First Order Mathematical Logic

A Blaisdell Book in Pure and Applied Mathematics

Consulting Editor
George Springer, Indiana University

First Order
Mathematical Logic

Angelo Margaris
The Ohio State University

Blaisdell Publishing Company

A Division of Ginn and Company
Waltham, Massachusetts, Toronto, London

To My Mother

Preface

This book is for junior, senior, and beginning graduate students of mathematics who have little or no acquaintance with abstract mathematics.

The entire book can be covered in one semester. The latter parts of Sections 23, 24, 28, and 29 and the proofs of some lemmas in Section 26 may be omitted if time presses. The examples involving fields, lattices, and Boolean algebras may safely be omitted. Chapter 1 should be covered very rapidly. A short course can be based on the first 25 sections.

I thank Elliott Mendelson for reading the manuscript and offering many valuable suggestions, and Lisl Novak Gaal and J. Barkley Rosser for introducing me to logic. The notes and references indicate the sources of this book. I wish to acknowledge my special debt to the books of Church, Kleene, Mendelson, and Rosser and to the monograph of Tarski, Mostowski, and Robinson.

A. M.

Columbus, Ohio
December 1966

Contents

1   INTRODUCTION

2   THE PREDICATE CALCULUS

3   FIRST ORDER THEORIES

First Order Mathematical Logic

1

INTRODUCTION

The logic that mathematicians use to prove their theorems is itself a part of mathematics, in the same way that algebra, analysis, and geometry are parts of mathematics. In this book we study logic as a mathematical theory.

This first chapter is introductory and preliminary. It has three purposes. First, it is an overture, introducing briefly some themes that are developed later. Second, it supplies the rudimentary logic and set theory that are necessary to construct a mathematical theory of logic. Third, it clears the way for a smooth advance later by disposing of some minor notions and conventions.

1 Rules of Inference

A *statement* is a declarative sentence that is either true or false (but not both). Some examples are:

$$\text{George Washington was the first President of the United States} \tag{1}$$

$$2 + 2 = 5 \tag{2}$$

$$\text{There are no positive integers } a, b, c, n \\ \text{with } n > 2 \text{ such that } a^n + b^n = c^n \tag{3}$$

1

(1) is true.   (2) is false.   (3) is the famous Fermat conjecture whose truth or falsehood is unknown at this time.

Let P and Q be statements.   Then P *and* Q and P *or* Q are also statements.   The words *and* and *or* stand for operations on statements in the same way that in ordinary algebra, $+$ and $\cdot$ stand for operations on numbers.   We write $P \wedge Q$ for P *and* Q, and $P \vee Q$ for P *or* Q.

A typical rule of ordinary algebra is: For all integers a and b, $a + b = b + a$.   The rules of logic are called *rules of inference*.   An example of a rule of inference is: For all statements P and Q, the statement P may be inferred from the statement $P \wedge Q$.   We write this rule in the following convenient form:

$$\frac{P \wedge Q}{P} \tag{4}$$

An interpretation of (4) is: For all statements P and Q, if $P \wedge Q$ is true, then P is also true.   Some other rules of inference are:

$$\frac{P \wedge Q}{Q \wedge P} \tag{5}$$

$$\frac{P}{P \vee Q} \tag{6}$$

$$\frac{P \vee Q}{Q \vee P} \tag{7}$$

We write the statement *If P, then Q* as $P \to Q$.   Some rules of inference involving $\to$ are

$$\frac{P \to Q,\ P}{Q} \qquad \text{(modus ponens)} \tag{8}$$

$$\frac{P \to Q,\ Q \to S}{P \to S} \qquad \text{(transitivity)} \tag{9}$$

$$\frac{P \vee Q,\ P \to S,\ Q \to S}{S} \qquad \text{(proof by cases)} \tag{10}$$

$$\frac{P}{Q \to P} \tag{11}$$

We give names to some of the more important rules of inference and give the same name to closely related rules.

We write *not P* as $\sim P$. $\sim P$ is false if P is true, and is true if P is false.   A rule of inference involving $\sim$ is

$$\frac{(\sim Q) \to (\sim P)}{P \to Q} \qquad \text{(contraposition)} \tag{12}$$

Some rules of inference state outright conclusions.

$$\overline{P \vee \sim P} \qquad \text{(excluded middle)} \qquad (13)$$

$$\overline{P \to \sim\sim P} \qquad \text{(double negation)} \qquad (14)$$

$$\overline{(\sim\sim P) \to P} \qquad \text{(double negation)} \qquad (15)$$

The meaning of (13) is that $P \vee \sim P$ is true outright for every state-ment P because of the way that $\vee$ and $\sim$ enter into the construction of $P \vee \sim P$. Similarly, (14) and (15) are true outright.

Some rules of inference can be derived from others.

EXAMPLE 1.

$$\frac{P}{\sim\sim P}$$

Proof.

$$\frac{P, \quad \overline{P \to \sim\sim P} \quad (14)}{\sim\sim P} \quad (8)$$

EXAMPLE 2.

$$\frac{(\sim P) \to Q}{(\sim Q) \to P}$$

Proof.

$$\frac{\dfrac{(\sim P) \to Q, \quad \overline{Q \to \sim\sim Q} \quad (14)}{(\sim P) \to \sim\sim Q} \quad (9)}{(\sim Q) \to P} \quad (12)$$

EXERCISES

1. Which of the following sentences are statements?

   (a) Spinach was growing on Mars on March 15, 1492.
   (b) Which way to the Union Station?
   (c) Go jump in the lake!

2. Derive each of the following rules from (4) through (15).

(a) $\dfrac{\sim\sim P}{P}$

(b) $\dfrac{P \to Q,\ (\sim P) \to Q}{Q}$ (proof by cases)

(c) $\dfrac{(\sim P) \to Q,\ (\sim P) \to \sim Q}{P}$ (proof by contradiction)

(d) $\overline{P \to P}$

(e) $\dfrac{(\sim P) \to P}{P}$ (proof by contradiction)

(f) $\dfrac{P \to Q}{(\sim Q) \to (\sim P)}$ (contraposition)

(g) $\dfrac{P,\ \sim P}{Q}$

3. Later we shall establish some criteria for correct rules of inference. Now draw on your experience to classify each of the following rules as correct or incorrect. Keep in mind that a rule is incorrect if and only if there is an example in which the statements above the line are true and the statement below the line is false.

(a) $\dfrac{P \to Q,\ Q}{P}$ (modus moron)

(b) $\dfrac{P \vee Q}{P}$

(c) $\dfrac{P \to \sim P}{\sim P}$

(d) $\dfrac{P \to S,\ Q \to S}{(P \vee Q) \to S}$

(e) $\dfrac{P \to (Q \wedge \sim Q)}{\sim P}$

(f) $\dfrac{\sim(P \to Q)}{P \wedge \sim Q}$

(g) $\dfrac{(P \wedge Q) \to S}{P \to S}$

ANSWERS

1. (a).

3. (c)–(f) are correct; (a), (b), and (g) are incorrect.

2 Set Theory

From such phrases as *a class of students, a collection of books,* and *a gaggle of geese,* we abstract the notion of *set*: a set of students, a set of books, a set of geese.   Given an object a and a set A, either a is in A or it is not, and that is all that matters.   For example, Mickey Mantle is in the set of baseball players; 3 is not in the set of even numbers.

The following statements have the same meaning:

> a is in the set A
> a is an element of the set A
> a is a member of the set A
> $a \in A$

$a \notin A$ means that a is not in A.

The set consisting of the objects $x_1, x_2, \ldots, x_n$ is denoted by $\{x_1, x_2, \ldots, x_n\}$.   For example, $\{1, \pi, \text{George Washington}\}$ is the set consisting of the elements $1, \pi,$ and George Washington.   For large sets this notation is awkward, and for very large sets (as we shall show) it is impossible.   Therefore we use the device of denoting a set by giving a property shared by all the elements of the set and no other objects. Let $P(x)$ be a property that an object x may or may not have.   For example, if $P(x)$ is *x is an even number,* then 2 has the property (because 2 is an even number), and 3 does not have the property (because 3 is not an even number). $\{x \mid P(x)\}$ is the set of all objects that have the property $P(x)$.   (It is read: the set of all x such that $P(x)$.)   For example, $\{x \mid x \text{ is an even number}\}$ is the set of all even numbers. Hence $2 \in \{x \mid x \text{ is an even number}\}$, and $3 \notin \{x \mid x \text{ is an even number}\}$.

Let R be the set of real numbers.   Let A, B, C be any sets.   The following statements have the same meaning.   The first defines the others.

> Every member of A is also a member of B
> A is included in B
> A is a subset of B
> $A \subseteq B$

Examples. $\{1, 3, 5\} \subseteq \{2, 1, 4, 5, 3, 7\}$. $\{x \mid x \in R \text{ and } x \text{ is positive}\}$ $\subseteq R$.   Note that $A \subseteq A$ for every set A.

The following statements have the same meaning.

A and B have precisely the same members
$A \subseteq B$ and $B \subseteq A$
$A = B$

Examples. $\{1, 3, 5\} = \{3, 5, 1\}$. $\{1, 3\} = \{1, 3, 1\}$.   Note that neither order nor repetition of elements is pertinent to the notion of set.

The *empty set* $\varnothing$ is the set with no elements.   By the definition of equality for sets, there is only one empty set.   In Example 8 in Section 11 we prove that $\varnothing \subseteq A$ for every set A.

If x is any object, then $\{x\}$ is the set with precisely one element, namely x. $\{x\}$ is called a *unit* set or *singleton* set.

$A \cup B$ (read: A union B) is defined to be $\{x \mid x \in A \text{ or } x \in B \text{ or both}\}$.

Examples. $\{1, 2, 3\} \cup \{3, 4, 5\} = \{1, 2, 3, 4, 5\}$. $\{1, 2, 3\} \cup \{1, 3\} = \{1, 2, 3\}$. $\{1, 2, 3\} \cup \{4\} = \{1, 2, 3, 4\}$. $\{x \mid x \in R \text{ and } x \geqslant 0\} \cup \{x \mid x \in R \text{ and } x \leqslant 0\} = R$.

$A \cap B$ (read: A intersection B) is defined to be $\{x \mid x \in A \text{ and } x \in B\}$.

Examples. $\{1, 2, 3\} \cap \{3, 4, 5\} = \{3\}$. $\{1, 2, 3\} \cap \{1, 3\} = \{1, 3\}$. $\{1, 2, 3\} \cap \{4, 5\} = \varnothing$. $\{x \mid x \in R \text{ and } x \geqslant 0\} \cap \{x \mid x \in R \text{ and } x \leqslant 0\} = \{0\}$.

The following properties of sets are immediate from the definitions of $\subseteq$, $=$, $\cup$, and $\cap$.

(1) If $A \subseteq B$ and $B \subseteq C$, then $A \subseteq C$
(2) $A \cup B = B \cup A$
(3) $(A \cup B) \cup C = A \cup (B \cup C)$
(4) $A \cap B = B \cap A$
(5) $(A \cap B) \cap C = A \cap (B \cap C)$
(6) $A \subseteq A \cup B$
(7) $A \cap B \subseteq A$

A function is a set A, called the *domain* (of definition), together with a rule that assigns to each element of A some unique object.

Examples. The wife function: assign to each married American man his wife. The square function: assign to each real number x its square x^2. The Fort Knox function: assign Fort Knox to each human being.

If f is a function with domain A, and a is in A, then the unique object assigned to a by f is written $f(a)$, and is called the *value* of f at a.

Examples. If f is the square function, then $f(2) = 4$. If f is the Fort Knox function, then f(John Doe) = Fort Knox.

If f and g are functions, then $f = g$ if and only if f and g have the same domain, and $f(x) = g(x)$ for every x in the common domain.

Let n be a positive integer. A *sequence of n terms* is a list $(a_1, a_2, \ldots, a_n)$ of n objects, called *terms*, with repetitions permitted. A *sequence of 0 terms* is the empty set. A *finite sequence* is a sequence of n terms for some nonnegative integer n. For example, $(1, 3, 7, 3, 4)$ is a finite sequence of five terms. Two finite sequences $(a_1, \ldots, a_n)$ and $(b_1, \ldots, b_m)$ are *equal* if and only if they have the same number of terms $(n = m)$, and $a_i = b_i$ for $i = 1, 2, \ldots, n$. For finite sequences, the notions of order and repetition are critical. Thus $(1, 2, 3) \neq (2, 3, 1)$ and $(1, 2, 1) \neq (1, 2)$. ($\neq$ means not equal.)

For our purposes the *ordered n-tuple* $(a_1, \ldots, a_n)$ is the same thing as the finite sequence $(a_1, \ldots, a_n)$. An ordered 2-tuple (a_1, a_2) is also called an *ordered pair*.

If A is a set and n is a positive integer, then A^n is the set of all ordered n-tuples $(a_1, \ldots, a_n)$ of elements of A. For example, R^2 is the set of all ordered pairs (a_1, a_2) of real numbers. Geometrically, R^2 is the set of all points in the plane.

An *n-place operation* on A is a function whose domain is A^n and whose values all lie in A. Addition is a 2-place operation on R since it assigns to each ordered pair (a, b) of real numbers the real number $a + b$. $\wedge$ is a 2-place operation on the set of statements since it assigns to each ordered pair (P, Q) of statements the statement $P \wedge Q$. The function f with domain R^3, defined by $f(a, b, c) = a(b + c)$, is a 3-place operation on R. The function g with domain R, defined by $g(a) = -a$, is a 1-place operation on R.

A 2-place operation is also called a *binary operation*. For binary operations, it is customary to write $a + b$ or $a \cdot b$ or $a \circ b$ instead of $f(a, b)$. Let $\circ$ be a binary operation on A. $\circ$ is *associative* if and only if $(a \circ b) \circ c = a \circ (b \circ c)$ for all a, b, c in A. If $\circ$ is associative, one can prove by induction that $a_1 \circ a_2 \circ \cdots \circ a_n$ does not depend on the way that the elements $a_1, \ldots, a_n$ are associated. For $n = 4$, this means that

$$((a_1 \circ a_2) \circ a_3) \circ a_4 = a_1 \circ ((a_2 \circ a_3) \circ a_4) = (a_1 \circ a_2) \circ (a_3 \circ a_4)$$
$$= (a_1 \circ (a_2 \circ a_3)) \circ a_4 = a_1 \circ (a_2 \circ (a_3 \circ a_4))$$

$\circ$ is *commutative* if and only if $a \circ b = b \circ a$ for all a, b in A. If $\circ$ is both associative and commutative, then one can prove by induction that $a_1 \circ a_2 \circ \cdots \circ a_n$ is independent of both the order and the association of the elements $a_1, \ldots, a_n$.

An *infinite sequence* is a list $(a_1, a_2, a_3, \ldots, a_i, \ldots)$ of objects, with one object for each positive integer i. As for finite sequences, the objects are called *terms* and repetitions are permitted. Two infinite sequences $(a_1, a_2, a_3, \ldots, a_i, \ldots)$ and $(b_1, b_2, b_3, \ldots, b_i, \ldots)$ are equal if and only if $a_i = b_i$ for each positive integer i.

An *enumeration* of a set A is a sequence (finite or infinite) such that every term is in A and every element of A is a term. For example, $(1, 2, 3)$ and $(3, 2, 1, 3)$ are enumerations of the set $\{1, 2, 3\}$.

A set is *finite* if and only if it can be enumerated by a finite sequence. A set is *infinite* if and only if it is not finite. For example, $\{1, 2, 3\}$ is a finite set because it is enumerated by $(1, 2, 3)$.

THEOREM 1.   *The set of positive integers is infinite.*

Proof. Suppose, for contradiction, that the set of positive integers is finite. Then it can be enumerated by a finite sequence $(a_1, a_2, \ldots, a_n)$. Let $a = a_1 + a_2 + a_3 + \cdots + a_n$. Then $a > a_i$ for $i = 1, 2, \ldots, n$. Hence a is a positive integer that is not a term of the sequence $(a_1, \ldots, a_n)$.

THEOREM 2.   *Let $A \subseteq B$. If B is finite, then A is also finite. Hence, by contraposition, if A is infinite, then B is also infinite.*

Proof. Suppose B is finite. Let $(b_1, \ldots, b_n)$ be an enumeration of B by a finite sequence. We cross out the terms that are not elements of A. The result is a finite sequence that enumerates A. Hence A is also finite.

A set is *countable* if and only if it can be enumerated. Every finite set is countable, and some infinite sets are countable. For example, the set of positive integers is countable because $(1, 2, 3, \ldots, n,$ $n + 1, \ldots)$ is an enumeration.

THEOREM 3. *The set of rational numbers is countable.*

Proof. First we show that the set of positive rationals is countable. Let n be a positive integer greater than 1. All the positive rationals whose numerator and denominator add up to n can be enumerated in order of increasing numerator. For example, for $n = 6$, we have $\frac{1}{5}, \frac{2}{4}, \frac{3}{3}, \frac{4}{2}, \frac{5}{1}$. Now we start with $n = 2$ to get $\frac{1}{1}$. Then we follow with $n = 3$ to get $\frac{1}{2}, \frac{2}{1}$. Then we follow with $n = 4$ to get $\frac{1}{1}, \frac{1}{2}, \frac{2}{1}, \frac{1}{3}, \frac{2}{2}, \frac{3}{1}$. We continue in this manner: $\frac{1}{1}, \frac{1}{2}, \frac{2}{1}, \frac{1}{3}, \frac{2}{2}, \frac{3}{1}, \frac{1}{4}, \frac{2}{3}, \frac{3}{2}, \frac{4}{1}, \frac{1}{5}, \frac{2}{4}, \frac{3}{3}, \frac{4}{2}, \frac{5}{1}, \frac{1}{6},$ $\frac{2}{5}, \frac{3}{4}, \frac{4}{3}, \frac{5}{2}, \frac{6}{1}, \ldots$. Each positive rational appears in this list. To enumerate all the rationals we start with 0 and interlace the positive and negative rationals: $0, \frac{1}{1}, -\frac{1}{1}, \frac{1}{2}, -\frac{1}{2}, \frac{2}{1}, -\frac{2}{1}, \frac{1}{3}, -\frac{1}{3}, \frac{2}{2}, -\frac{2}{2}, \ldots$.

THEOREM 4. *Let $A \subseteq B$. If B is countable, then A is countable. Hence, by contraposition, if A is uncountable, then B is also uncountable.*

Proof. Suppose B is countable. In a given enumeration of B we cross out the terms that are not elements of A. The result is an enumeration of A.

A 1–1 (*one to one*) *correspondence* between the set A and the set B is a pairing of the elements of A with the elements of B such that each a in A corresponds to one and only one b in B, and each b in B corresponds to one and only one a in A.

THEOREM 5. *Suppose there is a 1–1 correspondence between A and B. Then A is finite (or infinite, or countable, or uncountable) if and only if B is finite (or infinite, or countable, or uncountable).*

Proof. Suppose A is countable. Let $(a_1, a_2, \ldots)$ be an enumeration of A. Let b_i be the element of B corresponding to a_i. Then $(b_1, b_2, \ldots)$ is an enumeration of B, and hence B is also countable. Similarly, if B is countable, then A is also countable. Hence A is countable if and only if B is countable. Then by contraposition, A is uncountable if and only if B is uncountable. Now suppose A is finite. Then A can be enumerated by a finite sequence $(a_1, \ldots, a_n)$. Again letting b_i be the element of B corresponding to a_i, we have that $(b_1, \ldots, b_n)$ is an enumeration of B, and hence B is finite.   The argument is reversible, and hence A is finite if and only if B is finite.   Then, by contraposition, A is infinite if and only if B is infinite.

THEOREM 6.   *The set of real numbers is uncountable.*

Proof.   Let $A = \{x \mid x \in R \text{ and } 0 \leqslant x < 1\}$.   We show that A is uncountable.   Then R is uncountable by Theorem 4.   Every element of A can be expressed as a proper decimal.   (.237 and .01052 are proper decimals; 2.61 and 5.0203 are improper decimals.)   The subset $\{.1, .01, .001, .0001, \ldots\}$ of A is in 1–1 correspondence with the set of positive integers and is therefore infinite by Theorems 1 and 5.   Hence A is infinite by Theorem 2.   Before we go on, we will clear up two minor points.   First, some elements of A have decimal representations that terminate, and others do not.   (For example, $\frac{1}{4} = .25$, and $\frac{1}{3} = .3333\ldots$)   To put all the elements of A on the same footing, we add 0's to the terminating decimals.   (Thus we replace .25 by .250000....)   Then we work with the set of nonterminating proper decimals.   The second point is that this set is not quite in 1–1 correspondence with A. For example, .250000... and .2499999... represent the same real number.   We agree to always use the representation that ends with 0's instead of the one that ends with 9's.

With the preliminaries out of the way, the main bout begins.   We show that A is uncountable.   The proof is by contradiction.   Suppose A is countable.   Since A is infinite, A can be enumerated by an infinite sequence

$$
\begin{array}{ll}
1. & .a_{11}a_{12}a_{13}a_{14}\cdots \\
2. & .a_{21}a_{22}a_{23}a_{24}\cdots \\
3. & .a_{31}a_{32}a_{33}a_{34}\cdots \\
\vdots & \quad\vdots \\
i. & .a_{i1}a_{i2}a_{i3}a_{i4}\cdots \\
\vdots & \quad\vdots
\end{array}
$$

The first term is $.a_{11}a_{12}a_{13}a_{14}\ldots$, the second term is $.a_{21}a_{22}a_{23}a_{24}\ldots$, and so on.   Each a_{ij} is one of the digits 0, 1, 2, 3, 4, 5, 6, 7, 8, 9, and a_{ij} is the jth digit of the ith term of the sequence.   We define a proper decimal $.b_1b_2b_3\ldots$ as follows.   For each i,

$$
b_i = \begin{cases} 2 & \text{if } a_{ii} = 3 \\ 3 & \text{if } a_{ii} \neq 3 \end{cases}
$$

Then for every i, $b_i \neq a_{ii}$. Then for every i, $.b_1 b_2 b_3 \ldots \neq .a_{i1} a_{i2} a_{i3} \ldots$ because they differ in the ith digit.   Hence $.b_1 b_2 b_3 \ldots$ is an element of A that is not a term of the sequence.   But the sequence was supposed to be an enumeration of A.   This contradiction shows that A is uncountable.

EXERCISES

1. $\subseteq$ is transitive by (1).   Show that $\in$ is not transitive, i.e., give an object b, a set B, and a set β such that $b \in B$ and $B \in \beta$ but $b \notin \beta$.
2. Is $\{R\}$ the same set as R?   Why?
3. Give the domains of the wife function; the square function; the Fort Knox function.
4. How is the wife function affected if the domain is changed to
   (a) the set of all married men?
   (b) the set of all American men?
5. The *range* of a function f is the set of all values of f.   What is the range of the wife function? the square function? the Fort Knox function? the operation of addition on the set of positive integers?
6. The domain of the function f is the set of integers, and $f(x) = x^2$ for every integer x.   Is f the same as the square function?   Why?
7. The domain of the function f is R, and $f(x) = |x|$ (the absolute value of x) for every real number x.   The domain of the function g is R, and $g(x) = +\sqrt{x^2}$ for every real number x.   Is f the same function as g?
8. For all real numbers a and b, $f(a, b) = a/b$.   Is f an operation on R?   Why?
9. Give an example of a 4-place operation.
10. Use (1) through (7) to prove

    (a) $B \subseteq A \cup B$
    (b) $A \cap B \subseteq B$

11. Use Theorems 3 and 4 to prove that the set of integers is countable. Then give a direct proof, i.e., give an enumeration.
12. Prove that if a set is countable, then it can be enumerated without repetitions.
13. Prove that the set of all squares of positive integers is countable.
14. Prove that R^2 is uncountable.

ANSWERS

1. $1 \in \{1\}$ and $\{1\} \in \{\{1\}, \{2\}\}$, but $1 \notin \{\{1\}, \{2\}\}$.
2. No. For one thing, $\{R\}$ is finite and R is infinite.
3. The set of all married American men; R; the set of all human beings.
4. (a) No longer a function because some married men have more than one wife. (b) No longer a function because some American men are unmarried.
5. The set of all women married to American men (which is not the same as the set of all married American women); $\{x \mid x \in R$ and $x \geqslant 0\}$; $\{$Fort Knox$\}$; the set of all positive integers greater than 1.
6. No. The domains are different.
7. Yes.
8. No. $f(a, 0)$ is not a real number. The same rule applied to A^2, where A is the set of all real numbers different from 0, is an operation on A.
9. For all a, b, c, d in $R, f(a, b, c, d) = (a + b)(c + d)$.

3   Axiomatic Theories

A *theory* consists of two sets of statements. The first set determines the subject matter of the theory; the second set is a subset of the first and is called the set of *acceptable* statements. In the experimental sciences, "acceptable" means "true" in the sense of being in accordance with reality, and the final appeal is to observation and experiment. Thus in the theory of nuclear physics, the acceptable statements are the true statements about atomic nuclei. In some theories, acceptability has little relation to truth in this sense. For example, in the theory of chess, "A bishop moves diagonally" is an acceptable statement because the rulebook says it is.

The theories of mathematics are *axiomatic theories*. In an axiomatic theory, the acceptable statements are called *theorems*, or *provable* statements, and are defined to be the statements deducible by logic alone from certain initially specified acceptable statements called *axioms*. An axiomatic theory familiar to every high school graduate is Euclid's geometry.

In an axiomatic theory, the question "Is this statement true?" is not relevant. The proper question is, "Does this statement follow from the axioms by logic alone?"

In an axiomatic theory, a *formal proof* is a finite sequence $S_1, \ldots, S_n$ of statements such that each S_i $(1 \leqslant i \leqslant n)$ is either an axiom or is inferred from one or more previous S_j's by a rule of inference. The statements $S_1, \ldots, S_n$ are called the *steps* of the proof.

A *theorem* is a statement that is the last step of some proof. To prove a theorem means to produce a proof whose last step is the theorem.

Every axiom is a theorem, because the finite sequence consisting of a single step—the axiom itself—is a proof of the axiom.

Formal proofs are seldom found outside of logic books. Because a formal proof includes *every* step, the formal proofs of simple theorems are often very long. The proofs in the mathematical literature, which we call *working proofs,* are in comparison outlines, giving only the mathematical highlights and suppressing the logical details which will only distract the knowledgeable reader.

A formal proof leaves nothing to the imagination. There is an effective procedure for deciding whether or not a formal proof is correct. Every step can be checked to see if it is justified as an axiom or by some rule of inference, with the checker relying only on the forms of the steps—not their meaning. No intelligence beyond the ability to follow routine instructions is necessary to check a formal proof. A digital computer can be programmed to check formal proofs.

Checking a proof can be reduced to a mechanical procedure, but finding a proof is a different matter. Mathematicians have always proceeded on the basis that finding a proof is a creative act, requiring insight, inspiration, perseverance, and luck. Recent developments in mathematical logic justify this attitude. Mathematicians have proved that for many important mathematical theories there is no mechanical procedure for finding a proof.

To make sure that every formal proof can be effectively checked without recourse to the meaning of the steps, every statement of an axiomatic theory must have a definite recognizable form. For a simple example, consider a theory in which the only statements are those constructed from the symbols "1," "2," "3," and " $=$," with the symbols having their usual meanings. Some statements of the theory are

$$12 = 3 \qquad 312 = 312 \qquad 111 = 11$$

The following expressions are not statements of the theory.

$$= 12 \qquad 213 \qquad 2 = \ = 2$$

Is $21 = 13 = 21$ a statement? We settle all questions about possible statements in the following way. We define a statement to be any finite sequence of the symbols "1," "2," "3," and " $=$ " in which " $=$ " occurs exactly once, and this occurrence is neither the first nor the last symbol in the sequence. Then $21 = 13 = 21$ is not a statement.

The definition of statement above is *formal* because it involves only the form of certain expressions, not their meaning. The axiomatic theories we shall study are formal axiomatic theories. The axiomatic theories of everyday mathematics are informal theories. In an informal theory, the statements are made in a natural language (e.g., English). Symbols are used, but they are abbreviations for meaningful words and phrases. In a formal theory, the statements are written in a specially constructed symbolic language and are manipulated in accordance with specified rules which make no appeal to any possible meaning of the statements.

The construction of a formal axiomatic theory begins with the specification of a finite set of *formal symbols*, and a *string* is defined to be a finite sequence of formal symbols.

A formal axiomatic theory has the following properties.

The notion of statement is effective; i.e., there is an effective procedure for deciding whether or not a string is a statement.

The notion of axiom is effective; i.e., there is an effective procedure for deciding whether or not a statement is an axiom.

The notion of logical inference is effective; i.e., given a finite sequence $S_1, \ldots, S_k$ of statements, there is an effective procedure for deciding whether or not S_k is inferred from one or more of $S_1, \ldots, S_{k-1}$ by a rule of inference.

Because the notions of axiom and logical inference are effective, the notion of proof is effective. That is, there is an effective procedure for deciding whether or not a sequence of statements is a proof.

The prime purpose of a formal theory is to make the notion of proof effective.

A formal theory can be communicated to a reader only in a language he already knows. (The same situation arises in teaching a foreign language.) The symbolic language in which the statements of a formal theory are written is called the *object* language. The language used to present the formal theory is called the *metalanguage*. We shall use English as the metalanguage. A statement in the object language is a statement *of* the theory; a statement in the metalanguage is a statement *about* the theory. We shall use a special symbolism for the object language. Then it is easy to distinguish a statement in the object language from a statement in the metalanguage, because the former is written in the distinctive symbolism of the theory, and the latter is written in ordinary English. A provable statement of the formal theory is called a *formal* theorem. A statement proved in the metalanguage about the formal theory is called a *metatheorem*.

EXERCISES

1. State two ways in which a "proof" can be infinite. Why are infinite formal proofs not permitted?
2. Prove: All girls are beautiful.
3. A certain formal theory has exactly two axioms,

$$2 + 2 = 4 \rightarrow (2 + 2 = 4 \rightarrow 2 + 3 = 6)$$
$$2 + 2 = 4$$

and has modus ponens (see Section 1) as its one and only rule of inference. Find all the theorems of this theory, and give a formal proof of each one.
4. An axiomatic theory is *consistent* if and only if there is at least one statement of the theory that is not a theorem. In a certain formal theory, (a) if P and Q are statements, then $P \rightarrow Q$ is also a statement; (b) every statement of the form $P \rightarrow Q$ is a theorem; and (c) modus ponens is one of the rules of inference. Show that this theory is not consistent.

ANSWERS

1. The proof may have infinitely many steps, or one of the steps may be infinite, i.e., have infinitely many symbols. The purpose of any proof is to convince the reader; an "infinite proof" can convince no one because no one can read it all.
2. Let T be an axiomatic theory whose one and only axiom is: All girls are beautiful. Then this statement is not only provable—it is axiomatic.
3. The theorems are the two axioms and $2 + 2 = 4 \rightarrow 2 + 3 = 6$ and $2 + 3 = 6$.

4   Predicates and Quantifiers

Our primary interest is in *first order theories*.   In a first order theory, some set of objects is selected, and all the statements of the theory are statements about these objects.   The set of objects is called the *domain*, and the objects in the domain are called *individuals*.   Any set that is not empty can serve as a domain.   In this chapter most of the examples are from three domains: the set of human beings, the set of real numbers, and the set 0, 1, 2, 3, ... of nonnegative integers.   By *number theory* we mean the theory of nonnegative integers.   Whenever we say *number* we mean *nonnegative integer*.

In the statement "Sam Jones loves Mary Potholder," the subject is "Sam Jones" and the predicate is "loves Mary Potholder."   We write this predicate as

$$\text{\_\_\_\_ loves Mary Potholder} \tag{1}$$

where the dash reserves a place for the missing subject.

In logic, the notion of predicate is extended to include expressions in which the object rather than the subject is missing.   For example,

$$\text{Sam Jones loves \_\_\_\_} \tag{2}$$

is a predicate.   Further, both subject and object may be missing, as in

$$\text{\_\_\_\_ loves \_\_\_\_} \tag{3}$$

which is a 2-place predicate.   A 3-place predicate of number theory is

$$\text{\_\_\_\_} + \text{\_\_\_\_} = \text{\_\_\_\_} \tag{4}$$

If n is a positive integer, then an *n-place predicate* is an expression containing n different kinds of blanks that becomes a statement when the blanks are replaced by names of individuals.   When a predicate contains more than one occurrence of the same kind of blank, it is understood that the same name of an individual is to be filled in for each occurrence.   For example,

$$\text{\_\_\_\_} + \text{\_\_\_\_} = 7 \tag{5}$$

is a 1-place predicate of number theory, from which we can get the statements $2 + 2 = 7$ and $8 + 8 = 7$, but not $2 + 3 = 7$.   In contrast,

$$\text{\_\_\_\_} + \text{\_\_\_\_} = 7 \tag{6}$$

is a 2-place predicate, from which we can get $2 + 3 = 7$. From (6) we can also get $2 + 2 = 7$. It is permissible to use the same name of an individual to fill in different kinds of blanks; what is forbidden is filling in different names for the same kind of blank.

Because the notation for predicates becomes unwieldy when there are many different kinds of blanks, we shall henceforth use variables instead of dashes. For variables we use x, y, z, t, k, and n. In this notation, (1) becomes

$$x \text{ loves Mary Potholder} \tag{7}$$

and (3) becomes

$$x \text{ loves } y \tag{8}$$

and (4) becomes

$$x + y = z \tag{9}$$

and (5) becomes

$$x + x = 7. \tag{10}$$

A predicate is not a statement because it is neither true nor false. However, a predicate has the form of a statement, and many operations defined for statements apply also to predicates. For example, the operation $\land$ can be applied to the predicates $x < 2$ and $x + y = 7$ to give the predicate $x < 2 \land x + y = 7$.

A *formula* is an expression that is either a statement or a predicate. For technical reasons, formulas are used in many places where one expects to find only statements. For example, in many formal theories the steps of a proof are permitted to be formulas.

The following statements have the same meaning.

> All human beings are greedy
> Every human being is greedy
> Each human being is greedy
> For every human being x, x is greedy $\tag{11}$

The phrase *for every x* is called a *universal quantifier*, and we shall write it as $\forall x$. In logical symbolism, (11) is written as

$$\forall x(x \text{ is greedy}) \tag{12}$$

Although $\forall x$ means *for every x*, the restriction to some given domain (in this case the domain of human beings) is understood.

The following statements have the same meaning.

> There is a greedy human being
> There exists a greedy human being
> At least one human being is greedy
> Some human being is greedy
> There exists a human being x such that x is greedy   (13)

The phrase *there exists an x such that* is called an *existential quantifier*, and we shall write it as $\exists x$. In logical symbolism, (13) is written as

$$\exists x(x \text{ is greedy}) \qquad (14)$$

Again the restriction to some given domain is understood.

The *scope* of a quantifier is the formula to which the quantifier applies, and is indicated by parentheses. (12) and (14) illustrate how quantifiers can be coupled with predicates to give statements.

Two or more quantifiers may be used in tandem. In the following examples, we begin with a statement in symbolic form and give several translations.

EXAMPLE 1.

$$\exists x \forall y(x \text{ loves } y)$$

> There is an x such that for every y, x loves y
> There is a human being who loves every human being
> Somebody loves everybody

EXAMPLE 2.

$$\forall y \exists x(x \text{ loves } y)$$

> For every y there is an x such that x loves y
> Every human being is loved by some human being
> Everybody is loved by somebody

EXAMPLE 3.

$$\exists x \exists y(x \text{ loves } y)$$

> There is an x such that there is a y such that x loves y
> There is an x and there is a y such that x loves y
> There is a human being who loves some human being
> Somebody loves somebody

EXAMPLE 4.

$$\forall x \forall y (x \text{ loves } y)$$

For every x, for every y, x loves y
For every x and y, x loves y
Every human being loves every human being
Everybody loves everybody

EXAMPLE 5.

$$\forall x \forall y \exists z (x + y = z) \qquad \text{(number theory)}$$

For every x, for every y, there is a z such that $x + y = z$
For every x and y there is a z such that $x + y = z$
Given any two numbers x and y, there is a number z such that $x + y = z$
The sum of any two numbers is a number

EXAMPLE 6.

$$\forall x \forall y \forall z ((x + y) + z = x + (y + z)) \qquad \text{(number theory)}$$

For every x, for every y, for every z, $(x + y) + z = x + (y + z)$
For every x, y, and z, $(x + y) + z = x + (y + z)$
Addition of numbers is associative

In the statement

$$\sum_{k=1}^{k=5} k^2 = 55 \tag{15}$$

k is a dummy variable. When (15) is written out as

$$1^2 + 2^2 + 3^2 + 4^2 + 5^2 = 55$$

k does not appear at all. In (15), k can be changed to some other variable without altering the meaning. Similarly, in

$$\int_0^1 \cos x \, dx = \sin 1 \tag{16}$$

x is a dummy variable. The statement

$$\int_0^1 \cos t \, dt = \sin 1 \tag{17}$$

has exactly the same meaning as (16).

In logic a dummy variable is called a *bound* variable.   In the formula

$$\exists x(x < y) \tag{18}$$

x is a bound variable, but y is not a bound variable.   When (18) is written as

There is a number less than y

x disappears, but y is still present.   If we think of y as being some fixed number, (18) says something about y.   A variable that is not bound is *free*. y is a free variable in (18).   In the formula

$$\sum_{k=1}^{k=n} k = n(n + 1)/2 \tag{19}$$

k is a bound variable, and n is a free variable.   Similarly, in

$$\int_0^x \cos t\, dt = \sin x \tag{20}$$

t is a bound variable, and x is a free variable.

A variable may be bound in different ways, but we shall consider only variables bound by quantifiers.

An occurrence of a variable v in a formula P is *bound* if and only if it is the explicit occurrence in a quantifier $\forall v$ or $\exists v$, or if it is in the scope of a quantifier $\forall v$ or $\exists v$.   An occurrence of a variable is *free* if and only if it is not bound.   A variable is *bound* or *free* in P according as it has a bound or free occurrence in P.

In (18), both occurrences of x are bound, and the occurrence of y is free.   In the formula $x < y$, which is a part of (18), both the occurrence of x and the occurrence of y are free because there are no quantifiers in this formula.   This example illustrates that *free* and *bound* are relative to a given formula.

The same variable may be both free and bound in the same formula. In the formula

$$(\exists x(x < 7)) \land (x + z = 8) \tag{21}$$

the first two occurrences of x (from left to right) are bound, but the third occurrence of x is free because it is not in the scope of the quantifier $\exists x$.   As far as meaning is concerned, the free and bound occurrences of the same variable in a formula have nothing to do with each other. In the formula

$$\int_0^x \cos x\, dx = \sin x \tag{22}$$

the first and last occurrences of x are free, and the other two occurrences are bound. (22) is confusing and is better written as

$$\int_0^x \cos t \, dt = \sin x \tag{23}$$

We shall avoid formulas in which the same variable occurs both free and bound, but we do not forbid them, because to do so would complicate the definition of formula. In the formula

$$(\exists x(x < y)) \wedge (\forall x(x > 0)) \tag{24}$$

all occurrences of x are bound, but the first two occurrences of x have nothing to do with the last two occurrences because they are bound by a different quantifier. (24) can just as well be written

$$(\exists x(x < y)) \wedge (\forall z(z > 0)) \tag{25}$$

For the most part, we shall avoid formulas such as (24), but again we do not forbid them.

A precise definition of formula can be given for each formal theory. Now we define statement and predicate in terms of formula.

A *statement* is a formula with no free variables. A *predicate* is a formula with one or more free variables. An *n-place predicate* is a formula with exactly n distinct free variables.

Some examples from number theory follow.

$$\exists x \forall y(xy = x) \tag{26}$$

is a statement since it has no free variables.

$$\exists x(x + y = y) \tag{27}$$

is a 1-place predicate since y is the one and only free variable.

$$(\forall x(x + y = y + x)) \wedge (\exists z(z < t)) \tag{28}$$

is a 2-place predicate since it has exactly two free variables y and t.

If P is an n-place predicate, and v is free in P, then the formula $\forall v P$ is an $(n - 1)$-place predicate. (If P is a 1-place predicate, then $\forall v P$ is a statement.) If v is not free in P, then $\forall v P$ is still an n-place predicate; in this case, $\forall v P$ has the same meaning as P. There is no point in applying $\forall v$ to a formula P in which v is not free, but again we believe it is not worth the trouble to forbid such constructions. The same remarks hold also for the existential quantifier $\exists v$.

EXERCISES

1. For each of the following predicates of number theory, give a true statement and a false statement that result by substituting the names of numbers for the variables:

   (a) $x < y$
   (b) $xy = x + y$
   (c) $x + yz = (x + y)(x + z)$
   (d) $x + x = xx$

2. If a name of an individual is substituted for one of the variables in an n-place predicate, what is the result?

3. If two 2-place predicates are made into one by inserting $\wedge$ between them, how many places does the resulting predicate have?

4. (a) Give a 1-place predicate of number theory with the property that every statement that results from the predicate by substitution is true.

   (b) Repeat (a) for a 2-place predicate.

   (c) Repeat (a) with "true" replaced by "false."

5. Translate each of the following statements into reasonably good English statements that involve no variables.

   (a) $\exists x \forall y(y \text{ loves } x)$
   (b) $\forall y \exists x(y \text{ loves } x)$
   (c) $\forall x \forall y \exists z(x + z = y)$ (number theory)
   (d) $\exists x \exists y \forall z(x + z = yz)$ (number theory)
   (e) $\forall x \exists y \forall z(z \geqslant y \to z > x)$ (number theory)

6. For each of the following formulas, write "B" for "bound" or "F" for "free" under each occurrence of each variable.

   (a) $\exists y(x < y)$
   (b) $\exists z \forall y(z = y \vee y = x)$
   (c) $(\forall x(x > 0)) \wedge (\exists y(y = x))$
   (d) $(\exists z(x + y = z)) \vee ((\forall x(x > 2)) \to (\exists y(y = z)))$

ANSWERS

2. An $(n - 1)$-place predicate if $n > 1$; a statement if $n = 1$.

3. Two, three, or four.

5. (a) Somebody is loved by everybody. (b) Everybody loves somebody. (c) The difference of two numbers is a number. (d) and (e) are best not written in ordinary English. We give an answer for

(d); you can probably do better: (d) There exist two numbers with the property that the sum of one number and an arbitrary number is equal to the product of the other number and the same arbitrary number. (This answer is not quite correct. What has been overlooked?)

5   Statement Connectives

If P and Q are any statements, then the statement P *and* Q is called the *conjunction* of P and Q, and we write it as $P \wedge Q$. According to the usual meaning of *and*, $P \wedge Q$ is true if and only if each of P and Q is true.

We call "truth" and "falsehood" *truth values*, and abbreviate them as T and F. The table below gives the intended interpretation of $\wedge$.

P	Q	$P \wedge Q$
T	T	T
F	T	F
T	F	F
F	F	F

The first two columns list all the possible assignments of truth values to the pair $\{P, Q\}$, and the last column gives the corresponding truth value for $P \wedge Q$. The table above is an example of a truth value table, or briefly, *truth table*. An example of a conjunction is $2 + 2 = 4 \wedge 3 + 2 = 7$, which is false because $3 + 2 = 7$ is false.

If P and Q are any statements, then the statement P *or* Q is called the *disjunction* of P and Q, and we write it as $P \vee Q$. We choose that meaning of *or* for which $P \vee Q$ is true if and only if P or Q or both are true. The truth table for disjunction is

P	Q	$P \vee Q$
T	T	T
F	T	T
T	F	T
F	F	F

An example of a disjunction is $2 + 2 = 4 \vee 3 + 2 = 7$, which is true because $2 + 2 = 4$ is true.

The interpretation of *or* given in the truth table above is the *inclusive* interpretation, which is standard in mathematics, and is sometimes rendered as *and/or*. The other interpretation of *or*, called the *exclusive* interpretation, is probably more common in ordinary discourse. In the exclusive interpretation, *P or Q* is true if and only if exactly one of the pair $\{P, Q\}$ is true.

The *negation* of a statement is formed by inserting the word *not* in the proper place (perhaps accompanied by some slight change in wording), or by writing *it is false that* in front of the statement. The negation of

Texas is the largest state

is

Texas is not the largest state

The negation of

Mary Potholder loves candy

is

Mary Potholder does not love candy

The negation of

Everyone loves a fat man

is

It is false that everyone loves a fat man

We write the negation of P as $\sim P$. The negation of P is true when P is false and is false when P is true. The truth table for negation is

P	$\sim P$
T	F
F	T

A statement of the form *If P, then Q* is called a *conditional*, and we write it as $P \rightarrow Q$. The truth table for $\rightarrow$ is

P	Q	$P \rightarrow Q$
T	T	T
F	T	T
T	F	F
F	F	T

That the truth-table interpretation of $\rightarrow$ captures the full meaning of *If P, then Q* is not at all obvious. Now we confine ourselves to the remark that the truth-table interpretation conforms to standard mathematical usage. In Chapter 2 we prove some metatheorems that justify this interpretation.

In a conditional $P \to Q$, P is called the *antecedent* and Q the *consequent*. The truth table for the conditional can be summarized as follows: A conditional is true if and only if the antecedent is false or the consequent is true.

In mathematics, the following statements have the same meaning, and each is translated as $P \to Q$.

> If P, then Q.
> P only if Q.
> P implies Q.
> Q if P.
> Q provided P.
> Q when(ever) P.
> P is a sufficient condition for Q.
> Q is a necessary condition for P.

A statement of the form $(P \to Q) \land (Q \to P)$ is called a *biconditional*, and we abbreviate it as $P \leftrightarrow Q$. The truth table for the biconditional is

P	Q	$P \leftrightarrow Q$
T	T	T
F	T	F
T	F	F
F	F	T

and is completely determined by the truth tables for $\to$ and $\land$ as the following construction shows.

P	Q	$P \to Q$	$Q \to P$	$(P \to Q) \land (Q \to P)$
T	T	T	T	T
F	T	T	F	F
T	F	F	T	F
F	F	T	T	T

In mathematics, the following statements have the same meaning, and each is translated as $P \leftrightarrow Q$.

> P if and only if Q
> P is equivalent to Q
> P is a necessary and sufficient condition for Q

$Q \leftrightarrow P$ has the same meaning as $P \leftrightarrow Q$, i.e., $P \leftrightarrow Q$ is true if and only if $Q \leftrightarrow P$ is true.   Hence P and Q can be interchanged in each of

the statements above.   However, $Q \rightarrow P$ does not have the same
meaning as $P \rightarrow Q$. $Q \rightarrow P$ is called the *converse* of $P \rightarrow Q$, and its
truth value can be different from the truth value of $P \rightarrow Q$.

The symbols $\wedge$, $\vee$, $\sim$, $\rightarrow$, and $\leftrightarrow$ are called *statement connectives*.
With each connective there is associated an operation on statements.
$\sim$ is called a *singulary* connective, because the associated operation is a
singulary (1-place) operation; the other four connectives are called
binary connectives because their associated operations are binary
(2-place) operations.

The operations associated with statement connectives can also be
applied to predicates.   For example, $x > 2 \wedge x > 5$ is a formula.

To simplify the appearance of formulas, we adopt a convention for
the omission of parentheses.   The symbols $\leftrightarrow$, $\rightarrow$, $\wedge$, $\vee$, and $\sim$ are
ranked in the given order with $\wedge$ and $\vee$ having equal rank.   The
examples below illustrate the convention.   The formulas with parentheses omitted appear on the left.

$$P \wedge Q \rightarrow R \qquad (P \wedge Q) \rightarrow R$$
$$P \vee Q \leftrightarrow R \qquad (P \vee Q) \leftrightarrow R$$
$$\sim Q \rightarrow \sim P \qquad (\sim Q) \rightarrow (\sim P)$$
$$\sim P \rightarrow Q \leftrightarrow R \qquad ((\sim P) \rightarrow Q) \leftrightarrow R$$

EXERCISES

1. Give the truth value of each of the following statements of number
   theory:

   (a) $\sim(2 > 1 \wedge 2 > 4)$
   (b) $\sim(2 > 1 \vee 2 > 4)$
   (c) $4 > 3 \wedge \forall x \exists y (y < x)$
   (d) $\forall x \forall y (x < y \vee y \leqslant x)$
   (e) $2 < 1 \rightarrow \exists x (x < 0)$
   (f) $2 < 1 \leftrightarrow 2 < 3$
   (g) $(\forall x (x = 1)) \leftrightarrow 6 + 5 = 10$
   (h) $2 + 2 = 5 \rightarrow 2 + 2 = 4$
   (i) $(\sim(1 = 0 \wedge 0 = 0)) \rightarrow 2 = 3$
   (j) $(\sim(1 = 0 \vee 0 = 0)) \rightarrow 2 = 3$

2. Give the conditions under which $P \rightarrow Q$ is true and its converse is
   false.

3. Write $\bar{\vee}$ for the exclusive *or* and give the truth table for $\bar{\vee}$.

4. The truth table for $\sim(P \wedge Q)$ is constructed as follows:

P	Q	$P \wedge Q$	$\sim(P \wedge Q)$
T	T	T	F
F	T	F	T
T	F	F	T
F	F	F	T

Construct the truth table for $\sim P \wedge \sim Q$ and for $\sim P \vee \sim Q$ and state which of these two is the same as the truth table for $\sim(P \wedge Q)$.

5. (a) Show that the truth table for $P \vee Q$ is the same as the truth table for $\sim P \rightarrow Q$. (b) Show that the truth table for $P \wedge Q$ is the same as the truth table for $\sim(P \rightarrow \sim Q)$.

6. Use the convention to eliminate as many parentheses as possible.

(a) $((P \rightarrow R) \wedge ((\sim Q) \rightarrow R)) \rightarrow ((P \vee Q) \rightarrow R)$
(b) $P \rightarrow (Q \leftrightarrow (P \leftrightarrow Q))$
(c) $(\sim P) \rightarrow ((\sim P) \vee Q)$

ANSWERS

1. (a), (d), (e), (g), (h), and (j) are true, the others false.
2. P is false and Q is true.
6. (a) $(P \rightarrow R) \wedge (\sim Q \wedge R) \rightarrow (P \vee Q \rightarrow R)$. (b) No change. (c) $\sim P \rightarrow \sim P \vee Q$.

6   The Interpretation of Predicates and Quantifiers

Let $G(x)$ and $H(x)$ be 1-place predicates in the domain D, $G(x, y)$ and $H(x, y)$ be 2-place predicates in D, and $G(x_1, \ldots, x_n)$ be an n-place predicate in D.

Let $G(x, y)$ be the predicate $x < y$ of number theory. $G(x, y)$ can be interpreted as a function that assigns to each ordered pair (d_1, d_2) of numbers the statement $d_1 < d_2$, which we denote by $G(d_1, d_2)$. Thus $1 < 2$ is $G(1, 2)$, and $2 < 1$ is $G(2, 1)$. Since each statement is true or false, we can also interpret G as a function that assigns to each ordered pair (d_1, d_2) of numbers a truth value T or F. Thus $G(1, 2) = T$ since $1 < 2$ is true, and $G(2, 1) = F$ since $2 < 1$ is false.

We shall interpret $G(x_1, \ldots, x_n)$ as a function that assigns to each ordered n-tuple $(d_1, \ldots, d_n)$ of individuals the truth value of the statement that results when "d_i" is substituted for "x_i" in $G(x_1, \ldots, x_n)$.

We use this interpretation of predicates to interpret the quantifiers $\forall x$ and $\exists x$. $\forall x G(x)$ is true if and only if $G(d) = T$ for every individual d. For example, in number theory $\forall x(0 \leqslant x)$ is true because $0 \leqslant 0$, $0 \leqslant 1$, $0 \leqslant 2, \ldots$ are all true, but $\forall x(2 < x)$ is false because $2 < 1$ is false. $\exists x G(x)$ is true if and only if $G(d) = T$ for at least one individual d. In number theory $\exists x(2 < x)$ is true since $2 < 3$ is true, but $\exists x(x < 0)$ is false because $0 < 0$, $1 < 0$, $2 < 0, \ldots$ are all false.

EXAMPLE 1.   Every statement of the form

$$(\exists x G(x)) \leftrightarrow (\sim \forall x \sim G(x)) \tag{1}$$

is true.

Proof.   Let D be any domain and let $G(x)$ be any 1-place predicate in D. We show that $\exists x G(x)$ and $\sim \forall x \sim G(x)$ have the same truth value. Then (1) is true by the truth table for $\leftrightarrow$. Suppose that $\exists x G(x)$ is true. Then by the interpretation for $\exists$, $G(d_0)$ is true for some d_0 in D. Then $\sim G(d_0)$ is false by the truth table for $\sim$. Then $\forall x \sim G(x)$ is false by the interpretation for $\forall$. Then $\sim \forall x \sim G(x)$ is true by the truth table for $\sim$. Now suppose that $\exists x G(x)$ is false. Then $G(d)$ is false for every d in D by the interpretation for $\exists$. Then $\sim G(d)$ is true for every d in D by the truth table for $\sim$. Then $\forall x \sim G(x)$ is true by the interpretation for $\forall$. Then $\sim \forall x \sim G(x)$ is false by the truth table for $\sim$.

EXAMPLE 2.   Every statement of the form

$$((\forall x G(x)) \vee (\forall x H(x))) \rightarrow (\forall x(G(x) \vee H(x))) \tag{2}$$

is true.

Proof.   Let D be any domain and let $G(x)$ and $H(x)$ be any 1-place predicates in D. We note that $G(x) \vee H(x)$ is also a 1-place predicate in D. If $(\forall x G(x)) \vee (\forall x H(x))$ is false, then (2) is true by the truth table for $\rightarrow$. So suppose that $(\forall x G(x)) \vee (\forall x H(x))$ is true. Then by the truth table for $\vee$, either $\forall x G(x)$ or $\forall x H(x)$ is true. Suppose $\forall x G(x)$ is true. Then $G(d)$ is true for every d in D by the interpretation for $\forall$. Then $G(d) \vee H(d)$ is true for every d in D by the truth table for $\vee$. Then $\forall x(G(x) \vee H(x))$ is true by the interpretation for $\forall$. Then (2) is true by the truth table for $\rightarrow$. Similarly, if $\forall x H(x)$ is true, then (2) is true.

EXAMPLE 3.   There is a false statement of the form

$$(\forall x(G(x) \lor H(x))) \to ((\forall xG(x)) \lor (\forall xH(x))) \qquad (3)$$

Proof.   We give two examples.   First, in number theory, let $G(x)$ be *x is even* and $H(x)$ be *x is odd*.   For every number d, d *is even* $\lor$ d *is odd* is true.   Hence $\forall x(x$ is even $\lor$ x is odd) is true by the interpretation for $\forall$.   Now $\forall x(x$ is even) and $\forall x(x$ is odd) are both false.   Hence $(\forall x(x$ is even)) $\lor$ $(\forall x(x$ is odd)) is false by the truth table for $\lor$.   Hence

$$(\forall x(x \text{ is even} \lor x \text{ is odd})) \to ((\forall x(x \text{ is even})) \lor (\forall x(x \text{ is odd})))$$

is false by the truth table for $\to$.   For the second example, let D consist of the two elements d_1 and d_2.   Let $G(x)$ and $H(x)$ be defined in D as follows: $G(d_1) = T$, $G(d_2) = F$, $H(d_1) = F$, $H(d_2) = T$.   Then by the truth table for $\lor$, $G(d_1) \lor H(d_1)$ is true because $G(d_1)$ is true, and $G(d_2) \lor H(d_2)$ is true because $H(d_2)$ is true.   Hence $\forall x(G(x) \lor H(x))$ is true by the interpretation for $\forall$.   Now by the interpretation for $\forall$, $\forall xG(x)$ is false because $G(d_2)$ is false, and $\forall xH(x)$ is false because $H(d_1)$ is false.   Hence $(\forall xG(x)) \lor (\forall xH(x))$ is false by the truth table for $\lor$.   Hence (3) is false by the truth table for $\to$.

EXAMPLE 4.   Every statement of the form

$$(\forall x\forall yG(x, y)) \leftrightarrow (\forall y\forall xG(x, y)) \qquad (4)$$

is true.

Proof.   Let D be any domain, and let $G(x, y)$ be any 2-place predicate in D.   We show that $\forall x\forall yG(x, y)$ and $\forall y\forall xG(x, y)$ have the same truth value.   Then (4) is true by the truth table for $\leftrightarrow$.   Suppose $\forall x\forall yG(x, y)$ is true.   Then, by the interpretation for $\forall$, we have in turn: $\forall yG(d, y)$ is true for every d in D, $G(d, e)$ is true for every d and e in D, $\forall xG(x, e)$ is true for every e in D, and finally, $\forall y\forall xG(x, y)$ is true.   Now suppose that $\forall x\forall yG(x, y)$ is false.   Then by the interpretation for $\forall$ we have in turn: $\forall yG(d_0, y)$ is false for some d_0 in D, $G(d_0, e_0)$ is false for some d_0 and e_0 in D, $\forall xG(x, e_0)$ is false, and finally, $\forall y\forall xG(x, y)$ is false.

EXAMPLE 5.

$$\text{There is a cruel dictator} \qquad (5)$$

has the same meaning as

$$\text{There is a human being } d \text{ such that}$$
$$d \text{ is cruel and } d \text{ is a dictator} \qquad (6)$$

In the domain of human beings, the symbolic form of (6) is

$$\exists x(x \text{ is cruel} \wedge x \text{ is a dictator}) \tag{7}$$

Hence (7) is the symbolic translation of (5).

EXERCISES

1. Show that every statement of the following form is true.

    (a) $(\forall x G(x)) \rightarrow (\exists x G(x))$
    (b) $(\forall x G(x)) \leftrightarrow (\sim\exists x \sim G(x))$
    (c) $((\forall x G(x)) \wedge (\forall x H(x))) \leftrightarrow (\forall x(G(x) \wedge H(x)))$
    (d) $(\exists x(G(x) \vee H(x))) \leftrightarrow ((\exists x G(x)) \vee (\exists x H(x)))$
    (e) $(\exists x \exists y G(x, y)) \leftrightarrow (\exists y \exists x G(x, y))$

2. Show that there is a false statement of the form

$$((\exists x G(x)) \wedge (\exists x H(x))) \rightarrow (\exists x(G(x) \wedge H(x)))$$

3. Translate the following statements of number theory into logical symbolism.

    (a) There is an even number.
    (b) There is an even square.
    (c) There is an odd number greater than 0.

7   The Predicate Calculus and First Order Theories

The most important system of logic for mathematics is the first order predicate calculus, which we call the *predicate calculus*. The predicate calculus supplies all the language and logic necessary to state and prove any theorem of a first order theory. In this section we shall consider only the linguistic aspect of the predicate calculus.

The *logical operators* are the statement connectives and the quantifiers $\forall$ and $\exists$.

Some of these operators can be defined in terms of the others. Let P and Q be formulas, and v a variable. We define $\wedge$, $\vee$, and $\exists$ in terms of $\sim$, $\rightarrow$, and $\forall$.

    $P \vee Q$ is an abbreviation for $\sim P \rightarrow Q$.
    $P \wedge Q$ is an abbreviation for $\sim(P \rightarrow \sim Q)$.
    $P \leftrightarrow Q$ is an abbreviation for $(P \rightarrow Q) \wedge (Q \rightarrow P)$.
    $\exists v P$ is an abbreviation for $\sim \forall v \sim P$.

These definitions are justified by various remarks, examples, and exercises in Sections 5 and 6. The choice of fundamental operators is a matter of taste. Other popular choices are $\{\wedge, \sim, \forall\}$ and $\{\vee, \sim, \exists\}$.

We begin with some examples of first order theories and then abstract from them the predicate calculus.

EXAMPLE 1. The theory L of linearly ordered sets. A *linearly ordered set* is a nonempty set D together with a 2-place predicate $<$ in D having the following properties.

L1.   For every x in D it is false that $x < x$.
L2.   For every x, y, z in D, if $x < y$ and $y < z$, then $x < z$.
L3.   For every x and y in D, $x < y$ or $x = y$ or $y < x$.

Examples of linearly ordered sets are the integers and the reals with the usual meaning of $<$.

We formulate L as a formal theory. The formal symbols are the logical operators

$$\sim \qquad \rightarrow \qquad \forall$$

the punctuation marks

$$(\qquad)$$

the 2-place predicate symbols

$$= \qquad <$$

and an infinite sequence

$$x \ y \ z \ x_1 \ y_1 \ z_1 \ x_2 \ y_2 \ \cdots$$

of variables.

A *string* is a finite sequence of formal symbols.

Formula is defined as follows: (1) If u and v are variables, then $(u < v)$ and $(u = v)$ are formulas (atomic formulas). (2) If P and Q are formulas, then $(P \rightarrow Q)$ is a formula. (3) If P is a formula, then $\sim P$ is a formula. (4) If P is a formula and v is a variable, then $\forall v P$ is a formula. (5) Only strings are formulas, and a string is a formula only if its being so follows from one of (1) through (4).

Briefly, a formula is a string constructed from atomic formulas by a finite number (perhaps zero) of applications of the logical operations. For example, $(x < y)$ is a formula by (1). Then $\forall x (x < y)$ is a formula by (4).   Then $\sim\forall x(x < y)$ is a formula by (3).   Also $(y < z)$ is a formula by (1).   Then $\sim(y < z)$ is a formula by (3).   Then

$$(\sim\forall x(x < y) \rightarrow \sim(x < z))$$

is a formula by (2).   Then $\forall z(\sim\forall x(x < y) \rightarrow \sim(x < z))$ is a formula by (4).

L1 through L3 above are the *axioms* of L.   We translate L1 through L3 into logical symbolism as follows.

L1. $\forall x \sim(x < x)$
L2. $\forall x \forall y \forall z(((x < y) \wedge (y < z)) \rightarrow (x < z))$
L3. $\forall x \forall y(((x < y) \vee (x = y)) \vee (y < x))$

EXAMPLE 2.   The theory AG of abelian groups.

An *abelian group* is a nonempty set D together with a binary operation $+$ on D and a particular element 0 of D with the following properties.

AG1.   For every x, y, z in D , $(x + y) + z = x + (y + z)$.
AG2.   For every x in D , $x + 0 = x$.
AG3.   For every x in D there is a y in D such that $x + y = 0$.
AG4.   For every x and y in D , $x + y = y + x$.

Examples of abelian groups are the integers and the reals with the usual meanings of $+$ and 0.
The formal symbols of AG are

$$\sim \quad \rightarrow \quad \forall \quad (\quad)$$

the 2-place predicate symbol

$$=$$

the 2-place operation symbol

$$+$$

the constant symbol

$$0$$

and an infinite sequence of variables

$$x \ y \ z \ x_1 \ y_1 \ z_1 \ x_2 \ y_2 \ \cdots$$

Term is defined as follows.   (1) Every variable is a term.   (2) 0 is a term.   (3) If r and s are terms, then $(r + s)$ is a term.   (4) Only strings are terms, and a string is a term only if its being so follows from one of (1) through (3).

Some terms are

$$x, \quad 0, \quad (x + 0), \quad (0 + x), \quad ((x + z) + 0), \quad ((x + y) + (x + z))$$

If r and s are terms, then $(r = s)$ is an atomic formula. Clauses (2) through (5) of the definition of formula are exactly the same as for L.

The axioms AG1 through AG4 translate into the following:

AG1. $\forall x \forall y \forall z(((x + y) + z) = (x + (y + z)))$
AG2. $\forall x((x + 0) = x)$
AG3. $\forall x \exists y((x + y) = 0)$
AG4. $\forall x \forall y((x + y) = (y + x))$

Comparing L and AG, we note that each predicate symbol gives rise to atomic formulas and that the operation symbol of AG applied to terms yields new terms. In L, the only terms are the variables and need no special mention.

With these examples as a guide, we formulate the linguistic part of the predicate calculus.

The formal symbols are

$$\sim \qquad \rightarrow \qquad \forall \qquad (\qquad) \qquad ,$$

together with (a) an infinite sequence of *variables*, (b) for each positive integer n an infinite sequence of n-place *predicate symbols*, (c) for each positive integer n an infinite sequence of n-place *operation symbols*, and (d) an infinite sequence of *constant symbols*.

Term is defined as follows: (1) Every variable is a term. (2) Every constant symbol is a term. (3) If F is an n-place operation symbol, and $t_1, \ldots, t_n$ are terms (not necessarily distinct), then $F(t_1, \ldots, t_n)$ is a term. (4) Only strings are terms, and a string is a term only if its being so follows from (1), (2), or (3).

Formula is defined as follows: (1) If G is an n-place predicate symbol, and $t_1, \ldots, t_n$ are terms (not necessarily distinct), then $G(t_1, \ldots, t_n)$ is a formula (an atomic formula). (2) If P and Q are formulas, then $(P \rightarrow Q)$ is a formula. (3) If P is a formula, then $\sim P$ is a formula. (4) If P is a formula and v is a variable, then $\forall v P$ is a formula. (5) Only strings are formulas, and a string is a formula only if its being so follows from one of (1) through (4).

Every formula of every first order theory can be expressed in the symbolism of the predicate calculus. For example, to formulate the theory L of linearly ordered sets, we use the first two 2-place predicate symbols G and H for $=$ and $<$. Then axioms L1 through L3 are written as follows:

L1. $\forall x(\sim H(x, x))$

L2. $\forall x \forall y \forall z((H(x, y) \wedge H(y, z)) \rightarrow H(x, z))$

L3. $\forall x \forall y((H(x, y) \vee G(x, y)) \vee H(y, x))$

In L we have no use for the operation symbols and the constant symbols and the predicate symbols different from G and H. We simply discard them.

To formulate the theory AG of abelian groups, we use the first 2-place predicate symbol G for $=$, the first 2-place operation symbol F for $+$, and the first constant symbol c for 0. Then the axioms are written as follows:

AG1. $\forall x \forall y \forall z G(F(F(x, y), z), F(x, F(y, z)))$

AG2. $\forall x G(F(x, c), x)$

AG3. $\forall x \exists y G(F(x, y), c)$

AG4. $\forall x \forall y G(F(x, y), F(y, x))$

We discard all the operation symbols, predicate symbols, and constant symbols except for F, G, and c. If we agree to write $(x = y)$ for $G(x, y)$, $(x + y)$ for $F(x, y)$, and 0 for c, then we are back to the more familiar notation. Similarly, in L we can write $(x = y)$ for $G(x, y)$ and $(x < y)$ for $H(x, y)$.

Every formula of the predicate calculus uses only a finite number of variables, but there is no upper bound on the number of variables that may appear in a formula. Therefore we supply an infinite sequence of variables. Every familiar first order theory uses only a finite number of operation symbols, predicate symbols, and constant symbols, but again we supply infinite sequences of these symbols to make sure that we have enough for any given theory.

We have not displayed the operation symbols, predicate symbols, and constant symbols. These symbols may be chosen in any way that makes the notion of formula effective. In Chapter 2 we give one choice that achieves this purpose.

In presenting the predicate calculus we have used the symbols "P," "v," "r," "G," "F," and "c." These symbols are not formal symbols. They are symbols in the metalanguage. "P" stands for a formula, "v" for a variable, "r" for a term, "G" for a predicate symbol, "F" for an operation symbol, and "c" for a constant symbol.

We close this section with one more example of a first order theory.

EXAMPLE 3.   Let N be number theory.   We use the 2-place predicate symbols = and < , the 2-place operation symbols + and · (multiplication), and an infinite sequence of constant symbols

$$0 \quad 1 \quad 2 \quad 3 \quad 4 \ldots$$

We do not give the axioms for N here.   In Chapter 3 we give a different formulation, complete with axioms.   Until then we use this formulation of N as a source of examples.   Let r and s be terms. $(r \leqslant s)$ is an abbreviation for $(r < s) \vee (r = s)$.   We shall sometimes write $s > r$ in place of $r < s$, and $s \geqslant r$ in place of $r \leqslant s$.   We also write rs in place of $r \cdot s$ and omit many parentheses in accordance with the usual conventions of number theory.

EXERCISES

1. State why each first order theory must have at least one predicate symbol.
2. An *interpretation* I for a first order theory T is a nonempty set D together with an n-place predicate in D for each n-place predicate symbol of T, an n-place operation in D for each n-place operation symbol of T, and an element of D for each constant symbol of T. Each statement of T translates in a natural manner into a statement about D. A *model* for T is an interpretation for T in which the axioms of T are true statements. For example, a model for the theory of abelian groups is (in the usual mathematical terminology) an abelian group.

   (a) Give an interpretation for the theory L in which L1 and L2 are true but L3 is false.
   (b) Give a model for AG in which D consists of a single element, and verify that every axiom is true.
   (c) Let D be the set of positive real numbers.   Interpret + as (multiplication) and 0 as 1.   Is this a model for AG?
   (d) Add axioms to L that say (in the symbolism of the predicate calculus)

   L4.   For every x, y in D, if $x < y$, then there is a z in D such that $x < z$ and $z < y$.
   L5.   For every x in D there is a y in D such that $y < x$.
   L6.   For every x in D there is a y in D such that $x < y$.

(e) Give interpretations in which (i) L1 through L3 are true but L4 is false; (ii) L1 through L4 are true but L5 is false; (iii) L1 through L5 are true but L6 is false; (iv) L1 through L6 are true.

3. Define *term* and *formula* for N.
4. Are the following strings formulas or abbreviations for formulas of N ? Why ?

(a) $\forall xy(x + y = y + x)$
(b) $\exists 0 \forall x(x + 0 = x)$

ANSWERS

1. With no predicate symbols there can be no atomic formulas and hence no formulas.
2. (c) Yes.
4. No for both. In $\forall v P$, v must be a variable.

8 The Omission of Parentheses

To simplify the appearance of formulas we adopt some conventions for the omission of parentheses. Final parentheses are omitted in formulas. For example, we write $P \to (Q \to R)$ in place of $(P \to (Q \to R))$. The parentheses in $(Q \to R)$ are retained to distinguish $P \to (Q \to R)$ from $(P \to Q) \to R$. Similarly, final parentheses are omitted in terms. For example, we write $x + (y + z)$ in place of $(x + (y + z))$.

We rank the operators $\leftrightarrow$, $\to$, $\wedge$, $\vee$, $\forall$, $\exists$, $\sim$ in the given order, with $\wedge$ and $\vee$ having equal rank and $\forall$, $\exists$, and $\sim$ having equal rank. This means that $\forall$, $\exists$, and $\sim$ have minimum possible scope. For example, in $\sim \forall v P \to Q$, the scope of $\sim$ is $\forall v P$, and the scope of $\forall v$ is P. The examples below illustrate this convention. The abbreviated formulas appear on the left. Square brackets [ ] in the right-hand formulas indicate conventions already built into the definition of formula. (That is, these brackets should not be there at all; they are used only for these examples.)

$$\sim P \to Q \wedge R \qquad [\sim P] \to (Q \wedge R)$$
$$P \wedge S \to \sim Q \leftrightarrow R \qquad ((P \wedge S) \to [\sim Q]) \leftrightarrow R$$
$$\sim \forall v P \to \exists u Q \qquad [\sim [\forall v P]] \to \exists u Q$$
$$\forall v \sim \exists u Q \vee S \to R \qquad ((\forall v [\sim [\exists u Q]]) \vee S) \to R$$

Dots are used to replace parentheses. An operator with a dot outranks all operators with no dots in a given formula. For example, $P \wedge. Q \to R$ is an abbreviation for $P \wedge (Q \to R)$. An operator with n dots outranks all operators with less than n dots. If two operators have the same number of dots, then the normal rank holds between them. We give some examples. The abbreviated formulas appear on the left.

$$\sim P \vee. Q \leftrightarrow R \qquad\qquad \sim P \vee (Q \leftrightarrow R)$$
$$P \wedge: Q \to. R \leftrightarrow S \qquad\qquad P \wedge (Q \to (R \leftrightarrow S))$$
$$\forall v.P \to Q .\leftrightarrow. \forall v P \to \forall v Q \qquad \forall v(P \to Q) \leftrightarrow (\forall v P \to \forall v Q)$$

We do not use dots with $\sim$. Because our description of the use of dots is vague, we shall use them sparingly and with caution to avoid ambiguity.

For iterated conjunctions and disjunctions we use the convention of association to the left. For example, $P \wedge Q \wedge R \wedge S$ is an abbreviation for $((P \wedge Q) \wedge R) \wedge S$. This convention is not used with $\to$ and $\leftrightarrow$.

EXERCISES

1. Use the conventions to eliminate all parentheses.

   (a) $(\forall v(P \vee Q)) \leftrightarrow ((\forall v P) \vee (\exists v Q))$
   (b) $((\forall v P) \wedge (\forall v Q)) \to ((\exists v(P \wedge Q))$
   (c) $((P \to R) \wedge (Q \to R)) \to ((P \vee Q) \to R)$
   (d) $P \to (Q \leftrightarrow (P \leftrightarrow Q))$
   (e) $\sim(\forall v(((\sim P) \wedge Q) \to R))$

2. Rewrite without using dots, but using the other conventions.

   (a) $\sim P :\vee: Q \wedge \sim R .\vee. R \wedge \sim Q$
   (b) $P :\wedge: Q .\vee. R .\to. P \leftrightarrow Q$
   (c) $\sim \forall v :P \to. \sim Q \leftrightarrow R$

ANSWERS

1. (a) $\forall v.P \vee Q .\leftrightarrow. \forall v P \vee \forall v Q$
   (b) $\forall v P \wedge \forall v Q .\to. \exists v.P \wedge Q$
   (c) $P \to R .\wedge. Q \to R .\to. P \vee Q \to R$
   (d) $P \to: Q .\leftrightarrow. P \leftrightarrow Q$
   (e) $\sim\forall v.\sim P \wedge Q \to R$

2. (a) $\sim P \vee ((Q \wedge \sim R) \vee (R \wedge \sim Q))$
   (b) $P \wedge (Q \vee R \rightarrow (P \rightarrow Q))$
   (c) $\sim \forall v (P \rightarrow (\sim Q \leftrightarrow R))$

9   Substitution of a Term for a Variable

Let P be a formula, v a variable, and t a term. Then $P(t/v)$ is the formula that results when each free occurrence of v in P is replaced by an occurrence of t. We say that $P(t/v)$ is the result of *substituting* t for v in P.

EXAMPLE 1. P is $\exists y(y > x)$. Below we list some terms, and alongside each term the result of substituting this term for x in P.

2	$\exists y(y > 2)$	$P(2/x)$
z	$\exists y(y > z)$	$P(z/x)$
$2z$	$\exists y(y > 2z)$	$P(2z/x)$
$z + 2$	$\exists y(y > z + 2)$	$P(z + 2/x)$
$x + z$	$\exists y(y > x + z)$	$P(x + z/x)$
y	$\exists y(y > y)$	$P(y/x)$

$P(2/x)$ says that there is a number greater than 2, and $P(z/x)$ says that there is a number greater than z. But $P(y/x)$ says that there is a number greater than itself. When y is substituted for x in P, y falls within the scope of the quantifier $\exists y$ and becomes bound. As a result, $P(y/x)$ does not say the same thing about y that P does about x. This kind of substitution is of no use in the predicate calculus and can lead to error. The useful substitutions are singled out by the definition below.

Let u and v be variables and P a formula. P *admits* u for v if and only if every free occurrence of v in P becomes a free occurrence of u in $P(u/v)$.

In Example 1, P does not admit y for x but admits every variable other than y for x. We extend the definition to terms. Let t be a term, v a variable, and P a formula. Then P *admits* t for v if and only if P admits u for v for every variable u that occurs in t. In Example 1, P admits t for x if and only if y does not occur in t.

EXERCISES

1. Let P be $\forall y(x < y) \lor \exists z(y = z)$.
   (a) What is $P(x_1/x)$, $P(y/x)$, $P(z/x)$, $P(2x/x)$, $P(x + y/x)$, $P(3 + y/x)$?
   (b) Which of the following terms does P admit for x: x_1, y, z, $2x$, $x + y$, $3 + y$?
   (c) What is $P(x/y)$?
   (d) What is $P(x/x)$?

2. Does P always admit v for v?   What is $P(v/v)$?

ANSWERS

1. (a) $\forall y(x_1 < y) \lor \exists z(y = z)$, $\forall y(y < y) \lor \exists z(y = z)$,
   $\forall y(z < y) \lor \exists z(y = z)$, $\forall y(2x < y) \lor \exists z(y = z)$,
   $\forall y(x + y < y) \lor \exists z(y = z)$, $\forall y(3 + y < y) \lor \exists z(y = z)$
   (b) x_1, z, $2x$
   (c) $\forall y(x < y) \lor \exists z(x = z)$
   (d) P

10   Removing and Inserting Quantifiers

The rule of *specialization* is

$$\frac{\forall v P}{P(t/v)}$$ provided P admits the term t for v

The idea is that if P is true for every v, then in particular it is true for t.

EXAMPLE 1.

$$\frac{\forall x(x \geqslant 0)}{x \geqslant 0} \qquad \frac{\forall x(x \geqslant 0)}{y \geqslant 0} \qquad \frac{\forall x(x \geqslant 0)}{2 \geqslant 0} \qquad \frac{\forall x(x \geqslant 0)}{1 + yz \geqslant 0}$$

The rule of *existential introduction* is

$$\frac{P(t/v)}{\exists v P}$$ provided P admits the term t for v

The idea is that if P is true for t, then there is a v for which P is true.

EXAMPLE 2.

$$\frac{x > 2}{\exists x(x > 2)} \qquad \frac{y > 2}{\exists x(x > 2)} \qquad \frac{5 > 2}{\exists x(x > 2)} \qquad \frac{1 + y > 2}{\exists x(x > 2)}$$

The rule of *generalization* is

$$\frac{P}{\forall v P} \qquad \text{provided } v \text{ is not restricted}$$

The only interesting applications of this rule occur when v is free in P. The idea is that if P is true for v, and v is not restricted (i.e., stands for an arbitrary element of the domain), then P is true for every element of the domain.

EXAMPLE 3.   Let f be the function that assigns to each real number x the real number x^2, and let g be the function that assigns to each real number x the real number $2x$.   Then the derivative of f exists and is g.

Proof.   Let x be a fixed but arbitrary real number.   Then for $h \neq 0$, we have

$$\lim_{h \to 0} \frac{(x + h)^2 - x^2}{h} = \lim_{h \to 0} \frac{x^2 + 2xh + h^2 - x^2}{h}$$

$$= \lim_{h \to 0} \frac{2xh + h^2}{h} = \lim_{h \to 0} (2x + h) = 2x$$

We have shown that the derivative of f at x exists and is $2x$.   Since x is arbitrary, the derivative of f exists and is $2x$ for *every* x.

The rule of *existential elimination* is

$$\frac{\exists v P}{P(u/v)} \qquad \text{where } u \text{ is a variable that is not restricted}$$

The idea is that if P is true for some v, then we can choose some object u for which P is true.   We call existential elimination "Rule C" ("C" for "choose").   The precise restrictions on generalization and Rule C are given in Chapter 2.   Now we give some examples that show how careless use of these rules can lead to error.

EXAMPLE 4.   We begin with the true statement $\exists x(x < 2)$ of number theory, apply Rule C to get $x < 2$, and then generalize to get the false statement $\forall x(x < 2)$.   When P is inferred from $\exists x P$ by Rule C, x becomes restricted and is not eligible for generalization.

EXAMPLE 5.   We begin with the two true statements $\exists x(x < 2)$ and $\exists x(x > 2)$ of number theory.   Rule C applied to each statement gives

$x < 2$ and $x > 2$. Then we infer $x < 2 \land x > 2$. Then existential introduction gives the false statement $\exists x(x < 2 \land x > 2)$. The error lies in using the same variable x in both applications of Rule C. After $x < 2$ is inferred from $\exists x(x < 2)$ by Rule C, x becomes restricted and is not eligible for another use of Rule C. We may now apply Rule C to $\exists x(x > 2)$ to get $y > 2$, but no false statement results from $x < 2 \land y > 2$. The idea is that in inferring $x < 2$ from $\exists x(x < 2)$ by Rule C, we choose some integer x that is less than 2. In inferring $y > 2$ from $\exists x(x > 2)$ we choose an integer y that is greater than 2. If we also call the second integer x, then we are assuming (incorrectly) that there is an integer x that is both less than 2 and greater than 2.

EXAMPLE 6. We begin with the true statement $\forall y \exists x(y < x)$ of number theory, apply specialization to get $\exists x(y < x)$, and then apply Rule C to get $y < x$. Then we generalize to get $\forall y(y < x)$, and finally we apply existential introduction to get the false statement $\exists x \forall y(y < x)$. The error occurs in the application of generalization. When Rule C is applied to $\exists x(y < x)$ to give $y < x$, both x and y become restricted. Example 4 shows why x should be restricted. That y should become restricted when Rule C is applied to pass from $\exists x(y < x)$ to $y < x$ is perhaps surprising. This example shows why the restriction is necessary.

From Examples 4 through 6 we see that a variable becomes restricted when it occurs free in a formula that is inferred by Rule C.

EXAMPLE 7. We begin with the true statement $\exists x \forall y(y + x = y)$ of number theory, strip away the quantifiers by Rule C and specialization to get $y + x = y$, and then reinsert the quantifiers in reverse order by existential introduction and generalization to get $\forall y \exists x(y + x = y)$. The result is a true statement and no error occurs. In applying Rule C to $\exists x \forall y(y + x = y)$ to get $\forall y(y + x = y)$, only x becomes restricted because y is not free in $\forall y(y + x = y)$. Therefore in the final step we can safely generalize on y. Note that there are no restrictions on specialization and existential introduction (except that P admits t for v, which is always satisfied when t is v).

EXERCISES

1. For each statement in list I state which statements in list II may be inferred from it by one or more applications of the four rules for

removing and inserting quantifiers, and give the step-by-step derivation.

I. $2 < 5$, $\exists y \forall x(yx = x)$, $\forall x(x \geqslant 0)$, $\forall x \exists y(x < y)$.

II. $\exists y \forall x(x < y)$, $\exists y(2 < y)$, $3 \geqslant 0$, $\exists x(x < 5)$,
    $\forall x \exists y(yx = x)$, $\exists y(y \geqslant 0)$, $\exists x \exists y(x < y)$.

Example.

$$\frac{\dfrac{\forall x(x \geqslant 0)}{y \geqslant 0}}{\exists y(y \geqslant 0)}$$ specialization
    existential introduction

2. Give a working proof from a mathematics book in which all four of the rules for removing and inserting quantifiers are used.

11   Denials

A *denial* of a statement P is a statement which has the same meaning as $\sim P$. $\sim P$ is the simplest denial of P but not always the most useful.   For example, the negation of

$$\forall x \forall y \exists z(x + y = z) \tag{1}$$

is

$$\sim \forall x \forall y \exists z(x + y = z) \tag{2}$$

Equivalent to (2) is

$$\exists x \exists y \forall z \sim (x + y = z) \tag{3}$$

which is a more useful denial.   In (3), the quantifiers come at the beginning, and hence the rules for removing quantifiers can be applied. In general, it is desirable to transfer the negation sign in front of a statement as far as possible into the statement.   We list below some rules which provide a means of finding useful denials of statements. We say that two statements are *equivalent* if they have the same meaning.

(a) $\sim(P \lor Q)$ is equivalent to $\sim P \land \sim Q$
(b) $\sim(P \land Q)$ is equivalent to $\sim P \lor \sim Q$
(c) $\sim \exists x P$ is equivalent to $\forall x \sim P$
(d) $\sim \forall x P$ is equivalent to $\exists x \sim P$
(e) $\sim(P \rightarrow Q)$ is equivalent to $P \land \sim Q$

The rules apply not only to statements but to formulas and also to formulas that are parts of other formulas.

EXAMPLE 1.   We show how to pass from (2) to (3) using the rules above. (d) applied to (2) gives

$$\exists x \sim \forall y \exists z (x + y = z) \qquad (4)$$

Then (d) applied to (4) gives

$$\exists x \exists y \sim \exists z (x + y = z) \qquad (5)$$

Finally, (c) applied to (5) gives (3).

EXAMPLE 2.   The negation of

$$\forall x (P \lor Q) \qquad (6)$$

is

$$\sim \forall x (P \lor Q) \qquad (7)$$

which, by (d), is equivalent to

$$\exists x \sim (P \lor Q) \qquad (8)$$

Then, by (a), (8) is equivalent to

$$\exists x (\sim P \land \sim Q) \qquad (9)$$

EXAMPLE 3.   The negation of

$$\exists x (P \rightarrow Q) \qquad (10)$$

is

$$\sim \exists x (P \rightarrow Q) \qquad (11)$$

which, by (c), is equivalent to

$$\forall x \sim (P \rightarrow Q) \qquad (12)$$

Then, by (e), (12) is equivalent to

$$\forall x (P \land \sim Q) \qquad (13)$$

EXAMPLE 4.   A denial of

$$\forall x \exists y (y \leqslant x) \qquad (14)$$

is

$$\exists x \forall y \sim (y \leqslant x) \qquad (15)$$

Logic can take us no further, but number theory enables us to replace $\sim(y \leqslant x)$ by $y > x$ to get

$$\exists x \forall y (y > x) \tag{16}$$

EXAMPLE 5.   In most applications, the most useful denial of

$$P_1 \wedge \cdots \wedge P_n \rightarrow Q \tag{17}$$

is

$$P_1 \wedge \cdots \wedge P_n \wedge \sim Q \tag{18}$$

which results by (e) when (17) is considered to be of the form $P \rightarrow Q$.

EXAMPLE 6.   The formula

$$\exists \delta (\delta > 0 \wedge Q) \tag{19}$$

occurs as a part of many formulas in mathematical analysis.   Using (c) and (b), a denial of (19) is

$$\forall \delta (\sim \delta > 0 \vee \sim Q) \tag{20}$$

The mathematician is interested only in positive δ's.   Since $\sim P \vee \sim Q$ is equivalent to $P \rightarrow \sim Q$, (20) is equivalent to

$$\forall \delta (\delta > 0 \rightarrow \sim Q) \tag{21}$$

which is the most useful denial in practice.

EXAMPLE 7.   In the domain of human beings we set out to translate into logical symbolism the statement

$$\text{Every dictator is cruel} \tag{22}$$

A denial of (22) is

$$\text{There is a dictator who is not cruel} \tag{23}$$

By Example 5 in Section 6, (23) translates into

$$\exists x (x \text{ is a dictator} \wedge \sim(x \text{ is cruel})) \tag{24}$$

Because a denial of a denial of P is equivalent to P, we now find a denial of (24).   (c) and (b) give

$$\forall x (\sim(x \text{ is a dictator}) \vee \sim\sim(x \text{ is cruel})) \tag{25}$$

Since $\sim P \vee \sim\sim Q$ is equivalent to $\sim P \vee Q$ which is equivalent to $P \to Q$, we finally get

$$\forall x(x \text{ is a dictator} \to x \text{ is cruel}) \qquad (26)$$

as the translation of (22).

If P is false, then the conditional $P \to Q$ is true. We say that it is *vacuously* true. In Chapter 2 we show that we can get by with modus ponens as the only rule of inference. If $P \to Q$ is vacuously true, then Q may be true or false, but there is no danger of inferring a false Q from modus ponens on $P \to Q$ and P because P is false.

EXAMPLE 8. Let A be a set. We shall prove that $\varnothing \subseteq A$. By Example 7, $\varnothing \subseteq A$ translates into $\forall x(x \in \varnothing \to x \in A)$. Let d be any element of the domain. $d \in \varnothing \to d \in A$ is vacuously true. Hence $\forall x(x \in \varnothing \to x \in A)$ is true by the interpretation for $\forall$. We say that $\varnothing \subseteq A$ is vacuously true.

It is customary in mathematics to say that the converse of $\forall x(P \to Q)$ is $\forall x(Q \to P)$. Thus the converse of "Every integer is a real number" is "Every real number is an integer."

EXERCISES

1. Find a useful denial of each of the following formulas.

    (a) $\exists y \forall x(xy = x)$
    (b) $\forall x \forall y(x < y \vee x \geqslant y)$
    (c) $P \wedge \sim Q \to \sim R$
    (d) $\sim \forall x \forall y \exists z(xz = y)$
    (e) $\forall \varepsilon \exists \delta \forall x.|x - c| < \delta \to |f(x) - f(c)| < \varepsilon$
    (f) $\forall \varepsilon . \varepsilon > 0 \to \exists \delta(\delta > 0 \wedge \forall x(|x - c| < \delta \to |f(x) - f(c)| < \varepsilon))$
    (g) $\forall \varepsilon \exists n \forall m . m > n \to |a_m - a| < \varepsilon$
    (h) $\exists y(y \in M) \to \exists x(x \in M \wedge \forall z(z \in M \to x \leqslant z))$
    (i) $\forall M . 0 \in M \wedge \forall x(x \in M \to x + 1 \in M) \to \forall x(x \in M)$

2. In the domain of human beings, translate into symbolic form.

    (a) Everybody is greedy
    (b) Nobody is greedy
    (c) Every college dean is greedy
    (d) No college dean is greedy
    (e) Not all freshman girls are beautiful
    (f) All freshman girls are not beautiful

ANSWERS

1. (a) $\forall y \exists x (xy \neq x)$
   (b) $\exists x \exists y (\sim(x < y) \wedge \sim(x \geqslant y))$
   (c) $P \wedge \sim Q \wedge R$
   (d) $\forall x \forall y \forall z (xz = y)$
   (e) $\exists \varepsilon \forall \delta \exists x . |x - c| < \delta \wedge |f(x) - f(c)| \geqslant \varepsilon$
   (f) $\exists \varepsilon . \varepsilon > 0 \wedge \forall \delta (\delta > 0 \to \exists x (|x - c| < \delta \wedge |f(x) - f(c)| \geqslant \varepsilon))$
   (g) $\exists \varepsilon \forall n \exists m . m > n \wedge |a_m - a| \geqslant \varepsilon$
   (h) $\exists y (y \in M) \wedge \forall x (x \in M \to \exists z (z \in M \wedge x > z))$
   (i) $\exists M . 0 \in M \wedge \forall x (x \in M \to x + 1 \in M) \wedge \exists x (\sim x \in M)$

2. (a) $\forall x (x$ is greedy$)$
   (b) $\forall x \sim (x$ is greedy$)$
   (c) $\forall x (x$ is a college dean $\to x$ is greedy$)$
   (d) $\forall x (x$ is a college dean $\to \sim(x$ is greedy$))$
   (e) $\sim \forall x (x$ is a freshman girl $\to x$ is beautiful$)$ or
       $\exists x (x$ is a freshman girl and $\sim(x$ is beautiful$))$
   (f) $\forall x (x$ is a freshman girl $\to \sim(x$ is beautiful$))$

2

THE PREDICATE CALCULUS

In this chapter we shall formulate and develop the first order predicate calculus as a formal axiomatic theory. We shall make a fresh start, pushing Chapter 1 to the background.

12   Formulation

The formal symbols are

$$\sim \quad \rightarrow \quad \forall \quad (\quad , \quad) \quad \alpha \quad \beta \quad \gamma \quad x \quad | \quad \#$$

A *string* is a finite sequence of formal symbols.

A *variable* is a string consisting of an occurrence of x followed by zero or more occurrences of $|$. In other words, the variables are x, $x|$, $x||$, $x|||$, ..., and we call this order of the variables the *alphabetic order*.

An *n-place predicate symbol* (n a positive integer) is a string consisting of an occurrence of α followed by n occurrences of $\#$ followed by zero or more occurrences of $|$. Thus the 2-place predicate symbols are $\alpha\#\#$, $\alpha\#\#|$, $\alpha\#\#||$, $\alpha\#\#|||$, ...

An *n-place operation symbol* (n a positive integer) is a string consisting of an occurrence of β followed by n occurrences of $\#$ followed by zero or more occurrences of $|$. Thus the 2-place operation symbols are $\beta\#\#$, $\beta\#\#|$, $\beta\#\#||$, $\beta\#\#|||$, ...

A *constant symbol* is a string consisting of an occurrence of γ followed by zero or more occurrences of $|$. The constant symbols are γ, $\gamma|$, $\gamma||$, ...

Term is defined as follows: (1) Every variable is a term. (2) Every constant symbol is a term. (3) If F is an n-place operation symbol, and $t_1, \ldots, t_n$ are terms (not necessarily distinct), then $F(t_1, \ldots, t_n)$ is a term. (4) Only strings are terms, and a string is a term only if its being so follows from (1), (2), or (3).

Formula is defined as follows: (1) If G is an n-place predicate symbol, and $t_1, \ldots, t_n$ are terms (not necessarily distinct), then $G(t_1, \ldots, t_n)$ is a formula (an atomic formula). (2) If P and Q are formulas, then $(P \to Q)$ is a formula. (3) If P is a formula, then $\sim P$ is a formula. (4) If P is a formula and v is a variable, then $\forall v P$ is a formula. (5) Only strings are formulas, and a string is a formula only if its being so follows from (1), (2), (3), or (4).

A *subformula* of the formula P is a consecutive part of P that is itself a formula.

An occurrence of a variable v in a formula P is *bound* if and only if it occurs in a subformula of P of the form $\forall v Q$. An occurrence of v in P is *free* if and only if it is not a bound occurrence. The variable v is *free* or *bound* in P according as it has a free or bound occurrence in P.

A *statement* or *closed formula* is a formula with no free variables. If P is a formula and $v_1, \ldots, v_n$ are the distinct variables that are free in P in the order (from left to right) in which they first occur free in P, then $\forall v_1 \cdots \forall v_n P$ is the *closure* of P.

If P is a formula, v is a variable, and t is a term, then $P(t/v)$ is the result of replacing each free occurrence of v in P by an occurrence of t.

If v and u are variables and P is a formula, then P *admits u for v* if and only if there is no free occurrence of v in P that becomes a bound occurrence of u in $P(u/v)$. If t is a term, then P *admits t for v* if and only if P admits for v every variable in t.

We use "P," "Q," "R," "S," "U," and "V" to stand for formulas, "u," "v," and "w" to stand for variables, "G" and "H" to stand for predicate symbols, "F" to stand for an operation symbol, "r," "s," and "t" to stand for terms, and "c" to stand for a constant symbol.

The conventions of Section 8 for the omission of parentheses are carried over.

$P \vee Q$ is an abbreviation for $\sim P \to Q$
$P \wedge Q$ is an abbreviation for $\sim(P \to \sim Q)$
$P \leftrightarrow Q$ is an abbreviation for $(P \to Q) \wedge (Q \to P)$
$\exists v P$ is an abbreviation for $\sim \forall v \sim P$

The only reason for defining the variables, predicate symbols, operation symbols, and constant symbols as we have done above is to show that they can all be defined using only a finite number of formal symbols.

The notions of string, variable, predicate symbol, operation symbol, constant symbol, term, formula, and statement are all effective.

This completes the description of the linguistic aspect of the predicate calculus. We turn now to the notion of deduction.

Let P, Q, and S be any formulas, v any variable, and t any term. Then each of the following formulas is an axiom.

A1. $P \to . Q \to P$
A2. $S \to . P \to Q :\to: S \to P . \to . S \to Q$
A3. $\sim Q \to \sim P . \to . P \to Q$
A4. $\forall v(P \to Q) . \to . \forall v P \to \forall v Q$
A5. $\forall v P \to P(t/v)$ provided P admits t for v
A6. $P \to \forall v P$ provided v is not free in P

Further, if P is an axiom, and v is free in P, then $\forall v P$ is also an axiom (axiom generalization, or Ax Gen).

There is exactly one rule of inference: from $P \to Q$ and P to infer Q (modus ponens).

A1 through A6 are called *axiom schemes*. Each axiom scheme provides infinitely many axioms, which we call *instances* of the axiom scheme. For each axiom provided by an axiom scheme, Ax Gen provides a finite number of additional axioms. Although the number of axioms is infinite, the notion of axiom is effective because each axiom has one of six recognizable forms.

If Q is inferred by modus ponens on $P \to Q$ and P, we call $P \to Q$ the *major premiss* and P the *minor premiss*.

Let Δ be a finite set of formulas. We define "deduction from Δ," which reduces to "proof" when Δ is the empty set.

A deduction from Δ is a finite sequence $S_1, \ldots, S_n$ of formulas such that for each S_i ($1 \leqslant i \leqslant n$), at least one of the following holds.

1. S_i is an axiom   (axiom)
2. S_i is in Δ (assumption)
3. There exist positive integers j and k, each less than i, such that S_k is $S_j \rightarrow S_i$ (modus ponens)

The following statements have the same meaning.

There is a deduction $S_1, \ldots, S_n$ from Δ such that S_n is Q
There is a deduction of Q from Δ
Δ yields Q
$\Delta \vdash Q$

A *proof* is a deduction from the empty set.   The following statements have the same meaning.

$\varnothing \vdash Q$ ($\Delta \vdash Q$ with Δ empty)
$\vdash Q$
Q is a theorem
Q is provable

The formulas in Δ are called *assumptions*.   If Δ is the empty set, then each step in a deduction from Δ is justified as an axiom or by modus ponens, and hence the deduction is a proof according to the definition of proof given in Section 3 (replacing "statement" by "formula").   If Δ is not empty, and one or more steps in a deduction from Δ are justified only as assumptions (clause 2), then this deduction is *not* a proof.   The last step is not proved outright, it is merely *deduced from* Δ.   Deductions are useful because they afford a means of *discovering* proofs (as we shall show).

In order to be able to write some formulas of the predicate calculus without cluttering up the page with weird symbols, we make the following conventions.   We write the variables (in alphabetic order) as

$$x \quad y \quad z \quad x_1 \quad y_1 \quad z_1 \quad x_2 \ldots$$

We write A, B, and C for the first three n-place predicate symbols (for every n).   Hence $A(x, y, z)$, $B(x, z)$, $A(x)$,   and $C(x, y, z, x_1)$ are formulas.

EXERCISES

1. For each of the six axiom schemes, give one axiom provided by the scheme.   (You may use A, B, C, x, y, z.)

2. Let P be an axiom with exactly three free variables. How many additional axioms derived from P can one get by using Ax Gen?

3. Write out the formula $A(x, y, z) \land \exists x B(x)$ in full, using no abbreviations or conventions.

4. Let $S_1, \ldots, S_n$ be a deduction from Δ. Prove that for every m $(1 \leqslant m \leqslant n)$, $S_1, \ldots, S_m$ is also a deduction from Δ.

5. Is $\vdash$ a formal symbol? Why?

ANSWERS

2. 15.

3. $\sim(\alpha\#\#\#(x, x|, x||) \to \sim\sim\forall x\sim\alpha\#|(x))$.

5. No. There are exactly 12 formal symbols, and $\vdash$ is not one of them.

13 The Statement Calculus

The statement calculus is that part of the predicate calculus that remains when axiom schemes A4 through A6 and Ax Gen are discarded. To put it another way, we use axiom schemes A1 through A3, modus ponens, and the same definition of deduction. We develop the statement calculus first, and then use it to develop the full predicate calculus.

THEOREM 1. $\vdash A(x) \to A(x)$

Proof. A formal proof of $A(x) \to A(x)$ is exhibited below.

$A(x) \to: A(x) \to A(x) . \to A(x) .:\to:. A(x) \to. A(x) \to A(x) :\to: A(x) \to A(x)$
$A(x) \to: A(x) \to A(x) .\to. A(x)$
$A(x) \to. A(x) \to A(x) :\to: A(x) \to A(x)$
$A(x) \to. A(x) \to A(x)$
$A(x) \to A(x)$

Theorem 1 is the statement, "$A(x) \to A(x)$ is a theorem." Because this statement is in the metalanguage, Theorem 1 is a metatheorem. Its proof is an argument in the metalanguage designed to convince the reader that there is a formal proof of $A(x) \to A(x)$. No argument is more convincing than the exhibition of such a formal proof.

If $\Delta = \{P_1, \ldots, P_k\}$, we write "$P_1, \ldots, P_k \vdash Q$" for "$\Delta \vdash Q$."

THEOREM 2. $\sim A(x) \vdash A(x) \to B(y)$

Proof.   A formal deduction of $A(x) \to B(y)$ from $\sim A(x)$ is exhibited below.

$$\sim A(x)$$
$$\sim A(x) .\to. \sim B(y) \to \sim A(x)$$
$$\sim B(y) \to \sim A(x)$$
$$\sim B(y) \to \sim A(x) .\to. A(x) \to B(y)$$
$$A(x) \to B(y)$$

No analysis (justification for the steps) is given in the proofs of Theorems 1 and 2 because the definition of deduction makes no provision for an analysis.   None is necessary; each step can be effectively checked to determine if it is an axiom or an assumption or if it is inferred from two earlier steps by modus ponens.   The formal proof of $A(x) \to A(x)$ can be analyzed as follows.   Step 1 is an axiom—the instance of A2 in which S is $A(x)$, P is $A(x) \to A(x)$, and Q is $A(x)$.   Step 2 is an axiom—the instance of A1 in which P is $A(x)$ and Q is $A(x) \to A(x)$. Step 3 is inferred by modus ponens on steps 1 and 2.   Step 4 is an axiom—the instance of A1 in which P is $A(x)$ and Q is $A(x)$.   Step 5 is inferred by modus ponens on steps 3 and 4.

Because this book is intended for human readers rather than deduction-checking robots, we shall henceforth supply an analysis with each formal deduction.   The amount of detail in an analysis is a matter of taste.   For the formal proof of $A(x) \to A(x)$, we like the following analysis.

1. $A(x) \to: A(x) \to A(x) .\to. A(x) .:\to:. A(x) .\to. A(x) \to$
    $A(x) :\to: A(x) \to A(x)$ A2
2. $A(x) :\to: A(x) \to A(x) .\to. A(x)$ A1
3. $A(x) .\to. A(x) \to A(x) :\to: A(x) \to A(x)$ MP, 1, 2
4. $A(x) .\to. A(x) \to A(x)$ A1
5. $A(x) \to A(x)$ MP, 3, 4

"A2" after step 1 indicates that step 1 is an instance of axiom scheme A2.   "MP, 1, 2" after step 3 indicates that step 3 is inferred by modus ponens on steps 1 and 2, with step 1 the major premiss and step 2 the minor premiss.   (We always give the number of the major premiss first.)

THEOREM 3. $\vdash \sim A(x) \to. A(x) \to B(y)$

Proof.

1. $\sim B(y) \to \sim A(x) \,.\to.\, A(x) \to B(y)$ A3
2. $\sim B(y) \to \sim A(x) \,.\to.\, A(x) \to B(y) \,.:\to:.\, \sim A(x) \,:\to:$
    $\sim B(y) \to \sim A(x) \,.\to.\, A(x) \to B(y)$ A1
3. $\sim A(x) \,:\to:\, \sim B(y) \to \sim A(x) \,.\to.\, A(x) \to B(y)$ MP, 2, 1
4. $\sim A(x) \,:\to:\, \sim B(y) \to \sim A(x) \,.\to.\, A(x) \to B(y) \,.:\to:.$
    $\sim A(x) \,.\to.\, \sim B(y) \to \sim A(x) \,:\to:\, \sim A(x) \,.\to.$
    $A(x) \to B(y)$ A2
5. $\sim A(x) \,.\to.\, \sim B(y) \to \sim A(x) \,:\to:\, \sim A(x) \,.\to.$
    $A(x) \to B(y)$ MP, 4, 3
6. $\sim A(x) \,.\to.\, \sim B(y) \to \sim A(x)$ A1
7. $\sim A(x) \,.\to.\, A(x) \to B(y)$ MP, 5, 6

THEOREM 4. $A(x) \to B(y),\ B(y) \to C(z),\ A(x) \vdash C(z)$

Proof.

1. $A(x) \to B(y)$ as
2. $B(y) \to C(z)$ as
3. $A(x)$ as
4. $B(y)$ MP, 1, 3
5. $C(z)$ MP, 2, 4

"as" is an abbreviation for "assumption."

The formal proof of $A(x) \to A(x)$ is easily modified to give a formal proof of $B(y) \to B(y)$ or $A(x) \to \sim C(z) \,.\to.\, A(x) \to \sim C(z)$. We need only replace $A(x)$ throughout by $B(y)$ or $A(x) \to \sim C(z)$. Indeed, a formal proof of $P \to P$ for any formula P can be obtained by replacing $A(x)$ throughout by P.

THEOREM 5. $\vdash P \to P$.   (For every formula P, $\vdash P \to P$.)

Proof.   Let P be a fixed but arbitrary formula.   Then the sequence of five steps below is a formal proof of $P \to P$.

1. $P \to:\, P \to P \,.\to.\, P \,.:\to:.\, P \to.\, P \to P \,:\to:\, P \to P$ A2
2. $P \to:\, P \to P \,.\to.\, P$ A1
3. $P \to.\, P \to P \,:\to:\, P \to P$ MP, 1, 2
4. $P \to.\, P \to P$ A1
5. $P \to P$

$P \to P$ is not a formula because "P" is not a formal symbol. We call $P \to P$ a *formula scheme*. Any particular formula of the form $P \to P$, such as $A(x) \to \sim C(z) . \to . A(x) \to \sim C(z)$, we call an *instance* of $P \to P$. Theorem 5 states that every instance of $P \to P$ is a theorem. Therefore we call $P \to P$ a *theorem scheme*. The proof of Theorem 5 gives a uniform and effective procedure for constructing a formal proof of any instance of $P \to P$.

From now on we shall prove theorem schemes instead of individual formal theorems.

THEOREM 6. $\vdash \sim P \to . P \to Q$

Proof. Let P and Q be fixed but arbitrary formulas. Then the sequence of seven steps below is a formal proof of $\sim P \to . P \to Q$.

1. $\sim Q \to \sim P . \to . P \to Q$ A3
2. $\sim Q \to \sim P . \to . P \to Q . : \to : . \sim P : \to : \sim Q \to \sim P . \to .$
    $P \to Q$ A1
3. $\sim P : \to : \sim Q \to \sim P . \to . P \to Q$ MP, 2, 1
4. $\sim P : \to : \sim Q \to \sim P . \to . P \to Q . : \to : . \sim P . \to . \sim Q \to$
    $\sim P : \to : \sim P . \to . P \to Q$ A2
5. $\sim P . \to . \sim Q \to \sim P : \to : \sim P . \to . P \to Q$ MP, 4, 3
6. $\sim P . \to . \sim Q \to \sim P$ A1
7. $\sim P . \to . P \to Q$ MP, 5, 6

We give below some examples to clarify the distinction between a theorem, a theorem scheme, the assertion that something is a theorem, and the assertion that something is a theorem scheme.

$A(x) \to A(x)$	A formula. Also a theorem.
$P \to P$	A formula scheme. Also a theorem scheme.
$\vdash A(x) \to A(x)$	The assertion "$A(x) \to A(x)$ is a theorem."
$\vdash P \to P$	The assertion "$P \to P$ is a theorem scheme."

EXERCISES

1. Give a formal proof of

$$A(x) \to B(y) . \to . A(x) : \to : A(x) \to B(y) . \to . B(y)$$

2. Is the following formal proof correct?   Why?

   1. $A(x) \to. B(y) \to A(x) :\to: A(x) \to B(y) .\to. A(x) \to A(x)$

                                  A2, S is $A(x)$, P is $B(y)$, Q is $A(x)$

   2. $A(x) \to. B(y) \to A(x)$ A1, P is $A(x)$, Q is $B(y)$

   3. $A(x) \to B(y) .\to. A(x) \to A(x)$ MP, 1, 2

   4. $A(x) \to. B(y) \to A(x) :\to: A(x) \to A(x)$

                      Substitute $B(y) \to A(x)$ for $B(y)$ in 3

   5. $A(x) \to A(x)$ MP, 4, 2

3. Give a formal deduction for each of the following.

   (a) $\sim A(x) \to \sim B(y),\ B(y),\ A(x) \to C(z) \vdash C(z)$

   (b) $\sim A(x) \to. B(y) \to \sim C(z),\ \sim A(x) \to B(y),\ C(z) \vdash A(x)$

4. Prove $\sim P \vdash P \to Q$

14   The Deduction Theorem

We write "$\Delta, P \vdash Q$" for "$\Delta \cup \{P\} \vdash Q$."   The deduction theorem is

$$\text{If } \Delta, P \vdash Q, \text{ then } \Delta \vdash P \to Q$$

Before proving the theorem, we give some examples.

EXAMPLE 1.   Theorem 13.2 is $\sim A(x) \vdash A(x) \to B(y)$.   Let Δ be the empty set, P be $\sim A(x)$, and Q be $A(x) \to B(y)$.   Then the deduction theorem applied to Theorem 13.2 gives $\vdash \sim A(x) .\to. A(x) \to B(y)$.

EXAMPLE 2.   Theorem 13.4 is $A(x) \to B(y),\ B(y) \to C(z),\ A(x) \vdash C(z)$.   Let $\Delta = \{A(x) \to B(y),\ B(y) \to C(z)\}$, P be $A(x)$, and Q be $C(z)$.   Then the deduction theorem applied to Theorem 13.4 gives

$$A(x) \to B(y),\ B(y) \to C(z) \vdash A(x) \to C(z) \tag{1}$$

Now let $\Delta = \{A(x) \to B(y)\}$, P be $B(y) \to C(z)$, and Q be $A(x) \to C(z)$.   The deduction theorem applied to (1) gives

$$A(x) \to B(y) \vdash B(y) \to C(z) .\to. A(x) \to C(z) \tag{2}$$

Now let Δ be the empty set, P be $A(x) \to B(y)$, and Q be $B(y) \to C(z) .\to. A(x) \to C(z)$.   The deduction theorem applied to (2) gives $\vdash A(x) \to B(y) :\to: B(y) \to C(z) .\to. A(x) \to C(z)$.

When Δ is the empty set, the deduction theorem becomes

$$\text{If } P \vdash Q, \text{ then } \vdash P \to Q \tag{3}$$

The usual way of proving a conditional $P \to Q$ in mathematics is to assume P and deduce Q. Now a deduction of Q from P is not the same thing as a proof of $P \to Q$. In a deduction of Q from P, P is an assumption and the last step is Q, while in a proof of $P \to Q$ there are no assumptions and the last step is $P \to Q$. But (3) says that every deduction of Q from P can be converted into a proof of $P \to Q$. From the standpoint of the logician, (3) justifies a common mathematical practice. From the standpoint of the mathematician, (3) indicates that the predicate calculus is in accordance with mathematical custom.

In passing from Δ, $P \vdash Q$ to $\Delta \vdash P \to Q$ by the deduction theorem, we say that the assumption P has been *discharged*. When an assumption is discharged by the deduction theorem it does not disappear; it is transferred across $\vdash$ to become the antecedent of a conditional.

THEOREM 3 (*The deduction theorem*).   If Δ, $P \vdash Q$, then $\Delta \vdash P \to Q$.

Proof. Let $S_1, \ldots, S_n$ be a deduction of Q from $\Delta \cup \{P\}$. First we supply an analysis if none is provided. The idea behind the proof is to convert each step S_i into $P \to S_i$, using only formulas in Δ as assumptions. Then $P \to S_n$ is $P \to Q$. The steps of the form $P \to S_i$ are called the *key* steps. In general, the sequence $P \to S_1, \ldots, P \to S_n$ is not a deduction from Δ, so we show how to insert steps before each key step to make the whole a deduction from Δ. We begin with S_1. S_1 is an axiom or is in Δ or is P.

Case 1. S_1 is an axiom. The following sequence of three steps is a deduction of $P \to S_1$ from Δ.

$$
\begin{array}{ll}
S_1 & \text{axiom} \\
S_1 \,.\!\to.\, P \to S_1 & \text{A1} \\
P \to S_1 & \text{MP}
\end{array}
$$

The sequence above is actually a proof of $P \to S_1$, since no step is justified as an assumption. By the definition of deduction, it is also a deduction from Δ. In a deduction from Δ, only formulas in Δ can be justified as assumptions, but there is no compulsion to use all, or even any, of the formulas in Δ.

Case 2. S_1 is in Δ. The following sequence of three steps is a deduction of $P \to S_1$ from Δ.

$$S_1 \qquad\qquad \text{assumption}$$
$$S_1 \mathrel{.\to.} P \to S_1 \qquad \text{A1}$$
$$P \to S_1 \qquad\qquad \text{MP}$$

Case 3. S_1 is P. Then $P \to S_1$ is $P \to P$, and we supply the five-step proof of $P \to P$.

So we have a sequence of three or five steps that is a deduction of $P \to S_1$ from Δ. Let us call this sequence $\mathscr{S}_1$. Now we consider S_2. Like S_1, S_2 is an axiom or is in Δ or is P. For each case we imitate the corresponding case for S_1, replacing S_1 throughout by S_2 to get a sequence of three or five steps that is a deduction of S_2 from Δ. Call this sequence $\mathscr{S}_2$. Now we write $\mathscr{S}_2$ after $\mathscr{S}_1$. The result is a sequence which is a deduction of $P \to S_2$ from Δ in which $P \to S_1$ and $P \to S_2$ are steps. For example, suppose S_1 is an axiom and S_2 is in Δ. Then $\mathscr{S}_1, \mathscr{S}_2$ is

$$\mathscr{S}_1 \begin{cases} 1. & S_1 & \text{axiom} \\ 2. & S_1 \mathrel{.\to.} P \to S_1 & \text{A1} \\ 3. & P \to S_1 & \text{MP, 2, 1} \end{cases}$$

$$\mathscr{S}_2 \begin{cases} 4. & S_2 & \text{assumption} \\ 5. & S_2 \mathrel{.\to.} P \to S_2 & \text{A1} \\ 6. & P \to S_2 & \text{MP, 5, 4} \end{cases}$$

Suppose that one of cases 1, 2, or 3 applies to each of $S_1, S_2, \ldots, S_m$. We proceed as above to get $\mathscr{S}_1, \mathscr{S}_2, \ldots, \mathscr{S}_m$, which is a deduction of $P \to S_m$ from Δ in which $P \to S_1, \ldots, P \to S_m$ are steps. Suppose that S_{m+1} is inferred from S_j and S_k by modus ponens.

Case 4. S_k is $S_j \to S_{m+1}$, and S_{m+1} is inferred by modus ponens on S_k and S_j. In the deduction $\mathscr{S}_1, \ldots, \mathscr{S}_m$ from Δ appear the following key steps:

(a) $P \to (S_j \to S_{m+1})$

and

(b) $P \to S_j$

Then $\mathscr{S}_{m+1}$ is

(i) $P \to (S_j \to S_{m+1}) \mathrel{.\to.} (P \to S_j) \to (P \to S_{m+1})$ \qquad A2

(ii) $P \to S_j \mathrel{.\to.} P \to S_{m+1}$ \qquad MP, (i), (a)

(iii) $P \to S_{m+1}$ \qquad MP, (ii), (b)

We continue in this manner through $S_1, \ldots, S_n$, getting a deduction $\mathscr{S}_1, \ldots, \mathscr{S}_n$ of $P \to Q$ from Δ. For each S_i, one of cases 1 through 4 applies. If one of cases 1, 2, or 3 applies, $\mathscr{S}_i$ depends only on S_i and can be written without reference to any other step. If S_i is inferred by modus ponens on S_k and S_j, then $P \to S_j$ and $P \to S_k$ occur in $\mathscr{S}_1, \ldots, \mathscr{S}_{i-1}$, and case 4 can be applied.

The proof above exhibits an effective step-by-step procedure for converting a deduction of Q from $\Delta \cup \{P\}$ into a deduction of $P \to Q$ from Δ. Below we show how to cast this step-by-step procedure into a proof by induction.

We prove by induction on n the following statement. For every positive integer n,

> If $S_1, \ldots, S_n$ is a deduction of S_n from $\Delta \cup \{P\}$, then there is a deduction of $P \to S_n$ from Δ in which $P \to S_1, \ldots, P \to S_n$ (4) are steps

Basis. If $n = 1$, then S_1 is an axiom or is in Δ or is P. Then one of cases 1 through 3 above applies.

Induction step. Assume that (4) is true for n, and consider a deduction $S_1, \ldots, S_n, S_{n+1}$ with $n + 1$ steps of S_{n+1} from $\Delta \cup \{P\}$. $S_1, \ldots, S_n$ is a deduction of S_n from $\Delta \cup \{P\}$. Therefore, by the induction hypothesis, there is a deduction $\mathscr{D}$ of $P \to S_n$ from Δ in which $P \to S_1, \ldots, P \to S_n$ occur as steps. S_{n+1} is an axiom or is in Δ or is P or is inferred by modus ponens on S_k and S_j. One of cases 1 through 4 applies. If S_{n+1} is inferred by modus ponens on S_k and S_j, then $j \leqslant n$ and $k \leqslant n$, and hence $P \to S_j$ and $P \to S_k$ occur in $\mathscr{D}$ and are available for use with case 4.

EXAMPLE 4. $\vdash \sim A(x) . \to . \, A(x) \to B(y)$

Proof.

1.	$\sim A(x)$	as
2.	$\sim A(x) . \to . \sim B(y) \to \sim A(x)$	A1
3.	$\sim B(y) \to \sim A(x)$	MP, 2, 1
4.	$\sim B(y) \to \sim A(x) . \to . \, A(x) \to B(y)$	A3
5.	$A(x) \to B(y)$	MP, 4, 3
6.	$\sim A(x) . \to . \, A(x) \to B(y)$	DT, 1–5

The proof in Example 4 is not a formal proof. Steps 1 through 5 constitute a deduction of $A(x) \to B(y)$ from $\sim A(x)$. In step 6 the deduction theorem is applied to give $\sim\!A(x)\,.\!\rightarrow.\,A(x)\rightarrow B(y)$. The sequence 1 through 6 is a set of instructions for constructing a formal proof. We call it a *proof outline*. Step 6 says, "Follow the proof of the deduction theorem to convert steps 1 through 5 into a proof of $\sim\!A(x)\,.\!\rightarrow.\,A(x)\rightarrow B(y)$."

From now on we shall give proof outlines instead of formal proofs. We indent steps to indicate which steps depend on which assumptions. In the proof outline above, steps 1 through 5 all lie in the same column as $\sim\!A(x)$ to indicate that they are deduced from the assumption $\sim\!A(x)$. At step 6, where $\sim\!A(x)$ is discharged, the formula moves to the left to indicate that it does not depend on $\sim\!A(x)$.

THEOREM 5. $\vdash \sim\!\sim\!P \rightarrow P$

Proof.

1.	$\sim\!\sim\!P$	as
2.	$\sim\!\sim\!P\,.\!\rightarrow.\,\sim\!P \rightarrow \sim\!\sim\!\sim\!P$	T13.6
3.	$\sim\!P \rightarrow \sim\!\sim\!\sim\!P$	MP, 2, 1
4.	$\sim\!P \rightarrow \sim\!\sim\!\sim\!P\,.\!\rightarrow.\,\sim\!\sim\!P \rightarrow P$	A3
5.	$\sim\!\sim\!P \rightarrow P$	MP, 4, 3
6.	P	MP, 5, 1
7.	$\sim\!\sim\!P \rightarrow P$	DT, 1–6

In the proof outline above, "T13.6" after step 2 means "At this point insert the formal proof of $\sim\!\sim\!P\,.\!\rightarrow.\,\sim\!P \rightarrow \sim\!\sim\!\sim\!P$ which can be extracted from the proof of Theorem 6 of Section 13." The proof outline above completely specifies a formal proof of $\sim\!\sim\!P \rightarrow P$. We do not give the formal proof, but we do compute the total number of steps in the formal proof. Steps 1 and 3 through 6 above each call for one step in a formal deduction. Step 2 calls for 7 steps. Hence steps 1 through 6 call for 12 steps which constitute a deduction of P from $\sim\!\sim\!P$. Step 7 calls for the deduction theorem to be applied to this 12-step deduction. The first step is replaced by 5 steps, and every other step is replaced by 3 steps. Hence the total number of steps in the formal proof of $\sim\!\sim\!P \rightarrow P$ is $3(12) + 2 = 38$.

By avoiding the deduction theorem and using a little ingenuity, one can find a shorter formal proof of $\sim\!\sim\!P \rightarrow P$. However, the technique of starting from assumptions and using the deduction theorem is a great help in discovering proofs.

THEOREM 6. $\vdash P \rightarrow \sim\sim P$

Proof.

1.	$\sim\sim\sim P \rightarrow \sim P$	T5
2.	$\sim\sim\sim P \rightarrow \sim P . \rightarrow . P \rightarrow \sim\sim P$	A3
3.	$P \rightarrow \sim\sim P$	MP, 2, 1

THEOREM 7. $\vdash P \rightarrow Q . \rightarrow . \sim Q \rightarrow \sim P$

Proof.

1.	$P \rightarrow Q$	as
2.	$\sim\sim P$	as
3.	$\sim\sim P \rightarrow P$	T5
4.	P	MP, 3, 2
5.	Q	MP, 1, 4
6.	$Q \rightarrow \sim\sim Q$	T6
7.	$\sim\sim Q$	MP, 6, 5
8.	$\sim\sim P \rightarrow \sim\sim Q$	DT, 1–7
9.	$\sim\sim P \rightarrow \sim\sim Q . \rightarrow . \sim Q \rightarrow \sim P$	A3
10.	$\sim Q \rightarrow \sim P$	MP, 9, 8
11.	$P \rightarrow Q . \rightarrow . \sim Q \rightarrow \sim P$	DT, 1–10

In the proof outline above, the assumption $\sim\sim P$ is discharged at step 8, and the assumption $P \rightarrow Q$ is discharged at step 11. At each discharge the column of formulas shifts to the left. Thus step 5 is deduced from both assumptions $P \rightarrow Q$ and $\sim\sim P$, step 9 is deduced from $P \rightarrow Q$ only, and step 11 is deduced from no assumptions.

THEOREM 8. $\vdash Q \rightarrow . \sim R \rightarrow \sim(Q \rightarrow R)$

Proof.

1.	Q	as
2.	$Q \rightarrow R$	as
3.	R	MP, 2, 1
4.	$(Q \rightarrow R) \rightarrow R$	DT, 1–3
5.	$(Q \rightarrow R) \rightarrow R . \rightarrow . \sim R \rightarrow \sim(Q \rightarrow R)$	T7
6.	$\sim R \rightarrow \sim(Q \rightarrow R)$	MP, 5, 4
7.	$Q \rightarrow . \sim R \rightarrow \sim(Q \rightarrow R)$	DT, 1–6

THEOREM 9. $\vdash S \rightarrow P : \rightarrow : \sim S \rightarrow P . \rightarrow . P$

Proof.

1.	$S \to P$	as
2.	$\sim P$	as
3.	$S \to P .\to. \sim P \to \sim S$	T7
4.	$\sim P \to \sim S$	MP, 3, 1
5.	$\sim S$	MP, 4, 2
6.	$\sim S .\to. \sim P \to \sim(\sim S \to P)$	T8
7.	$\sim P \to \sim(\sim S \to P)$	MP, 6, 5
8.	$\sim(\sim S \to P)$	MP, 7, 2
9.	$\sim P \to \sim(\sim S \to P)$	DT, 1–8
10.	$\sim P \to \sim(\sim S \to P) :\to: \sim S \to P .\to. P$	A3
11.	$\sim S \to P .\to. P$	MP, 10, 9
12.	$S \to P :\to: \sim S \to P .\to. P$	DT, 1–11

We conclude this section with some theorems that state some natural properties of deduction. Δ and Γ are finite sets of formulas.

THEOREM 10.   *If $\Delta \vdash Q$, then $\Delta \cup \Gamma \vdash Q$ for every Γ.*

Proof. Let $S_1, \ldots, S_n$ be a deduction of Q from Δ. Then $S_1, \ldots, S_n$ is also a deduction of Q from $\Delta \cup \Gamma$ with the same analysis. If S_i is an axiom, it is still an axiom. If S_i is inferred from S_k and S_j by modus ponens, it is still inferred from S_k and S_j by modus ponens. If S_i is an assumption, then it is in Δ and hence in $\Delta \cup \Gamma$, and hence is still an assumption.

COROLLARY 11.   If $\vdash Q$, then $\Gamma \vdash Q$ for every Γ.

THEOREM 12.   If $\Delta \vdash P$ and $\Gamma \vdash P \to Q$, then $\Delta \cup \Gamma \vdash Q$.

Proof. Let $S_1, \ldots, S_{n-1}, P$ be a deduction of P from Δ, and let $U_1, \ldots, U_{m-1}, P \to Q$ be a deduction of $P \to Q$ from Γ. Then $S_1, \ldots, S_{n-1}, P, U_1, \ldots, U_{m-1}, P \to Q, Q$ is a deduction of Q from $\Delta \cup \Gamma$ in which Q is justified by modus ponens on $P \to Q$ and P, and every other step is justified exactly as before.

COROLLARY 13.   *If $\Delta \vdash P$ and $\Delta \vdash P \to Q$, then $\Delta \vdash Q$.*

COROLLARY 14.   *If $\vdash P$ and $\Gamma \vdash P \to Q$, then $\Gamma \vdash Q$.*

COROLLARY 15.   *If $\Delta \vdash P$ and $\vdash P \to Q$, then $\Delta \vdash Q$.*

The proof of Theorem 12 involves nothing more than the definition of deduction and an application of modus ponens. Therefore we shall indicate an application of Theorem 12 (or any of its corollaries) by "modus ponens."

THEOREM 16. *If $P_1, \ldots, P_n \vdash Q$ and $\Delta \vdash P_i$ $(i = 1, 2, \ldots, n)$, then $\Delta \vdash Q$.*

Proof. In a deduction of Q from $\{P_1, \ldots, P_n\}$, replace each step which is a P_i by a deduction of P_i from Δ. The result is a deduction of Q from Δ.

COROLLARY 17. *If $P_1, \ldots, P_n \vdash Q$ and $\vdash P_i$ $(i = 1, 2, \ldots, n)$, then $\vdash Q$.*

The deduction theorem and Corollary 17 are the two ways of immediately converting a deduction into a proof.

EXERCISES

In Exercises 2, 4, 5, and 7, write A for $A(x)$ and B for $B(y)$.

1. Prove

(a) $P \to . Q \to R : \to : Q \to . P \to R$

(b) $P \to Q : \to : P \to (Q \to R) . \to . P \to R$

(c) $P \to (P \to Q) . \to . P \to Q$

(d) $P \lor \sim P$

(e) $\sim P \lor P$

(f) $P \lor Q \to Q \lor P$

(g) $P \land Q \to P$

(h) $P \land Q \to Q$

(i) $P \land Q \to Q \land P$

(j) $P \to . Q \to P \land Q$

(k) $(P \to Q) \to Q . \to . (Q \to P) \to P$

2. Follow faithfully the instructions in the proof of the deduction theorem to convert the proof outline of Example 4 into a formal proof of $\sim A(x) . \to . A(x) \to B(y)$.

3. In the proof of Theorem 5, step 5 is $\sim\sim P \to P$. Why can't we stop at step 5?

4. Give the 38-step proof of $\sim\sim A(x) \to A(x)$ called for by the proof outline of Theorem 5.

5. Give a formal proof of $\sim\sim A(x) \to A(x)$ with fewer than 38 steps.
6. How many steps are there in the formal proof of $A(x) \to B(y) .\to.$ $\sim B(y) \to \sim A(x)$ if the proof outlines of Theorem 7 and previous theorems are followed faithfully?
7. Give a formal proof of $A(x) \to B(y) .\to. \sim B(y) \to \sim A(x)$ with fewer than 70 steps.
8. Prove the converse of the deduction theorem: If $\Delta \vdash P \to Q$, then $\Delta, P \vdash Q$.

15   The Completeness Theorem for the Statement Calculus

In this section we shall prove that the statement calculus is a decidable theory; i.e., there is an effective procedure for deciding whether or not a formula is a theorem of the statement calculus. Recall that every formula is an atomic formula, or of the form $P \to Q$, or of the form $\sim P$, or of the form $\forall v P$.

A formula is *prime* if and only if it is an atomic formula or of the form $\forall v P$. For example, $A(x)$ and $\forall x(A(x) \to \sim B(x))$ are prime formulas. A formula P that is not prime is formed from prime formulas, called the *prime constituents* of P, by a finite number (greater than zero) of applications of $\sim$ and $\to$. For example, the prime constituents of $(A(x) \to \sim\forall y \sim B(y)) \to \sim\forall x(C(x) \to A(x))$ are $A(x)$, $\forall y \sim B(y)$, and $\forall x(C(x) \to A(x))$.

When a truth value T or F is assigned to each prime constituent of a formula P (with each occurrence of the same prime constituent in P assigned the same truth value), a unique truth value is assigned to P by the truth tables for $\sim$ and $\to$ given in Section 5.

EXAMPLE 1.   The truth table for $A(x) \to \sim B(y)$ is

$A(x)$	$B(y)$	$\sim B(y)$	$A(x) \to \sim B(y)$
T	T	F	F
F	T	F	T
T	F	T	T
F	F	T	T

There are 2 prime constituents, and hence 4 distinct assignments of truth values to the prime constituents. Each assignment results in a truth value for $A(x) \to \sim B(y)$. The truth table above may also be given in the following form.

$A(x)$	$\to$	$\sim$	$B(y)$
T	F	F	T
F	T	F	T
T	T	T	F
F	T	T	F

EXAMPLE 2.

$A(x)$	$\to$	$A(x)$
T	T	T
F	T	F

There is only one prime constituent, and hence 2 distinct assignments. $A(x) \to A(x)$ takes the value T for both assignments.

A formula is a *tautology* if and only if it takes the value T for every assignment of truth values to its prime constituents. For example, $A(x) \to A(x)$ is a tautology. Another tautology is $\sim A(x) . \to . A(x) \to B(y)$, as the truth table below shows.

$\sim$	$A(x)$	$. \to .$	$A(x)$	$\to$	$B(y)$
F	T	T	T	T	T
T	F	T	F	T	T
F	T	T	T	F	F
T	F	T	F	T	F

The notion of *tautology* is effective; i.e., there is an effective procedure (construct the truth table) for deciding whether or not a formula is a tautology. We shall show that a formula is a theorem of the statement calculus if and only if it is a tautology.

A formula scheme is *tautologous* if and only if it takes the value T for every assignment of truth values to the letters " P," " Q,"... that appear in it. For example, $P \to . Q \to P$ is tautologous, as the truth table below shows.

P	$. \to .$	Q	$\to$	P
T	T	T	T	T
F	T	T	F	F
T	T	F	T	T
F	T	F	T	F

LEMMA 3.   *Every axiom of the statement calculus is a tautology.*

Proof.   We prove that every instance of $P \to . Q \to P$ is a tautology. The proofs for A2 and A3 are similar. Let S be any instance of $P \to . Q \to P$. Then there exist subformulas P^* and Q^* of S such that S is $P^* \to . Q^* \to P^*$. Every assignment of truth values to the prime constituents of S results in truth values being assigned to P^* and Q^*. The truth table above shows that $P^* \to . Q^* \to P^*$ takes the value T for every assignment of truth values to P^* and Q^*. Hence S is a tautology.

LEMMA 4.   *If $P \to Q$ and P are tautologies, then Q is also a tautology. (Modus ponens applied to two tautologies gives a tautology.)*

Proof.   The truth table for $\to$ is given below.

	P	$\to$	Q
1.	T	T	T
2.	F	T	T
3.	T	F	F
4.	F	T	F

Suppose $P \to Q$ and P take the value T for every assignment to the prime constituents of P and Q. Then line 3 cannot occur because $P \to Q$ is never F, and lines 2 and 4 cannot occur because P is never F. Hence only line 1 can occur; i.e., Q always takes the value T.

THEOREM 5.   *Every theorem of the statement calculus is a tautology.*

Proof.   We prove that every step of every proof is a tautology. Then every theorem is a tautology since every theorem is the last step of some proof. Let $S_1, \ldots, S_n$ be a proof. We prove by induction on n that every step in $S_1, \ldots, S_n$ is a tautology. If $n = 1$, then S_1 is an axiom. By Lemma 3, every axiom is a tautology. Now suppose that for every proof with n steps, every step is a tautology, and consider a proof $S_1, \ldots, S_n, S_{n+1}$ with $n + 1$ steps. $S_1, \ldots, S_n$ is itself a proof. Hence by the induction hypothesis, the steps $S_1, \ldots, S_n$ are all tautologies. S_{n+1} is an axiom or is inferred by modus ponens. If S_{n+1} is an axiom, then S_{n+1} is a tautology. If S_{n+1} is inferred from S_k and S_j by modus ponens, then S_k and S_j are tautologies, since $j \leq n$ and $k \leq n$. Then, by Lemma 4, S_{n+1} is also a tautology.

The idea behind the proof of Theorem 5 is that every axiom is a tautology, and modus ponens applied to two tautologies gives a tautology. Then every theorem is a tautology since every theorem is the result of starting with some axioms and applying modus ponens a finite number of times. The induction proof makes this argument precise. We shall encounter other metatheorems whose proof requires induction. Usually we shall give the induction proof, but sometimes we shall merely give the underlying idea.

Now we prove: *Every tautology is a theorem of the statement calculus.* The proof is complicated and requires some preliminaries. First we need the following lemma:

Let P be a formula, and let every prime constituent of P be in the list $U_1, \ldots, U_k$ of distinct prime formulas. For a given assignment of truth values to $U_1, \ldots, U_k$, let U'_i $(1 \leqslant i \leqslant k)$ and P' be defined as follows: U'_i is U_i if U_i is assigned T, and U'_i is $\sim U_i$ if U_i is assigned F; P' is P if P takes the value T, and P' is $\sim P$ if P takes the value F. Then

$$U'_1, \ldots, U'_k \vdash P \tag{1}$$

We give an example before proving this lemma.

EXAMPLE 6. P is $A(x) \to \sim B(y)$. The table below shows the four assignments to the prime constituents $A(x)$ and $B(y)$, the corresponding truth value for $A(x) \to \sim B(y)$, and the assertion (1) for each assignment. We write A for $A(x)$ and B for $B(y)$.

A	B	$\sim B$	$A \to \sim B$	
T	T	F	F	$A, B \vdash \sim(A \to \sim B)$
F	T	F	T	$\sim A, B \vdash A \to \sim B$
T	F	T	T	$A, \sim B \vdash A \to \sim B$
F	F	T	T	$\sim A, \sim B \vdash A \to \sim B$

To illustrate the lemma, we go through the second assignment in detail. In the second assignment, A is assigned F, B is assigned T, and $A \to \sim B$ takes the value T. Hence A' is $\sim A$, B' is B, and $(A \to \sim B)'$ is $A \to \sim B$. Then (1) is

$$\sim A, B \vdash A \to \sim B \tag{2}$$

We prove (2) to illustrate the proof of the lemma. The idea is to prove (1) for every subformula of P that occurs in the construction of the truth table for P. For the assignment we are using, the table below lists the subformulas of P, their truth values, and the corresponding statement (1).

A	B	$\sim B$	$A \to \sim B$
F	T	F	T
$\sim A, B \vdash \sim A$	$\sim A, B \vdash B$	$\sim A, B \vdash \sim\sim B$	$\sim A, B \vdash A \to \sim B$

Thus, for the subformula $\sim B$, the given assignment of F to A and T to B gives $\sim B$ the value F. Hence A' is $\sim A$, B' is B, and $(\sim B)'$ is $\sim\sim B$. We prove $\sim A, B \vdash \sim A$; $\sim A, B \vdash B$; $\sim A, B \vdash \sim\sim B$; and $\sim A, B \vdash A \to \sim B$ in turn. $\sim A, B \vdash \sim A$ since the single step $\sim A$ is a deduction of $\sim A$ from $\sim A, B$. Similarly, $\sim A, B \vdash B$. Then modus ponens applied to $\sim A, B \vdash B$ and $\vdash B \to \sim\sim B$ (Theorem 14.6) gives $\sim A, B \vdash \sim\sim B$. Then modus ponens applied to $\sim A, B \vdash \sim A$ and $\vdash \sim A .\to. A \to \sim B$ (Theorem 13.6) gives $\sim A, B \vdash A \to \sim B$.

The sequence $\sim A, B \vdash \sim A$; $\sim A, B \vdash B$; $\sim A, B \vdash \sim\sim B$; $\sim A, B \vdash A \to \sim B$; parallels the construction of the truth table for $A \to \sim B$. $\sim A$ $B \vdash B$ and $\sim A, B \vdash \sim\sim B$ are not needed to prove $\sim A, B \vdash A \to \sim B$; because $A \to \sim B$ takes the truth value T when A is assigned F regardless of what truth value is assigned to B.

LEMMA 7. *Let P be a formula, and let every prime formula in P be in the list $U_1, \ldots, U_k$ of distinct prime formulas. For a given assignment of truth values to $U_1, \ldots, U_k$, let U'_i ($1 \leqslant i \leqslant k$) and P' be defined as follows: U'_i is U_i if U_i is assigned T, and U'_i is $\sim U_i$ if U_i is assigned F; P' is P if P takes the value T, and P' is $\sim P$ if P takes the value F. Then*

$$U'_1, \ldots, U'_k \vdash P' \tag{1}$$

Proof. Let $\Delta = \{U'_1, \ldots, U'_k\}$. Then (1) becomes

$$\Delta \vdash P' \tag{3}$$

We proceed by induction on the number n of symbols in P, counting as a symbol each occurrence of $\sim$ or $\to$ that is not an occurrence inside some U_i.

Basis. If $n = 0$, then P is some U_i, and hence P' is U'_i. Then P' is in Δ, and (3) is immediate.

Induction step. Suppose that (3) holds for every formula with n or fewer symbols, and consider P with $n + 1$ symbols.

Case 1. P is $\sim Q$ for some Q.   Since Q has n symbols, the induction hypothesis gives

$$\Delta \vdash Q' \tag{4}$$

Subcase 1.1. Q takes the value T.   Then P takes the value F, Q' is Q, P' is $\sim P$ (which is $\sim\sim Q$), and (4) is $\Delta \vdash Q$.   Then modus ponens applied to $\Delta \vdash Q$ and $\vdash Q \to \sim\sim Q$ (Theorem 14.6) gives $\Delta \vdash \sim\sim Q$, which is (3).

Subcase 1.2. Q takes the value F.   Then P takes the value T, Q' is $\sim Q$, P' is P (which is $\sim Q$), and (4) is $\Delta \vdash \sim Q$, which is (3).

Case 2. P is $Q \to R$ for some Q and R.   Since each of Q and R has n or fewer symbols, the induction hypothesis gives

$$\Delta \vdash Q' \tag{5}$$

and

$$\Delta \vdash R' \tag{6}$$

Subcase 2.1. R takes the value T.   Then P takes the value T, R' is R, P' is P (which is $Q \to R$), and (6) is $\Delta \vdash R$.   Then modus ponens applied to $\Delta \vdash R$ and $\vdash R \to . Q \to R$ (Axiom scheme A1) gives $\Delta \vdash Q \to R$, which is (3).

Subcase 2.2. Q takes the value F.   Then P takes the value T, Q' is $\sim Q$, and P' is P (which is $Q \to R$), and (5) is $\Delta \vdash \sim Q$.   Then modus ponens applied to $\Delta \vdash \sim Q$ and $\vdash \sim Q .\to. Q \to R$ (Theorem 13.6) gives $\Delta \vdash Q \to R$, which is (3).

Subcase 2.3. Q takes the value T and R takes the value F.   Then P takes the value F, Q' is Q, R' is $\sim R$, P' is $\sim P$ (which is $\sim(Q \to R)$), and (5) and (6) are $\Delta \vdash Q$ and $\Delta \vdash \sim R$.   Modus ponens applied to $\Delta \vdash Q$ and $\vdash Q .\to. \sim R \to \sim(Q \to R)$ (Theorem 14.8) gives $\Delta \vdash \sim R \to \sim(Q \to R)$.   Then modus ponens applied to $\Delta \vdash \sim R$ and $\Delta \vdash \sim R \to \sim(Q \to R)$ gives $\Delta \vdash \sim(Q \to R)$, which is (3).

EXAMPLE 8. P is $A .\to. \sim A \to B$.   (Again we write A for $A(x)$ and B for $B(y)$.) P is a tautology; hence P' is always P.   Then Lemma 7 gives $A, B \vdash P$; $\sim A, B \vdash P$; $A, \sim B \vdash P$; and $\sim A, \sim B \vdash P$.   We show that P is a theorem.   The deduction theorem applied to $A, B \vdash P$ and $A, \sim B \vdash P$ gives $A \vdash B \to P$ and $A \vdash \sim B \to P$.   Modus ponens applied to $A \vdash B \to P$ and $\vdash B \to P :\to: \sim B \to P .\to. P$ (Theorem 14.9) gives $A \vdash \sim B \to P .\to. P$.   Then modus ponens applied to

$A \vdash \sim B \to P$ and $A \vdash \sim B \to P .\to. P$ gives $A \vdash P$. Similarly, starting with $\sim A, B \vdash P$ and $\sim A, \sim B \vdash P$, we get $\sim A \vdash P$. Hence the assumption B' (which is B in some cases and $\sim B$ in the other cases) is eliminated. We go on to eliminate A' in the same way: The deduction theorem applied to $A \vdash P$ and $\sim A \vdash P$ gives $\vdash A \to P$ and $\vdash \sim A \to P$. Modus ponens applied to $\vdash A \to P$ and $\vdash A \to P :\to:$ $\vdash \sim A \to P .\to. P$ (Theorem 14.9) gives $\vdash \sim A \to P .\to. P$. Then modus ponens applied to $\vdash \sim A \to P$ and $\vdash \sim A \to P .\to. P$ gives $\vdash P$.

THEOREM 9 (*The completeness theorem for the statement calculus*).   *Every tautology is a theorem of the statement calculus.*

Proof.   Let P be a tautology. Let $U_1, \ldots, U_k$ be the distinct prime constituents of P. Let U_i' and P' be defined as in Lemma 7. Because P is a tautology, P' is P for every assignment. Hence by Lemma 7, $U_1', \ldots, U_k' \vdash P$ for every assignment to $U_1, \ldots, U_k$. In particular, $U_1', \ldots, U_{k-1}', U_k \vdash P$ and $U_1', \ldots, U_{k-1}', \sim U_k \vdash P$ for every assignment to $U_1', \ldots, U_{k-1}'$. Let $\Delta_i = U_1', \ldots, U_i'$ ($1 \leqslant i \leqslant k$). The deduction theorem applied to $\Delta_{k-1}, U_k \vdash P$ and $\Delta_{k-1}, \sim U_k \vdash P$ gives $\Delta_{k-1} \vdash U_k \to P$ and $\Delta_{k-1} \vdash \sim U_k \to P$. Modus ponens applied to $\Delta_{k-1} \vdash U_k \to P$ and $\vdash U_k \to P :\to: \sim U_k \to P .\to. P$ (Theorem 14.9) gives $\Delta_{k-1} \vdash \sim U_k \to P .\to. P$. Then modus ponens applied to $\Delta_{k-1} \vdash \sim U_k \to P$ and $\Delta_{k-1} \vdash \sim U_k \to P .\to. P$ gives $\Delta_{k-1} \vdash P$. Thus the assumption U_k' is eliminated. Similarly, $U_{k-1}', \ldots, U_1'$ are eliminated in turn, giving $\Delta_{k-2} \vdash P, \ldots, \Delta_1 \vdash P$, and finally, $\vdash P$.

THEOREM 10.   *A formula is a theorem of the statement calculus if and only if it is a tautology.*

Proof.   Theorems 5 and 9.

There are many ways of checking tautologies other than the method of truth tables. We give one below. The reader is encouraged to improvise. Let P be a formula. We suppose that P is not a tautology and proceed to fill in truth values for the subformulas of P until a contradiction (i.e., a conflict) results, or until each prime formula is assigned a truth value. If a contradiction results, then the initial assumption that P is not a tautology is false. Hence in this case P is a tautology. If each prime formula is assigned a truth value with no contradiction, then P is not a tautology, and we have a specific assignment for which it takes the value F. This method applies equally well to schemes.

EXAMPLE 11.   Suppose $P .\rightarrow. Q \rightarrow P$ is not tautologous. Then by the truth table for $\rightarrow$, P takes the value T and $Q \rightarrow P$ takes the value F. Since $Q \rightarrow P$ takes the value F, Q takes the value T, and P takes the value F. Hence P takes both T and F as values. This contradiction shows that $P .\rightarrow. Q \rightarrow P$ *is* tautologous.

EXAMPLE 12.   Suppose that $Q \rightarrow P .\rightarrow. \sim P$ is not tautologous. Then $Q \rightarrow P$ takes the value T, and $\sim P$ takes the value F. Then P takes the value T. We can assign either T or F to Q. Therefore $Q \rightarrow P .\rightarrow. \sim P$ is not tautologous, and further, it takes the value F when P is assigned T, and Q is assigned either T or F.

EXERCISES

1. For each formula scheme, construct the truth table and state if the scheme is tautologous. (A scheme with three distinct letters has 8 lines in its truth table.)

   (a) $P \rightarrow Q .\wedge. Q \rightarrow R .\rightarrow. P \rightarrow R$
   (b) $P .\wedge. P \rightarrow Q .\rightarrow. Q$
   (c) $P \rightarrow Q .\rightarrow. Q \rightarrow P$
   (d) $Q \wedge \sim Q$
   (e) $P \wedge Q \leftrightarrow \sim(\sim P \vee \sim Q)$
   (f) $P \vee Q \leftrightarrow (P \rightarrow Q) \rightarrow Q$
   (g) $(P \wedge Q) \wedge R \leftrightarrow P \wedge (Q \wedge R)$
   (h) $P \leftrightarrow \sim\sim P$
   (i) $P \rightarrow Q .\wedge. \sim P \rightarrow R .\rightarrow. Q \vee R$
   (j) $P \wedge \sim Q \rightarrow R \wedge \sim R .\rightarrow. P \rightarrow Q$
   (k) $\sim Q \rightarrow \sim P .\leftrightarrow. P \rightarrow Q$

2. Let P be $\sim B(y) \rightarrow \sim A(x) .\rightarrow. A(x) \rightarrow B(y)$. Let T be assigned to $A(x)$ and F be assigned to $B(y)$. Imitate Example 6 to show that $A(x), \sim B(y) \vdash Q'$ for every subformula Q of P, starting with the prime formulas and progressing to P. Do not use Lemma 7, but

make use of the proof of Lemma 7 to handle the various cases that arise.   Write A for $A(x)$ and B for $B(y)$.

16   Applications of the Completeness Theorem for the Statement Calculus

We now return to the full predicate calculus.   Every proof in the statement calculus is a proof in the predicate calculus, because the predicate calculus includes all the formulas, axioms, and rules of inference of the statement calculus.   Therefore every theorem of the statement calculus is a theorem of the predicate calculus.   By Theorem 10 in Section 15, this means that every tautology is a theorem of the predicate calculus.

We give below a list of tautologous schemes.

1. $P \lor Q \leftrightarrow Q \lor P$	
2. $P \land Q \leftrightarrow Q \land P$	commutative laws
3. $P \leftrightarrow Q .\leftrightarrow. Q \leftrightarrow P$	
4. $P \to. Q \to R .\leftrightarrow. Q \to. P \to R$	
5. $(P \lor Q) \lor R .\leftrightarrow. P \lor (Q \lor R)$	associative laws
6. $(P \land Q) \land R .\leftrightarrow. P \land (Q \land R)$	
7. $P \land (Q \lor R) .\leftrightarrow. (P \land Q) \lor (P \land R)$	distributive laws
8. $P \lor (Q \land R) .\leftrightarrow. (P \lor Q) \land (P \lor R)$	
9. $P \land P \leftrightarrow P$	idempotent laws
10. $P \lor P \leftrightarrow P$	
11. $P \leftrightarrow \sim\sim P$	double negation
12. $P \lor \sim P$	excluded middle
13. $P \to Q :\to: Q \to R .\to. P \to R$	transitivity of
14. $P \to Q .\land. Q \to R .\to. P \to R$	implication
15. $P \to Q .\leftrightarrow. \sim Q \to \sim P$	contraposition
16. $P \to \sim Q .\leftrightarrow. Q \to \sim P$	
17. $P \land Q \to R :\to: P \to. Q \to R$	law of exportation
18. $P \to. Q \to R :\to: P \land Q \to R$	law of importation
19. $P \land Q \to R .\leftrightarrow. P \to. Q \to R$	export–import law
20. $P \lor (P \land Q) \leftrightarrow P$	
21. $P \land (P \lor Q) \leftrightarrow P$	absorption laws
22. $P \to. P \to Q .\leftrightarrow. P \to Q$	
23. $P \to Q .\land. P \to R .\leftrightarrow. P \to Q \land R$	
24. $\sim(P \lor Q) \leftrightarrow \sim P \land \sim Q$	De Morgan's laws
25. $\sim(P \land Q) \leftrightarrow \sim P \lor \sim Q$	

26. $P \vee Q . \wedge . P \rightarrow R . \wedge . Q \rightarrow R . \rightarrow . R$ proof by cases

27. $\sim P \rightarrow R \wedge \sim R . \rightarrow . P$

28. $\sim P \rightarrow P . \rightarrow . P$

29. $P \rightarrow \sim P . \rightarrow . \sim P$ proof by

30. $P \wedge \sim Q \rightarrow R \wedge \sim R . \rightarrow . P \rightarrow Q$ contradiction

31. $P \wedge \sim Q \rightarrow \sim P . \rightarrow . P \rightarrow Q$

32. $P \wedge \sim Q \rightarrow Q . \rightarrow . P \rightarrow Q$

33. $P \rightarrow Q . \leftrightarrow . \sim P \vee Q$

34. $P \rightarrow Q . \leftrightarrow . \sim (P \wedge \sim Q)$

35. $P \vee Q . \leftrightarrow . (P \rightarrow Q) \rightarrow Q$

36. $P \vee Q . \leftrightarrow . \sim P \rightarrow Q$ relations between

37. $P \vee Q . \leftrightarrow . \sim (\sim P \wedge \sim Q)$ connectives

38. $P \wedge Q . \leftrightarrow . \sim (\sim P \vee \sim Q)$

39. $P \wedge Q . \leftrightarrow . \sim (P \rightarrow \sim Q)$

40. $P \leftrightarrow Q . \leftrightarrow . P \rightarrow Q . \wedge . Q \rightarrow P$

These schemes should be studied and interpreted until they become self-evident. For example, "$P \wedge Q \rightarrow R$" may be read, "If P and Q, then R." "$P \rightarrow . Q \rightarrow R$" may be read, "If P, then if Q then R." If we read them this way, it becomes apparent that they have the same meaning. Then the export–import law (19) becomes easy to remember and use.

Suppose $P_1 \rightarrow (P_2 \rightarrow \cdots \rightarrow (P_n \rightarrow Q) \cdots)$ is a tautology, and suppose that in some formal proof $P_1, P_2, \ldots, P_n$ occur as steps. Then we can get Q as a step in the following way. The completeness theorem for the statement calculus gives an effective procedure for constructing a proof of $P_1 \rightarrow (P_2 \rightarrow \cdots (P_n \rightarrow Q) \cdots)$. Then modus ponens in turn with $P_1, P_2, \ldots, P_n$ gives a sequence of steps that ends with Q.

EXAMPLE 1.

5. $yz \neq 0$

6. $z = 0 \wedge y0 = 0 \rightarrow yz = 0$

7. $y0 = 0$

8. $z \neq 0$ SC, 5–7

"SC" stands for "statement calculus." "SC, 5–7" after step 8 means that

$$\text{step } 5 \rightarrow (\text{step } 6 \rightarrow (\text{step } 7 \rightarrow \text{step } 8)) \qquad (1)$$

is a tautology. The instructions at step 8 are as follows: Construct the formal proof of (1).   Then write step $6 \to$ (step $7 \to$ step 8), which is justified by modus ponens on (1) and step 5.   Then write step $7 \to$ step 8, which is justified by modus ponens on step $6 \to$ (step $7 \to$ step 8) and step 6.   Then write step 8, which is justified by modus ponens on step $7 \to$ step 8 and step 7.   All the reader has to check is that (1) is a tautology.   This is straightforward.   A more satisfying procedure is to informally derive step 8 from steps 5 through 7 in the following way.   By the commutativity of conjunction, step 6 is equivalent to $y0 = 0 \wedge z = 0 \to yz = 0$.   This in turn is equivalent to $y0 = 0 \,.\to.\, z = 0 \to yz = 0$ by the law of exportation.   Then modus ponens with step 7 gives $z = 0 \to yz = 0$.   Then contraposition gives $yz \neq 0 \to z \neq 0$.   Then modus ponens with step 5 gives $z \neq 0$.

EXAMPLE 2.

2. $y = y \wedge x = y \,.\to.\, y = y \leftrightarrow y = x$
    $\vdots$
4. $y = y$
5. $x = y \to y = x$ SC, 2, 4

"SC, 2, 4" after step 5 means that

$$\text{step } 2 \to (\text{step } 4 \to \text{step } 5) \qquad (2)$$

is a tautology.   Then, as in Example 1, there is an effective procedure for filling in the formal steps between steps 4 and 5.   The reader can either accept that (2) is a tautology, or he can make out a truth table, or he can informally derive step 5 from steps 2 and 4, or he can verify that (2) is a tautology by the method of contradiction as follows: Suppose (2) is false.   Then steps 2 and 4 are true and step 5 is false. Since step 5 is a conditional, we have that $x = y$ is true and $y = x$ is false.   Since $x = y$ and $y = y$ (step 4) are true, the antecedent $y = y \wedge x = y$ of step 2 is true.   Since step 2 is true, the consequent $y = y \leftrightarrow y = x$ of step 2 is true.   But $y = y$ is true and $y = x$ is false. Hence $y = y \leftrightarrow y = x$ is false.   This contradiction shows that (2) is a tautology.

EXERCISES

1. For each of the following, state if the step justified by the statement calculus is correctly justified.

(a)   6. $\forall v \sim Q \rightarrow \forall v \sim P$
     7. $\sim Q \rightarrow \forall v \sim Q$
     8. $\sim \forall v \sim P \rightarrow Q$ SC, 6, 7

(b)   3. Q
     4. $P \rightarrow Q$ SC, 3

(c)   1. $\forall v \sim P \rightarrow \sim P(t/v)$
     2. $P(t/v) \rightarrow \sim \forall v \sim P$ SC, 1

(d)   8. $\forall v(P \leftrightarrow Q) .\rightarrow. \forall v P \rightarrow \forall v Q$
     9. $\forall v(P \leftrightarrow Q) .\rightarrow. \forall v Q \rightarrow \forall v P$
    10. $\forall v(P \leftrightarrow Q) .\rightarrow. \forall v P \leftrightarrow \forall v Q$ SC, 8, 9

(e) 17. $\sim \forall v P \rightarrow \exists v(P \rightarrow Q)$
         $\vdots$
   23. $\exists v Q \rightarrow \exists v(P \rightarrow Q)$
   24. $\forall v P \rightarrow \exists v Q .\rightarrow. \exists v(P \rightarrow Q)$ SC, 17, 23

(f)   4. $\exists y(x' = y')$
     5. $x = 0 \vee \exists y(x = y') \rightarrow x' = 0 \vee \exists y(x' = y')$ SC, 4

(g)   9. $P \wedge \sim Q \rightarrow R$
   10. $P \rightarrow Q \vee R$ SC, 9

(h)   2. $\sim P \rightarrow Q \vee \sim R$
     3. Q
     4. $R \rightarrow P$ SC, 2, 3

2. Prove the generalized deduction theorem:

$$\Delta, P_1, \ldots, P_n \vdash Q \text{ if and only if } \Delta \vdash P_1 \wedge \cdots \wedge P_n \rightarrow Q$$

ANSWERS

1. All but (h) are correctly justified.

17   Quantifiers

In this section we shall study the rules for removing and inserting quantifiers. The ideas are the same as in Section 10, but the details are considerably different. We begin with the rule of specialization.

THEOREM 1.   *If* $\Delta \vdash \forall v P$, *then* $\Delta \vdash P(t/v)$, *provided that* P *admits* t *for* v.

Proof. Suppose that $\Delta \vdash \forall v P$ and P admits t for v. Then modus ponens applied to $\Delta \vdash \forall v P$ and $\vdash \forall v P \rightarrow P(t/v)$ (Axiom Scheme A5) gives $\Delta \vdash P(t/v)$.

Theorem 1 allows us to use specialization in proof outlines. We indicate an application of Theorem 1 by "spec."

EXAMPLE 2.   Abelian groups.

$$
\begin{array}{lll}
1. & \forall x \forall y(x + y = y + x) & \text{axiom} \\
2. & \forall y(0 + y = y + 0) & \text{spec, 1} \\
3. & 0 + 0 = 0 + 0 & \text{spec, 2}
\end{array}
$$

In this example, Δ is the empty set. Step 1 is a deduction of $\forall x \forall y(x + y = y + x)$. Theorem 1 applied to step 1 gives step 2. Here v is x and P is $\forall y(x + y = y + x)$ and t is 0. (If c is a constant symbol, P always admits c for v.) Then Theorem 1 applied to step 2 gives step 3. Here v is y and P is $(0 + y = y + 0)$ and t is 0.

THEOREM 3. $\vdash P(t/v) \rightarrow \exists v P$ provided P admits t for v.

Proof.   Suppose P admits t for v.

$$
\begin{array}{lll}
1. & \forall v \sim P \rightarrow \sim P(t/v) & \text{A5} \\
2. & P(t/v) \rightarrow \sim \forall v \sim P & \text{SC, 1} \\
3. & P(t/v) \rightarrow \exists v P & \text{same as 2}
\end{array}
$$

Since $\exists v P$ is an abbreviation for $\sim \forall v \sim P$, step 3 is exactly the same as step 2 and is given only for clarification.

The next theorem allows us to use existential introduction in proof outlines.

THEOREM 4.   If $\Delta \vdash P(t/v)$, then $\Delta \vdash \exists v P$, provided that P admits t for v.

Proof.   Imitate the proof of Theorem 1, using Theorem 3 instead of Axiom Scheme A5.

We indicate an application of Theorem 4 by "$\exists$."

EXAMPLE 5.   Abelian groups

$$
\begin{array}{lll}
1. & \forall x(x + 0 = x) & \text{axiom} \\
2. & 0 + 0 = 0 & \text{spec, 1} \\
3. & \exists x(0 + x = 0) & \exists, 2
\end{array}
$$

Theorem 4 is applied to step 2 to give step 3. Δ is the empty set, v is x, P is $0 + x = 0$, and t is 0.

An important special case of A5 is

$$\forall v P \to P$$

which is obtained by letting t be v. P always admits v for v, and $P(v/v)$ is always P. Similarly, an important special case of Theorem 3 is

$$P \to \exists v P$$

THEOREM 6. $\vdash \forall v P \to \exists v P$

Proof.

1.	$\forall v P$	as
2.	P	spec
3.	$\exists v P$	$\exists$
4.	$\forall v P \to \exists v P$	DT, 1–3

In the proof outline above we used the convention that if the analysis for step k mentions no other step, then step k depends only on step $k - 1$. Thus we wrote "spec" instead of "spec, 1," and "$\exists$" instead of "$\exists$, 2."

Next we consider the rule of generalization.

A variable v is *not free in* Δ if and only if there is no formula in Δ with a free occurrence of v.

THEOREM 7.   *If* $\Delta \vdash Q$, *then* $\Delta \vdash \forall v Q$, *provided that* v *is not free in* Δ.

Proof.   Suppose that v is not free in Δ. We prove by induction on n the statement: For every n,

if $S_1, \ldots, S_n$ is a deduction from Δ, then there is a
deduction from Δ in which $\forall v S_1, \ldots, \forall v S_n$ occur as steps   (1)

Basis.   If $n = 1$, then S_1 is an axiom or is in Δ.

Case 1. S_1 is an axiom and v is free in S_1. Then $\forall v S_1$ is also an axiom by Ax Gen. Hence the single step $\forall v S_1$ is a deduction from Δ.

Case 2. S_1 is an axiom and v is not free in S_1. Then the following sequence of three steps is a deduction of $\forall v S_1$ from Δ.

1.	S_1	axiom
2.	$S_1 \to \forall v S_1$	A6
3.	$\forall v S_1$	MP, 2, 1

Case 3. S_1 is in Δ. Then v is not free in S_1. Then the following sequence of three steps is a deduction of $\forall v S_1$ from Δ.

$$
\begin{array}{lll}
1. & S_1 & \text{as} \\
2. & S_1 \to \forall v S_1 & \text{A6} \\
3. & \forall v S_1 & \text{MP, 2, 1}
\end{array}
$$

Induction step. We assume (1) and consider a deduction $S_1, \ldots, S_n$, S_{n+1} from Δ with $n + 1$ steps. $S_1, \ldots, S_n$ is itself a deduction from Δ. Hence by (1) there is a deduction $\mathcal{D}$ from Δ in which $\forall v S_1, \ldots, \forall v S_n$ occur as steps. If S_{n+1} is an axiom or is in Δ, then one of cases 1 through 3 above applies, and we append to $\mathcal{D}$ the necessary one or three steps to get a deduction from Δ in which $\forall v S_1, \ldots, \forall v S_n, \forall v S_{n+1}$ occur as steps.

Case 4. S_{n+1} is inferred from S_k and S_j by modus ponens, where S_k is $S_j \to S_{n+1}$. Since $j \leqslant n$ and $k \leqslant n$, the steps

(a) $\forall v S_j$

and

(b) $\forall v(S_j \to S_{n+1})$

occur in $\mathcal{D}$. Then to $\mathcal{D}$ we append

$$
\begin{array}{lll}
\text{(i)} & \forall v(S_j \to S_{n+1}) \,.\to.\; \forall v S_j \to \forall v S_{n+1} & \text{A4} \\
\text{(ii)} & \forall v S_j \to \forall v S_{n+1} & \text{MP, (i), (b)} \\
\text{(iii)} & \forall v S_{n+1} & \text{MP, (ii), (a)}
\end{array}
$$

The result is a deduction from Δ in which $\forall v S_1, \ldots, \forall v S_n, \forall v S_{n+1}$ occur as steps.

We indicate an application of Theorem 7 by "gen."

EXAMPLE 8.   Number theory

$$\vdash \forall x.2 < x \wedge x < 7 \to 2 < x$$

Proof.

$$
\begin{array}{lll}
1. & 2 < x \wedge x < 7 & \text{as} \\
2. & 2 < x & \text{SC} \\
3. & 2 < x \wedge x < 7 \to 2 < x & \text{DT, 1–2} \\
4. & \forall x.2 < x \wedge x < 7 \to 2 < x & \text{gen}
\end{array}
$$

In this example, Δ is the empty set at step 3, so x is not free in Δ.

EXAMPLE 9.   In this example from number theory, we show what can happen if the restriction on gen (v is not free in Δ) is violated.

1.	$x < 2$	as
2.	$\forall x(x < 2)$	gen
3.	$x < 2 \rightarrow \forall x(x < 2)$	DT, 1–2
4.	$\forall x.x < 2 \rightarrow \forall x(x < 2)$	gen

Step 4 is a false statement because $1 < 2 \rightarrow \forall x(x < 2)$ is false. We look with deep suspicion upon any "proof" of a false statement in number theory. The error occurs at step 2. Since x is free in the assumption $x < 2$, gen cannot be applied with x until this assumption is discharged. (The application of gen at step 4 is correct, because at step 4 Δ is the empty set.)

THEOREM 10. $\vdash \forall u \forall v P \rightarrow \forall v \forall u P$

   Proof.

1.	$\forall u \forall v P$	as
2.	$\forall v P$	spec
3.	P	spec
4.	$\forall u P$	gen
5.	$\forall v \forall u P$	gen
6.	$\forall u \forall v P \rightarrow \forall v \forall u P$	DT, 1–5

The proof of Theorem 10 uses two applications of gen. Since Theorem 7 provides for only one application, some explanation is necessary. Steps 1 through 3 show that $\forall u \forall v P \vdash P$. Since u is not free in the assumption, Theorem 7 gives $\forall u \forall v P \vdash \forall u P$ (step 4). Since v is not free in the assumption, Theorem 7 applied again gives $\forall u \forall v P \vdash \forall v \forall u P$ (step 5).

We now take up Rule C.

THEOREM 11. $\vdash \forall v(P \rightarrow Q) .\rightarrow. \exists v P \rightarrow Q$ *if v is not free in Q*

   Proof.   Suppose v is not free in Q.

1.	$\forall v(P \rightarrow Q)$	as
2.	$P \rightarrow Q$	spec
3.	$\sim Q \rightarrow \sim P$	SC
4.	$\forall v(\sim Q \rightarrow \sim P)$	gen

5.	$\forall v(\sim Q \to \sim P) . \to . \forall v \sim Q \to \forall v \sim P$	A4
6.	$\forall v \sim Q \to \forall v \sim P$	MP, 5, 4
7.	$\sim Q \to \forall v \sim Q$	A6
8.	$\sim \forall v \sim P \to Q$	SC, 6, 7
9.	$\exists v P \to Q$	same as 8
10.	$\forall v(P \to Q) . \to . \exists v P \to Q$	DT, 1–9

THEOREM 12.   *If $\Delta \vdash \exists v P$ and $\Delta, P \vdash Q$, then $\Delta \vdash Q$, provided that v is not free in Δ or Q.*

Proof.   Suppose $\Delta \vdash \exists v P$ and $\Delta, P \vdash Q$ and v is not free in Δ or Q. The deduction theorem gives $\Delta \vdash P \to Q$.   Since v is not free in Δ, gen gives $\Delta \vdash \forall v(P \to Q)$.   Since v is not free in Q, Theorem 11 gives $\vdash \forall v(P \to Q) . \to . \exists v P \to Q$.   Then modus ponens with $\Delta \vdash \forall v(P \to Q)$ gives $\Delta \vdash \exists v P \to Q$.   Then modus ponens with $\Delta \vdash \exists v P$ gives $\Delta \vdash Q$.

Theorem 12 is the Rule C theorem.   Here is how we use it in proof outlines.   Suppose $\exists v P$ is a step in a deduction from Δ, i.e., $\Delta \vdash \exists v P$. We take P as another assumption and go on to deduce Q.   Now we have $\Delta, P \vdash Q$.   If v is not free in Δ or Q, then Theorem 12 gives $\Delta \vdash Q$. We say that the assumption P is *discharged* by Theorem 12.   Note that P now disappears entirely.

EXAMPLE 13.   We illustrate the conventions used with Theorem 12 in proof outlines, taking for granted two theorems of number theory.

1.	$\exists x(x > 3)$	theorem
2.	$x > 3$	Cx
3.	$x > 3 \to x > 2$	theorem
4.	$x > 2$	MP, 3, 2
5.	$\exists x(x > 2)$	$\exists$
6.	$\exists x(x > 2)$	C, 2

Here Δ is the empty set, $\exists v P$ is $\exists x(x > 3)$, and Q is $\exists x(x > 2)$.   At step 1 we have $\vdash \exists x(x > 3)$.   At step 2 we take $x > 3$ as an assumption. At step 5 we have $x > 3 \vdash \exists x(x > 2)$.   Since x is not free in Δ or $\exists x(x > 2)$, Theorem 12 gives $\vdash \exists x(x > 2)$ at step 6.   "Cx" at step 2 means "Rule C with the variable x."   This notation serves three purposes.   First, it indicates that step 2 is the result of removing $\exists x$ from the preceding step.   Second, it signals that we intend to use

Theorem 12 later to discharge step 2.   Third, it singles out the variable that is involved in the application of Theorem 12.   Theorem 12 is applied at step 6.   "C, 2" means the Rule C assumption of step 2 is now discharged.   Note that officially step 2 is an assumption.   For that reason, steps 2 through 5 are indented.   When step 2 is discharged at step 6, the formula moves to the left to show that it no longer depends on step 2.

THEOREM 14. $\vdash \exists v(P \wedge Q) \to \exists vP \wedge \exists vQ$

Proof.

1.	$\exists v(P \wedge Q)$	as
2.	$P \wedge Q$	Cv
3.	P	SC
4.	$\exists vP$	$\exists$
5.	Q	SC, 2
6.	$\exists vQ$	$\exists$
7.	$\exists vP \wedge \exists vQ$	SC, 4, 6
8.	$\exists vP \wedge \exists vQ$	C, 2
9.	$\exists v(P \wedge Q) \to \exists vP \wedge \exists vQ$	DT, 1–8

In the proof outline above, Δ is $\{\exists v(P \wedge Q)\}$.   At step 1 we have $\exists v(P \wedge Q) \vdash \exists v(P \wedge Q)$.   Step 2 is the Rule C assumption.   At step 7 we have $\exists v(P \wedge Q)$, $P \wedge Q \vdash \exists vP \wedge \exists vQ$.   Since v is not free in $\exists v(P \wedge Q)$ or in $\exists vP \wedge \exists vQ$, Theorem 12 gives $\exists v(P \wedge Q) \vdash \exists vP \wedge \exists vQ$ (step 8).

THEOREM 15. $\vdash \forall v(P \to Q) \,.\to.\, \exists vP \to \exists vQ$

Proof.

1.	$\forall v(P \to Q)$	as
2.	$\exists vP$	as
3.	P	Cv
4.	$P \to Q$	spec, 1
5.	Q	MP, 4, 3
6.	$\exists vQ$	$\exists$
7.	$\exists vQ$	C, 3
8.	$\exists vP \to \exists vQ$	DT, 1–7
9.	$\forall v(P \to Q) \,.\to.\, \exists vP \to \exists vQ$	DT, 1–8

EXAMPLE 16.   Rule C may be used more than once in a proof outline.
We give an example from number theory.

1.	$\exists x(x < 2)$	theorem
2.	$\exists y(y > 2)$	theorem
3.	$x < 2$	Cx, 1
4.	$y > 2$	Cy, 2
5.	$x < 2 \wedge y > 2$	SC, 3, 4
6.	$x < 2 \wedge y > 2 \to x < y$	theorem
7.	$x < y$	MP, 6, 5
8.	$\exists y(x < y)$	$\exists$
9.	$\exists y(x < y)$	C, 4
10.	$\exists x \exists y(x < y)$	$\exists$
11.	$\exists x \exists y(x < y)$	C, 3

At step 8 we have $x < 2, y > 3 \vdash \exists y(x < y)$.   Then Theorem 12 gives
step 9.   Here P is $y > 3$, Q is $\exists y(x < y)$, Δ is $\{x < 2\}$, and v is y.   At
step 10 we have $x < 2 \vdash \exists x \exists y(x < y)$.   Then Theorem 12 gives step 11.
Here P is $x < 2$, Q is $\exists x \exists y(x < y)$, Δ is the empty set, and v is x.

The next proof illustrates how Rule C can be used twice on the same
formula.

THEOREM 17. $\vdash \exists u \exists v P \to \exists v \exists v\, P$

Proof.

1.	$\exists u \exists v P$	as
2.	$\exists v P$	Cu
3.	P	Cv
4.	$\exists u P$	$\exists$
5.	$\exists v \exists u P$	$\exists$
6.	$\exists v \exists u P$	C, 3
7.	$\exists v \exists u P$	C, 2
8.	$\exists u \exists v P \to \exists v \exists u P$	DT, 1–7

1. In Example 2, give a formal proof of $0 + 0 = 0 + 0$.
2. Prove Theorem 4.

3. Find the errors in the following incorrect proofs of false statements.

(a) $\vdash\forall y(y > 2)$ (number theory)

Proof.

1.	$3 > 2$	theorem
2.	$\exists x(x > 2)$	$\exists$
3.	$x > 2$	Cx
4.	$\forall x(x > 2)$	gen
5.	$y > 2$	spec
6.	$y > 2$	C, 3
7.	$\forall y(y > 2)$	gen

(b) $\vdash\exists y\forall x(x < y)$ (number theory)

Proof.

1.	$\forall x(x < x + 1)$	theorem
2.	$x < x + 1$	spec
3.	$\exists y(x < y)$	$\exists$
4.	$x < y$	Cy
5.	$\forall x(x < y)$	gen
6.	$\exists y\forall x(x < y)$	$\exists$
7.	$\exists y\forall x(x < y)$	C, 4

(c) $\vdash\exists x(x < 2 \land x > 2)$ (number theory)

Proof.

1.	$\exists x(x < 2)$	theorem
2.	$\exists x(x > 2)$	theorem
3.	$x < 2$	Cx, 1
4.	$x > 2$	Cx, 2
5.	$x < 2 \land x > 2$	SC, 3, 4
6.	$\exists x(x < 2 \land x > 2)$	$\exists$
7.	$\exists x(x < 2 \land x > 2)$	C, 4
8.	$\exists x(x < 2 \land x > 2)$	C, 3

(d) $\vdash\forall x(x > 2)$ (number theory)

Proof.

1.	$\sim(x > 2)$	as
2.	$3 > 2$	theorem

3.	$\exists x(x > 2)$	$\exists$
4.	$x > 2$	Cx
5.	$0 > 1$	SC, 1, 4
6.	$0 > 1$	C, 4
7.	$\sim(x > 2) \to 0 > 1$	DT, 1–6
8.	$\sim(0 > 1)$	theorem
9.	$x > 2$	SC, 7, 8
10.	$\forall x(x > 2)$	gen

(e) $\vdash \forall x(x > 2)$ (number theory)

Proof.

1.	$4 > 3$	theorem
2.	$\exists x(x > 3)$	$\exists$
3.	$x > 3$	Cx
4.	$x > 3 \to x > 2$	theorem
5.	$x > 2$	MP, 4, 3
6.	$x > 2$	C, 3
7.	$\forall x(x > 2)$	gen

(f) $\vdash \forall v \exists u P \to \exists u \forall v P$

Proof.

1.	$\forall v \exists u P$	as
2.	$\exists u P$	spec
3.	P	Cu
4.	$\forall v P$	gen
5.	$\exists u \forall v P$	$\exists$
6.	$\exists u \forall v P$	C, 3
7.	$\forall v \exists u P \to \exists u \forall v P$	DT, 1–6

18   Equivalence and Replacement

P is *equivalent* to Q if and only if $\vdash P \leftrightarrow Q$.

THEOREM 1. $\vdash \forall v(P \leftrightarrow Q) .\to. \forall v P \leftrightarrow \forall v Q$

Proof.

1.	$\forall v(P \leftrightarrow Q)$	as
2.	$\forall v P$	as
3.	$P \leftrightarrow Q$	spec, 1

4.	P	spec, 2
5.	Q	SC, 3, 4
6.	$\forall v Q$	gen
7.	$\forall v P \to \forall v Q$	DT, 1–6
8.	$\forall v (P \leftrightarrow Q) . \to . \forall v P \to \forall v Q$	DT, 1–7
9.	$\forall v (P \leftrightarrow Q) . \to . \forall v Q \to \forall v P$	similar to 1–8
10.	$\forall v (P \leftrightarrow Q) . \to . \forall v P \leftrightarrow \forall v Q$	SC, 8, 9

THEOREM 2.   (*The equivalence theorem.*)   Let U and V be formulas. Let P_U be a formula in which U occurs as a subformula. Let P_V be the result of replacing one or more specified occurrences (but not necessarily all occurrences) of U in P_U by occurrences of V. Let every variable that is free in U or V and bound in P_U be in the list $v_1, \ldots, v_k$. Then

$$\vdash \forall v_1 \cdots \forall v_k (U \leftrightarrow V) . \to . P_U \leftrightarrow P_V$$

Proof.   The proof is by induction on the number n of symbols in P_U, counting each occurrence of $\sim$, $\to$, or $\forall$ as a symbol. We first consider a special case.

Case 1. P_U is U. Then P_V is V. Then $\vdash \forall v_1 \cdots \forall v_k (U \leftrightarrow V) . \to . P_U \leftrightarrow P_V$ by k applications of spec and the statement calculus.

Basis.   If $n = 0$, then case 1 must hold.

Induction step.   Assume the theorem holds for every formula with n or fewer symbols, and consider P_U with $n + 1$ symbols. Suppose also that case 1 does not hold.

Case 2. P_U is $\sim Q_U$. By the induction hypothesis,

$$\vdash \forall v_1 \cdots \forall v_k (U \leftrightarrow V) . \to . Q_U \leftrightarrow Q_V$$

where Q_V is the result of replacing the specified occurrences of U in Q_U by occurrences of V. Then $\vdash \forall v_1 \cdots \forall v_k (U \leftrightarrow V) . \to . \sim Q_U \leftrightarrow \sim Q_V$ by the statement calculus.

Case 3. P_U is $Q_U \to R_U$. Let Q_V and R_V be defined as in case 2. By the induction hypothesis, $\vdash \forall v_1 \cdots \forall v_k (U \leftrightarrow V) . \to . Q_U \leftrightarrow Q_V$ and $\vdash \forall v_1 \cdots \forall v_k (U \leftrightarrow V) . \to . R_U \leftrightarrow R_V$. Then $\vdash \forall v_1 \cdots \forall v_k (U \leftrightarrow V) . \to . (Q_U \to R_U) \leftrightarrow (Q_V \to R_V)$ by the statement calculus.

Case 4. P_U is $\forall v Q_U$. Since v is bound in P_U, either v is in the list $v_1, \ldots, v_k$, or v is not free in U or V. In either case, v is not free in $\forall v_1 \cdots \forall v_k (U \leftrightarrow V)$. Assume $\forall v_1 \cdots \forall v_k (U \leftrightarrow V)$. The induction hypothesis gives $\forall v_1 \cdots \forall v_k (U \leftrightarrow V) . \to . Q_U \leftrightarrow Q_V$. Then modus ponens gives $Q_U \leftrightarrow Q_V$. Since v is not free in the assumption, gen gives $\forall v(Q_U \leftrightarrow Q_V)$. Theorem 1 gives $\forall v(Q_U \leftrightarrow Q_V) .\rightarrow. \forall v Q_U \leftrightarrow \forall v Q_V$. Then modus ponens gives $\forall v Q_U \leftrightarrow \forall v Q_V$. Hence $\vdash \forall v_1 \cdots \forall v_k (U \leftrightarrow V) .\rightarrow. \forall v Q_U \leftrightarrow \forall v Q_V$ by the deduction theorem.

COROLLARY 3.   *Let U, V, P_U, and P_V be as in Theorem 2.   If $\vdash U \leftrightarrow V$, then $\vdash P_U \leftrightarrow P_V$.*

Proof.   Suppose $\vdash U \leftrightarrow V$.   Then k applications of gen give $\vdash \forall v_1 \cdots \forall v_k(U \leftrightarrow V)$.   Then modus ponens with $\vdash \forall v_1 \cdots \forall v_k(U \leftrightarrow V) .\rightarrow. P_U \leftrightarrow P_V$ gives $\vdash P_U \leftrightarrow P_V$.

COROLLARY 4 (*The replacement theorem*).   *Let U, V, P_U, and P_V be as in Theorem 2.   If $\vdash U \leftrightarrow V$ and $\Delta \vdash P_U$, then $\Delta \vdash P_V$.*

Proof.   Suppose $\vdash U \leftrightarrow V$ and $\Delta \vdash P_U$.   Then $\vdash P_U \leftrightarrow P_V$ by Corollary 3.   Then the statement calculus with $\Delta \vdash P_U$ gives $\Delta \vdash P_V$.

In proof outlines, "equiv" indicates an application of Theorem 2 or Corollary 3, and "rep" indicates an application of Corollary 4.   The remainder of this section is devoted to applications of the replacement theorem.

THEOREM 5. $\vdash \forall v P \leftrightarrow \sim \exists v \sim P$

Proof.

1.	$\forall v P \leftrightarrow \sim\sim\forall v P$	taut
2.	$P \leftrightarrow \sim\sim P$	taut
3.	$\forall v P \leftrightarrow \sim\sim\forall v\sim\sim P$	rep, 1, 2
4.	$\forall v P \leftrightarrow \sim\exists v\sim P$	same as 3

"taut" after step 1 indicates that step 1 is a tautology.   Note that step 3 does not follow from step 1 by the statement calculus, because P is in the scope of the quantifier $\forall v$.   The replacement theorem is necessary to make a replacement within the scope of a quantifier.

In informal number theory, $\exists x(x < 2)$ and $\exists y(y < 2)$ have the same meaning.   In formal number theory, these two formulas are equivalent.

We first consider the formulas $x < 2$ and $y < 2$, which are similar according to the definition below.

We sometimes write $P(v)$ for a formula. The variable v may or may not be free in $P(v)$, and variables other than v may be free in $P(v)$.

Let u and v be distinct variables, and let $P(u)$ and $P(v)$ be formulas. $P(u)$ is *similar* to $P(v)$ if and only if v is not free in $P(u)$ and u is not free in $P(v)$, and $P(u)$ admits v for u and $P(v)$ admits u for v, and $P(v/u)$ is $P(v)$ and $P(u/v)$ is $P(u)$. Briefly, $P(u)$ is the same as $P(v)$, except that $P(u)$ has free occurrences of u in exactly those positions in which $P(v)$ has free occurrences of v.

The definition of similar is symmetric, i.e., if $P(u)$ is similar to $P(v)$, then $P(v)$ is similar to $P(u)$. We observe also that if $P(u)$ is similar to $P(v)$, then $\sim P(u)$ is similar to $\sim P(v)$.

THEOREM 6. $\vdash \forall u P(u) \leftrightarrow \forall v P(v)$ *if $P(u)$ is similar to $P(v)$.*

Proof.   Suppose $P(u)$ is similar to $P(v)$.

1.	$\forall u P(u)$	as
2.	$P(v)$	spec
3.	$\forall v P(v)$	gen
4.	$\forall u P(u) \to \forall v P(v)$	DT, 1–3
5.	$\forall v P(v) \to \forall u P(u)$	repeat 1–4, interchanging u and v
6.	$\forall u P(u) \leftrightarrow \forall v P(v)$	SC, 4, 5

THEOREM 7 (*Change of bound variable*).   *If $\Delta \vdash Q$, and Q' is the result of replacing one or more occurrences of $\forall u P(u)$ in Q by occurrences of $\forall v P(v)$, and $P(u)$ is similar to $P(v)$, then $\Delta \vdash Q'$.*

Proof.   Theorem 6 and the replacement theorem.

THEOREM 8. $\vdash \exists u P(u) \leftrightarrow \exists v P(v)$ *if $P(u)$ is similar to $P(v)$.*

Proof.   Suppose $P(u)$ is similar to $P(v)$.

1.	$\forall u \sim P(u) \leftrightarrow \forall v \sim P(v)$	T 6
2.	$\sim \forall u \sim P(u) \leftrightarrow \sim \forall v \sim P(v)$	SC
3.	$\exists u P(u) \leftrightarrow \exists v P(v)$	same as 2

THEOREM 9.   *If* $\Delta \vdash Q$, *and* Q' *is the result of replacing one or more occurrences of* $\exists u P(u)$ *in* Q *by occurrences of* $\exists v P(v)$, *and* $P(u)$ *is similar to* $P(v)$, *then* $\Delta \vdash Q'$.

Proof.   Theorem 8 and the replacement theorem.

EXAMPLE 10.   Suppose that in proving some theorem of number theory we need

$$y + x \leqslant x + y \tag{1}$$

and have already proved

$$\forall x \forall y (x + y \leqslant y + x) \tag{2}$$

If we try to get (1) from (2) by spec we run into trouble.   (Try it.) However, the difficulty is purely notational and easily overcome by changes of bound variables.   Recall that x, y, x_1, x_2 are distinct variables. $x + y \leqslant y + x$ is similar to $x + y_1 \leqslant y_1 + x$.   Hence Theorem 7 applied to (2) gives

$$\forall x \forall y_1 (x + y_1 \leqslant y_1 + x) \tag{3}$$

$\forall y_1 (x + y_1 \leqslant y_1 + x)$ is similar to $\forall y_1 (x_1 + y_1 \leqslant y_1 + x_1)$.   Then Theorem 7 applied to (3) gives

$$\forall x_1 \forall y_1 (x_1 + y_1 \leqslant y_1 + x_1) \tag{4}$$

Then spec applied to (4) gives $\forall y_1 (y + y_1 \leqslant y_1 + y)$, and another application of spec gives $y + x \leqslant x + y$.

EXAMPLE 11.   A theorem of abelian groups is $\forall x \forall y \exists z (x + z = y)$. Let t_1 and t_2 be any terms in which z does not occur.   We show that $\exists z (t_1 + z = t_2)$ is a theorem.   For example, $\exists z ((x + y) + z = (y + x) + x)$ is a theorem.   Let v_1 and v_2 be variables distinct from each other and from x, y, and z, and from each variable that occurs in t_1 or t_2.   Then $\exists z (x + z = y)$ is similar to $\exists z (x + z = v_2)$, and a change of bound variable gives $\forall x \forall v_2 \exists z (x + z = v_2)$.   Similarly, $\forall v_2 \exists z (x + z = v_2)$ is similar to $\forall v_2 \exists z (v_1 + z = v_2)$, and a change of bound variable gives $\forall v_1 \forall v_2 \exists z (v_1 + z = v_2)$. .   Then $\forall v_2 \exists z (v_1 + z = v_2)$ admits t_1 for v_1 since neither v_2 nor z occurs in t_1.   Then spec gives $\forall v_2 \exists z (t_1 + z = v_2)$. Similarly, $\exists z (t_1 + z = v_2)$ admits t_2 for v_2 since z does not occur in t_2, and spec gives $\exists z (t_1 + z = t_2)$.

The next theorem generalizes the method of Example 11.

THEOREM 12.   *Let* $\Delta \vdash \forall u_1 \cdots \forall u_n P$. *Let* $t_1, \ldots, t_n$ *be terms such that no variable bound in P occurs in any* t_i. *Then* $\Delta \vdash P(t_1/u_1, \ldots, t_n/u_n)$, *where* $P(t_1/u_1, \ldots, t_n/u_n)$ *is the result of replacing each free occurrence of* u_i *in P by an occurrence of* t_i *for* $i \leqslant i \leqslant n$.

Proof.   Let $v_1, \ldots, v_n$ be distinct variables that do not occur in $\forall u_1 \cdots \forall u_n P$ or in $t_1, \ldots, t_n$. Since no v_i occurs in $\forall u_1 \cdots \forall u_n P$, n changes of bound variables give $\Delta \vdash \forall v_1 \cdots \forall v_n P(v_1/u_1, \ldots, v_n/u_n)$. Since no variable bound in $\forall v_1 \cdots \forall v_n P(v_1/u_1, \ldots, v_n/u_n)$ is free in any t_i, n applications of spec give $\Delta \vdash P(t_1/u_1, \ldots, t_n/u_n)$.

We indicate an application of Theorem 12 by "spec." For example,

    1. $\forall x \forall y \exists z(x + z = y)$
    2. $\exists z((x + y) + z = (y + x) + x)$ spec

A change of bound variable is sometimes necessary in a proof outline that uses Rule C more than once.

EXAMPLE 13.   In Example 17.16 we proved $\exists x \exists y(x < y)$ starting with the theorems $\exists x(x < 2)$ and $\exists y(y > 2)$. Suppose we have $\exists x(x > 2)$ instead of $\exists y(y > 2)$. Then we would have to use Rule C twice with x, and Exercise 17.3(c) shows that we cannot use Rule C twice in the same proof outline with the same variable. We proceed as follows:

    1. $\exists x(x < 2)$ theorem
    2. $\exists x(x > 2)$ theorem
    3. $\exists y(y > 2)$ Theorem 7
    4. $x < 2$ $Cx, 1$
    5. $y > 2$ $Cy, 3$

Then we proceed as in Example 17.16. Henceforth we shall omit explicit mention of Theorem 7. For example, the above proof outline will appear as

    1. $\exists x(x < 2)$ theorem
    2. $\exists x(x > 2)$ theorem
    3. $x < 2$ $Cx, 1$
    4. $y > 2$ $Cy, 2$

EXERCISES

1. Prove: (a) P is equivalent to P; (b) if P is equivalent to Q, then Q is equivalent to P; (c) if P is equivalent to Q and Q is equivalent to R, then P is equivalent to R.

2. Is $x > 2 \leftrightarrow \forall y(y > x) .\rightarrow. \forall x(x > 2) \leftrightarrow \forall x \forall y(y > x)$ an instance of the equivalence theorem? Why?

3. Prove in number theory: If $\vdash x > 2 \rightarrow y > 2$, then $\vdash 3 > 2 \rightarrow \forall y(y > 2)$. Do you believe that $P(u) \leftrightarrow P(v)$ is probable if $P(u)$ is similar to $P(v)$? Why?

4. Prove $\vdash \forall u \forall v(P(u) \wedge P(v)) \leftrightarrow \forall u \forall v(P(u) \vee P(v))$ if $P(u)$ is similar to $P(v)$.

5. Prove $\vdash \forall v(P \vee Q) \rightarrow \exists v P \vee \forall v Q$ using Axiom Scheme A4, the replacement theorem, and the definitions of $\vee$ and $\exists$.

6. Prove in number theory $\vdash \forall x(x \leqslant 3 \rightarrow \forall y(y > 3 \rightarrow y > x)) \rightarrow \forall y(y \leqslant 3 \rightarrow \forall x(x > 3 \rightarrow x > y))$.

7. Let U, V, P_U, and P_V be as in Theorem 2. Suppose $\Delta \vdash U \leftrightarrow V$ and $\Delta \vdash P_U$ and no variable bound in P_U is free in Δ. Show that $\Delta \vdash P_V$.

19 Theorem Schemes

Below we list some of the more important theorem schemes of the predicate calculus. A few have already been proved and are stated again for ready reference. Some are proved in this section. Those whose proof involves nothing new are assigned as exercises.

1. $\forall v P \rightarrow P(t/v)$ if P admits t for v	(Axiom Scheme A5)
2. $\forall v P \rightarrow \exists v P$	(Theorem 17.6)
3. $\forall v P \leftrightarrow P$ if v is not free in P	(Theorem 1)
4. $\forall u P(u) \leftrightarrow \forall v P(v)$ if $P(u)$ is similar to $P(v)$	(Theorem 18.6)
5. $\forall u \forall v P \leftrightarrow \forall v \forall u P$	(Theorem 2)
6. $\forall v P \leftrightarrow {\sim}\exists v {\sim}P$	(Theorem 18.5)
7. $\forall v {\sim}P \leftrightarrow {\sim}\exists v P$	(Theorem 3)
8. $P(t/v) \rightarrow \exists v P$ if P admits t for v	(Theorem 17.3)
9. $\exists v P \leftrightarrow P$ if v is not free in P	
10. $\exists u P(u) \leftrightarrow \exists v P(v)$ if $P(u)$ is similar to $P(v)$	(Theorem 18.8)
11. $\exists u \exists v P \leftrightarrow \exists v \exists u P$	
12. $\exists u \forall v P \rightarrow \forall v \exists u P$	(Theorem 4)
13. $\exists v P \leftrightarrow {\sim}\forall v {\sim}P$	

14. $\exists v \sim P \leftrightarrow \sim \forall v P$

15. $\forall v(P \leftrightarrow Q) . \rightarrow . \forall v P \leftrightarrow \forall v Q$ (Theorem 18.1)

16. $\forall v(P \leftrightarrow Q) . \rightarrow . P \leftrightarrow \forall v Q$ if v is not free in P (Theorem 5)

17. $\forall v(P \leftrightarrow Q) . \rightarrow . P \leftrightarrow \forall v Q$ if v is not free in Q

18. $\forall v(P \leftrightarrow Q) . \rightarrow . \exists v P \leftrightarrow \exists v Q$ (Theorem 6)

19. $\forall v(P \leftrightarrow Q) . \rightarrow . P \leftrightarrow \exists v Q$ if v is not free in P

20. $\forall v(P \rightarrow Q) . \rightarrow . \forall v P \rightarrow \forall v Q$ (Axiom Scheme A4)

21. $\forall v(P \rightarrow Q) \leftrightarrow P \rightarrow \forall v Q$ if v is not free in P

22. $\forall v(P \rightarrow Q) . \rightarrow . \exists v P \rightarrow \exists v Q$ (Theorem 17.15)

23. $\forall v(P \rightarrow Q) \leftrightarrow \exists v P \rightarrow Q$ if v is not free in Q

24. $\forall v P \rightarrow \forall v Q . \rightarrow . \exists v(P \rightarrow Q)$

25. $\forall v \exists u(P \rightarrow Q) . \rightarrow . \exists v \forall u P \rightarrow \exists v \exists u Q$

26. $\forall v(P \wedge Q) \leftrightarrow \forall v P \wedge \forall v Q$ (Theorem 7)

27. $\forall v(P \wedge Q) \leftrightarrow \forall v P \wedge Q$ if v is not free in Q

28. $\forall v(P \wedge Q) \leftrightarrow P \wedge \forall v Q$ if v is not free in P

29. $\forall v P \wedge \exists v Q \rightarrow \exists v(P \wedge Q)$

30. $\forall v(P \vee Q) \rightarrow \forall v P \vee \exists v Q$ (Theorem 8)

31. $\forall v(P \vee Q) \leftrightarrow \forall v P \vee Q$ if v is not free in Q

32. $\forall v(P \vee Q) \leftrightarrow P \vee \forall v Q$ if v is not free in P

33. $\forall v P \vee \forall v Q \rightarrow \forall v(P \vee Q)$ (Theorem 9)

34. $\forall v P \vee \exists v Q \rightarrow \exists v(P \vee Q)$

35. $\exists v(P \rightarrow Q) \leftrightarrow \forall v P \rightarrow \exists v Q$ (Theorem 10)

36. $\exists v(P \rightarrow Q) \leftrightarrow \forall v P \rightarrow Q$ if v is not free in Q

37. $\exists v(P \rightarrow Q) \leftrightarrow P \rightarrow \exists v Q$ if v is not free in P

38. $\exists v P \rightarrow \forall v Q . \rightarrow . \forall v(P \rightarrow Q)$

39. $\exists v P \rightarrow \exists v Q . \rightarrow . \exists v(P \rightarrow Q)$

40. $\exists v(P \wedge Q) \rightarrow \exists v P \wedge \exists v Q$ (Theorem 17.14)

41. $\exists v(P \wedge Q) \leftrightarrow \exists v P \wedge Q$ if v is not free in Q

42. $\exists v(P \wedge Q) \leftrightarrow P \wedge \exists v Q$ if v is not free in P

43. $\exists v(P \vee Q) \leftrightarrow \exists v P \vee \exists v Q$

44. $\exists v(P \vee Q) \leftrightarrow \exists v P \vee Q$ if v is not free in Q

45. $\exists v(P \vee Q) \leftrightarrow P \vee \exists v Q$ if v is not free in P

THEOREM 1. $\vdash \forall v P \leftrightarrow P$ *if v is not free in P.*

Proof.   Suppose that v is not free in P.

1. $\forall v P \rightarrow P$ A5

2. $P \rightarrow \forall v P$ A6

3. $\forall v P \leftrightarrow P$ SC, 1, 2

THEOREM 2. $\vdash \forall u \forall v P \leftrightarrow \forall v \forall u P$

Proof.

1.	$\forall u \forall v P \rightarrow \forall v \forall u P$	T17.10
2.	$\forall v \forall u P \rightarrow \forall u \forall v P$	T17.10
3.	$\forall u \forall v P \leftrightarrow \forall v \forall u P$	SC, 1, 2

THEOREM 3. $\vdash \forall v \sim P \leftrightarrow \sim \exists v P$

Proof.

1.	$\forall v \sim P \leftrightarrow \sim \sim \forall v \sim P$	taut
2.	$\forall v \sim P \leftrightarrow \sim \exists v P$	same as 1

THEOREM 4. $\vdash \exists u \forall v P \rightarrow \forall v \exists u P$

Proof.

1.	$\exists u \forall v P$	as
2.	$\forall v P$	Cu
3.	P	spec
4.	$\exists u P$	$\exists$
5.	$\forall v \exists u P$	gen
6.	$\forall v \exists u P$	C, 2
7.	$\exists u \forall v P \rightarrow \forall v \exists u P$	DT, 1–6

THEOREM 5. $\vdash \forall v (P \leftrightarrow Q) .\rightarrow. P \leftrightarrow \forall v Q$ *if v is not free in P.*

Proof.   Suppose that v is not free in P.

1.	$\forall v (P \leftrightarrow Q) .\rightarrow. \forall v P \leftrightarrow \forall v Q$	T18.1
2.	$\forall v P \leftrightarrow P$	T1
3.	$\forall v (P \leftrightarrow Q) .\rightarrow. P \leftrightarrow \forall v Q$	SC, 1, 2 (or rep, 1, 2)

THEOREM 6. $\vdash \forall v (P \leftrightarrow Q) .\rightarrow. \exists v P \leftrightarrow \exists v Q$

Proof.

1.	$\forall v (P \leftrightarrow Q)$	as
2.	$\exists v P$	as
3.	$P \leftrightarrow Q$	spec, 1

4.	P	Cv, 2
5.	Q	SC, 3, 4
6.	$\exists vQ$	$\exists$
7.	$\exists vQ$	C, 4
8.	$\exists vP \to \exists vQ$	DT, 1–7
9.	$\forall v(P \leftrightarrow Q) .\to. \exists vP \to \exists vQ$	DT, 1–8
10.	$\forall v(P \leftrightarrow Q) .\to. \exists vQ \to \exists vP$	similar to 1–9
11.	$\forall v(P \leftrightarrow Q) .\to. \exists vP \leftrightarrow \exists vQ$	SC, 9, 10

THEOREM 7. $\vdash \forall v(P \wedge Q) \leftrightarrow \forall vP \wedge \forall vQ$

Proof.

1.	$\forall v(P \wedge Q)$	as
2.	$P \wedge Q$	spec
3.	P	SC
4.	$\forall vP$	gen
5.	Q	SC, 2
6.	$\forall vQ$	gen
7.	$\forall vP \wedge \forall vQ$	SC, 4, 6
8.	$\forall v(P \wedge Q) \to \forall vP \wedge \forall vQ$	DT, 1–7
9.	$\forall vP \wedge \forall vQ$	as
10.	$\forall vP$	SC
11.	P	spec
12.	$\forall vQ$	SC, 9
13.	Q	spec
14.	$P \wedge Q$	SC, 11, 13
15.	$\forall v(P \wedge Q)$	gen
16.	$\forall vP \wedge \forall vQ \to \forall v(P \wedge Q)$	DT, 9–15
17.	$\forall v(P \wedge Q) \leftrightarrow \forall vP \wedge \forall vQ$	SC, 8, 16

THEOREM 8. $\vdash \forall v(P \vee Q) \to \forall vP \vee \exists vQ$

Proof.

1.	$\forall v(P \vee Q)$	as
2.	$P \vee Q \leftrightarrow {\sim}Q \to P$	taut
3.	$\forall v({\sim}Q \to P)$	rep, 1, 2
4.	$\forall v({\sim}Q \to P) .\to. \forall v{\sim}Q \to \forall vP$	A4
5.	$\forall v{\sim}Q \to \forall vP$	MP, 4, 3

6. $\forall vP \vee \sim\forall v\sim Q$ SC
7. $\forall vP \vee \exists vQ$ same as 6
8. $\forall v(P \vee Q) \rightarrow \forall vP \vee \exists vQ$ DT, 1–7

THEOREM 9. $\vdash\forall vP \vee \forall vQ \rightarrow \forall v(P \vee Q)$

Proof.

1. $\forall vP$ as
2. P spec
3. $P \vee Q$ SC
4. $\forall v(P \vee Q)$ gen
5. $\forall vP \rightarrow \forall v(P \vee Q)$ DT, 1–4
6. $\forall vQ \rightarrow \forall v(P \vee Q)$ similar to 1–5
7. $\forall vP \vee \forall vQ \rightarrow \forall v(P \vee Q)$ SC, 5, 6

THEOREM 10. $\vdash\exists v(P \rightarrow Q) \leftrightarrow \forall vP \rightarrow \exists vQ$

Proof.

1. $\exists v(P \rightarrow Q)$ as
2. $\forall vP$ as
3. $P \rightarrow Q$ Cv, 1
4. P spec, 2
5. Q MP, 3, 4
6. $\exists vQ$ $\exists$
7. $\exists vQ$ C, 3
8. $\forall vP \rightarrow \exists vQ$ DT, 1–7
9. $\exists v(P \rightarrow Q) .\rightarrow. \forall vP \rightarrow \exists vQ$ DT, 1–8
10. $\sim\exists v(P \rightarrow Q)$ as
11. $\sim\sim\forall v\sim(P \rightarrow Q)$ same as 10
12. $\forall v\sim(P \rightarrow Q)$ SC
13. $\sim(P \rightarrow Q) \leftrightarrow P \wedge \sim Q$ taut
14. $\forall v(P \wedge \sim Q)$ rep, 12, 13
15. $\forall v(P \wedge \sim Q) \leftrightarrow \forall vP \wedge \forall v\sim Q$ T7
16. $\forall vP \wedge \forall v\sim Q$ SC, 14, 15
17. $\forall vP \wedge \sim\sim\forall v\sim Q$ SC
18. $\forall vP \wedge \sim\exists vQ$ same as 17
19. $\sim(\forall vP \rightarrow \exists vQ)$ SC

20. $\sim\exists v(P \to Q) \to \sim(\forall vP \to \exists vQ)$ DT, 10–19
21. $\forall vP \to \exists vQ \;.\to.\; \exists v(P \to Q)$ SC
22. $\exists v(P \to Q) \leftrightarrow \forall vP \to \exists vQ$ SC, 9, 21

Another proof of the second part (by cases):

10. $\sim\forall vP$ as
11. $\forall vP \leftrightarrow \sim\exists v\sim P$ T18.5
12. $\exists v\sim P$ SC, 10, 11
13. $\sim P$ Cv
14. $P \to Q$ SC
15. $\exists v(P \to Q)$ $\exists$
16. $\exists v(P \to Q)$ C, 13
17. $\sim\forall vP \to \exists v(P \to Q)$ DT, 10–16
18. $\exists vQ$ as
19. Q Cv
20. $P \to Q$ SC
21. $\exists v(P \to Q)$ $\exists$
22. $\exists v(P \to Q)$ C, 19
23. $\exists vQ \to \exists v(P \to Q)$ DT, 18–22
24. $\sim\forall vP \;\vee\; \exists vQ \to \exists v(P \to Q)$ SC, 17, 23
25. $\forall vP \to \exists vQ \;.\to.\; \exists v(P \to Q)$ SC

EXERCISES

1. Prove the unproved theorem schemes in any order, making maximum use of what has already been proved.
2. Prove the unproved theorem schemes in the order given, using only the statement calculus, theorem schemes 1 through 14 (for those following 14), and the rules for removing and inserting quantifiers.
3. For each of Theorem Schemes 27 through 34 and 40 through 45, find another theorem scheme that does not involve $\wedge$ or $\vee$ from which the given scheme follows by the replacement theorem. For example, 26 follows from 35 because 26 is equivalent to $\forall v\sim(P \to \sim Q) \leftrightarrow \sim(\forall vP \to \sim\forall vQ)$, which is equivalent to $\sim\exists v(P \to \sim Q) \leftrightarrow \sim(\forall vP \to \exists v\sim Q)$, which is equivalent to $\exists v(P \to \sim Q) \leftrightarrow \forall vP \to \exists v\sim Q$.

20   Normal Forms

A *truth value operation* is an operation on the set $\{T, F\}$ of truth values.

EXAMPLE 1.   The table below defines a 3-place truth value operation f.
p_1, p_2, p_3 are variables ranging over $\{T, F\}$.

	p_1	p_2	p_3	$f(p_1, p_2, p_3)$
1.	T	T	T	F
2.	F	T	T	F
3.	T	F	T	T
4.	F	F	T	F
5.	T	T	F	F
6.	F	T	F	F
7.	T	F	F	T
8.	F	F	F	F

Since $\{T, F\}$ has 2 elements, the domain $\{T, F\}^3$ of f has 2^3 elements.
For every n, $\{T, F\}^n$ has 2^n elements.   Each line of the table above
states what value f assigns to one of the 8 possible ordered triples
(p_1, p_2, p_3) of truth values.   For example, line 2 states that $f(F, T, T)$
$= F$.   The 8 lines of the table completely define f.

We define $\sim, \rightarrow, \wedge, \vee$, and $\leftrightarrow$ as truth value operations as follows:

$$\sim T = F \quad T \rightarrow T = T \quad T \wedge T = T \quad T \vee T = T \quad T \leftrightarrow T = T$$
$$\sim F = T \quad F \rightarrow T = T \quad F \wedge T = F \quad F \vee T = T \quad F \leftrightarrow T = F$$
$$\quad\quad\quad\quad T \rightarrow F = F \quad T \wedge F = F \quad T \vee F = T \quad T \leftrightarrow F = F$$
$$\quad\quad\quad\quad F \rightarrow F = T \quad F \wedge F = F \quad F \vee F = F \quad F \leftrightarrow F = T$$

All we have done is to reproduce the truth tables for $\sim, \rightarrow, \wedge, \vee$, and
$\leftrightarrow$.   It should come as no surprise that such identities as $p \leftrightarrow q =$
$(p \rightarrow q) \wedge (q \rightarrow p)$ are true.

To every formula P there corresponds a unique truth value operation
f as follows.   Let $P_1, \ldots, P_n$ be the distinct prime constituents of P in
the order in which they first occur from left to right.   Each assignment
$p_1, \ldots, p_n$ of truth values to $P_1, \ldots, P_n$ results in a unique truth value
for P.   Then f is defined by: for each assignment $p_1, \ldots, p_n$ to
$P_1, \ldots, P_n$, $f(p_1, \ldots, p_n)$ is the truth value thereby assigned to P.

EXAMPLE 2.   To the formula $(A(x) \vee B(y)) \wedge \sim(A(x) \wedge B(y))$ there
corresponds the operation f defined by

$$f(p_1, p_2) = (p_1 \vee p_2) \wedge \sim(p_1 \wedge p_2)$$

We can now describe a tautology as a formula whose corresponding truth value operation always takes the value T. A *contradiction* is a formula whose corresponding truth value operation always takes the value F. For example, $\sim A(x) \wedge A(x)$ is a contradiction.

We now show that for each truth value operation f there is a formula P with the same truth table, i.e., the truth value operation corresponding to P is f.

EXAMPLE 3.   We produce a formula with the same truth table as the operation f of Example 1. Let P_1, P_2, P_3 be distinct prime formulas. f takes the value T on lines 3 and 7. On line 3, $p_1 = T$, $p_2 = F$, and $p_3 = T$. Corresponding to line 3 we use the conjunction

$$P_1 \wedge \sim P_2 \wedge P_3$$

On line 7, $p_1 = T$, $p_2 = F$, and $p_3 = F$. Corresponding to line 7 we use the conjunction

$$P_1 \wedge \sim P_2 \wedge \sim P_3.$$

Then the disjunction

$$(P_1 \wedge \sim P_2 \wedge P_3) \vee (P_1 \wedge \sim P_2 \wedge \sim P_3)$$

of these conjunctions has the same truth table as f. To see this, let g be the operation corresponding to

$$(P_1 \wedge \sim P_2 \wedge P_3) \vee (P_1 \wedge \sim P_2 \wedge \sim P_3).$$

We show that $f = g$. g is defined by

$$g(p_1, p_2, p_3) = (p_1 \wedge \sim p_2 \wedge p_3) \vee (p_1 \wedge \sim p_2 \wedge \sim p_3).$$

First, suppose that $f(p_1, p_2, p_3) = T$. Then either $p_1 = T$, $p_2 = F$, $p_3 = T$, or $p_1 = T$, $p_2 = F$, $p_3 = F$. If $p_1 = T$, $p_2 = F$, $p_3 = T$, then

$$g(T, F, T) = (T \wedge \sim F \wedge T) \vee (T \wedge \sim F \wedge \sim T)$$
$$= (T \wedge T \wedge T) \vee (T \wedge T \wedge F) = T \vee F = T.$$

If $p_1 = T$, $p_2 = F$, $p_3 = F$, then

$$g(T, F, F) = (T \wedge \sim F \wedge F) \vee (T \wedge \sim F \wedge \sim F)$$
$$= (T \wedge T \wedge F) \vee (T \wedge T \wedge T) = F \vee T = T.$$

Hence, if $f(p_1, p_2, p_3) = T$, then also $g(p_1, p_2, p_3) = T$. Now suppose that $g(p_1, p_2, p_3) = T$. By the truth table for $\vee$, either

$$p_1 \wedge \sim p_2 \wedge p_3 = T \quad \text{or} \quad p_1 \wedge \sim p_2 \wedge \sim p_3 = T.$$

If $p_1 \wedge \sim p_2 \wedge p_3 = T$, then $p_1 = \sim p_2 = p_3 = T$ by the truth table
for $\wedge$. Then $p_1 = T, p_2 = F, p_3 = T$. We know that $f(T, F, T) = T$. If $p_1 \wedge \sim p_2 \wedge \sim p_3 = T$, then $p_1 = \sim p_2 = \sim p_3 = T$. Then
$p_1 = T, p_2 = F, p_3 = F$. We know that $f(T, F, F) = T$. Hence, if
$g(p_1, p_2, p_3) = T$, then also $f(p_1, p_2, p_3) = T$. Hence $f(p_1, p_2, p_3) = T$ if and only if $g(p_1, p_2, p_3) = T$. Therefore

$$f(p_1, p_2, p_3) = g(p_1, p_2, p_3)$$

for every ordered triple (p_1, p_2, p_3) of truth values, i.e., $f = g$.

EXAMPLE 4. f is defined by

p	q	$f(p, q)$
T	T	F
F	T	T
T	F	T
F	F	F

To f there corresponds every formula $(\sim P \wedge Q) \vee (P \wedge \sim Q)$, where
P and Q are distinct prime formulas.

EXAMPLE 5. f is defined by

p	q	$f(p, q)$
T	T	F
F	T	F
T	F	F
F	F	F

Let P and Q be distinct prime formulas. Then a formula with the
same truth table as f is $\sim P \wedge P \wedge Q$, which always takes the value F
because $\sim P \wedge P$ always takes the value F.

THEOREM 6 (*The operational completeness of the statement calculus*).
*Let f be an n-place truth value operation. Then there is a formula with
exactly n distinct prime constituents whose corresponding truth value
operation is f.*

Proof. Let $P_1, \ldots, P_n$ be distinct prime formulas. If every value
of f is F, then we use $\sim P_1 \wedge P_1 \wedge P_2 \wedge \cdots \wedge P_n$, for $\sim p_1 \wedge p_1 \wedge p_2 \wedge \cdots \wedge p_n$ always takes the value F. So suppose that f takes the

value T at least once. Let $(p_{11}, \ldots, p_{1n})$, $(p_{21}, \ldots, p_{2n})$, $\ldots$, $(p_{k1}, \ldots, p_{kn})$ be the k different ordered n-tuples of truth values to which f assigns the value T. For $1 \leqslant i \leqslant k$ and $1 \leqslant j \leqslant n$ we define P_{ij} by $P_{ij} = P_j$ if $p_{ij} = T$, and $P_{ij} = \sim P_j$ if $p_{ij} = F$. Let P be the formula $(P_{11} \wedge \cdots \wedge P_{1n}) \vee \cdots \vee (P_{k1} \wedge \cdots \wedge P_{kn})$. We show that f is the truth value operation corresponding to P. Suppose that $f(p_1, \ldots, p_n) = T$. Then for some i $(1 \leqslant i \leqslant k)$, $(p_1, \ldots, p_n) = (p_{i1}, \ldots, p_{in})$. Assign $p_{i1}, \ldots, p_{in}$ to $P_1, \ldots, P_n$. $P_{i1}, \ldots, P_{in}$ all take the value T by the definition of P_{ij}. Then $(P_{i1} \wedge \cdots \wedge P_{in})$ takes the value T by the truth table for $\wedge$. Then P takes the value T by the truth table for $\vee$. Now suppose that P takes the value T when $p_1, \ldots, p_n$ are assigned to $P_1, \ldots, P_n$. By the truth table for $\vee$, there is an i $(1 \leqslant i \leqslant k)$ such that $(P_{i1} \wedge \cdots \wedge P_{in})$ takes the value T. By the truth table for $\wedge$, $P_{i1}, \ldots, P_{in}$ each take the value T. We show that $(p_1, \ldots, p_n) = (p_{i1}, \ldots, p_{in})$, and hence $f(p_1, \ldots, p_n) = T$. We consider two cases. Suppose $p_{ij} = T$. Then $P_{ij} = P_j$ by the definition of P_{ij}. Since P_{ij} takes the value T, P_j takes the value T, i.e., $p_j = T = p_{ij}$. Suppose $p_{ij} = F$. Then $P_{ij} = \sim P_j$ by the definition of P_{ij}. Since P_{ij} takes the value T, P_j takes the value F, i.e., $p_j = F = p_{ij}$.

A set of statement connectives is *operationally complete* if and only if for each truth value operation f there is a formula or an abbreviation of a formula whose corresponding truth value operation is f and in which the only statement connectives that explicitly appear are those in the given set. Theorem 6 shows that the set $\{\wedge, \vee, \sim\}$ is operationally complete. Since $\wedge$ and $\vee$ can be defined in terms of $\to$ and $\sim$, it follows that $\{\to, \sim\}$ is also operationally complete. Since $p \vee q = \sim(\sim p \wedge \sim q)$, the set $\{\wedge, \sim\}$ is operationally complete. Similarly, the set $\{\vee, \sim\}$ is operationally complete.

A formula whose distinct prime constituents are $P_1, \ldots, P_n$ is in *disjunctive normal form* if and only if it has the form

$$(P_{11} \wedge \cdots \wedge P_{1n}) \vee (P_{21} \wedge \cdots \wedge P_{2n}) \vee \cdots \vee (P_{k1} \wedge \cdots \wedge P_{kn})$$

where each P_{ij} is either P_j or $\sim P_j$.

THEOREM 7. *Every formula that is not a contradiction is equivalent to a formula in disjunctive normal form.*

Proof. Let P be a formula that is not a contradiction, and let $P_1, \ldots, P_n$ be the prime constituents of P. Let f be the truth value operation corresponding to P. The proof of Theorem 6 shows how to construct a formula Q in disjunctive normal form whose prime constituents are $P_1, \ldots, P_n$ and whose truth value operation is f. Since P and Q have the same truth value operation, every assignment of truth values to $P_1, \ldots, P_n$ results in the same truth value being assigned to P and Q. Hence $P \leftrightarrow Q$ is a tautology by the truth table for $\leftrightarrow$. Hence $\vdash P \leftrightarrow Q$, i.e., P is equivalent to Q.

EXAMPLE 8.   Let P be $(A(x) \lor B(y)) \land \sim(A(x) \land B(y))$. The truth table for P is

$(A(x)$	$\lor$	$B(y))$	$\land$	$\sim$	$(A(x)$	$\land$	$B(y))$
T	T	T	F	F	T	T	T
F	T	T	T	T	F	F	T
T	T	F	T	T	T	F	F
F	F	F	F	T	F	F	F

The truth value operation f corresponding to P is defined by

p_1	p_2	$f(p_1, p_2)$
T	T	F
F	T	T
T	F	T
F	F	F

Then by Theorem 7, P is equivalent to

$$(\sim A(x) \land B(y)) \lor (A(x) \land \sim B(y))$$

A formula whose distinct prime constituents are $P_1, \ldots, P_n$ is in *conjunctive normal* form if and only if it has the form

$$(P_{11} \lor \cdots \lor P_{1n}) \land (P_{21} \lor \cdots \lor P_{2n}) \land \cdots \land (P_{k1} \lor \cdots \lor P_{kn})$$

where each P_{ij} is either P_j or $\sim P_j$.

THEOREM 9.   *Every formula that is not a tautology is equivalent to a formula in conjunctive normal form.*

Proof.   Let P be a formula that is not a tautology, and let $P_1, \ldots, P_n$ be the distinct prime constituents of P. Since P is not a tautology,

$\sim P$ is not a contradiction. Then by the proof of Theorem 7, $\sim P$ is equivalent to a formula $(P_{11} \wedge \cdots \wedge P_{1n}) \vee \cdots \vee (P_{k1} \wedge \cdots \wedge P_{kn})$ in disjunctive normal form, where each P_{ij} is either P_j or $\sim P_j$. By the statement calculus, P is equivalent to

$$\sim((P_{11} \wedge \cdots \wedge P_{1n}) \vee \cdots \vee (P_{k1} \wedge \cdots \wedge P_{kn}))$$

By the statement calculus, the latter is equivalent to

$$\sim(P_{11} \wedge \cdots \wedge P_{1n}) \wedge \cdots \wedge \sim(P_{k1} \wedge \cdots \wedge P_{kn})$$

By the statement calculus again, the latter is equivalent to

$$(\sim P_{11} \vee \cdots \vee \sim P_{1n}) \wedge \cdots \wedge (\sim P_{k1} \wedge \cdots \wedge \sim P_{kn})$$

If $P_{ij} = P_j$, then $\sim P_{ij} = \sim P_j$. If $P_{ij} = \sim P_j$, then $\sim P_{ij} = \sim\sim P_j$. In the latter case $\sim P_{ij}$ is equivalent to P_j. Now in

$$(\sim P_{11} \vee \cdots \vee \sim P_{1n}) \wedge \cdots \wedge (\sim P_{k1} \vee \cdots \vee \sim P_{kn})$$

we replace every $\sim\sim P_{ij}$ by P_{ij}. The resulting formula is equivalent to P by the statement calculus and is in conjunctive normal form.

EXAMPLE 10. Let P be $(A(x) \vee B(y)) \wedge \sim(A(x) \wedge B(y))$. From Example 8, the truth value operation g corresponding to $\sim P$ is defined by

p_1	p_2	$g(p_1, p_2)$
T	T	T
F	T	F
T	F	F
F	F	T

Hence a disjunctive normal form of $\sim P$ is

$$(A(x) \wedge B(y)) \vee (\sim A(x) \wedge \sim B(y))$$

Then a denial of $\sim P$ is $(\sim A(x) \vee \sim B(y)) \wedge (A(x) \vee B(y))$. This denial is equivalent to P and is in conjunctive normal form.

We move on to the predicate calculus. A formula P is in *prenex normal form* if and only if it is of the form $Z v_1 Z v_2 \cdots Z v_n Q$, where each Z is $\forall$ or $\exists$, no quantifiers occur in Q, and $n \geqslant 0$. (Briefly, all the quantifiers in P appear at the front.)

We show that every formula is equivalent to a formula in prenex normal form, using the following theorem schemes of Section 19.

7. $\forall v \sim P \leftrightarrow \sim \exists v P$
14. $\exists v \sim P \leftrightarrow \sim \forall v P$
21. $\forall v (P \to Q) \leftrightarrow P \to \forall v Q$ if v is not free in P
23. $\forall v (P \to Q) \leftrightarrow \exists v P \to Q$ if v is not free in Q
36. $\exists v (P \to Q) \leftrightarrow \forall v P \to Q$ if v is not free in Q
37. $\exists v (P \to Q) \leftrightarrow P \to \exists v Q$ if v is not free in P

EXAMPLE 10.   Let P be the formula $\forall x(x \geqslant 0) \to \exists y(y > 2)$ of number theory.   By 36 and the equivalence theorem, P is equivalent to

$$\exists x . x \geqslant 0 \to \exists y(y > 2) \tag{1}$$

By 37, $x \geqslant 0 \to \exists y(y > 2)$ is equivalent to $\exists y . x \geqslant 0 \to y > 2$.   Then by the equivalence theorem, (1) is equivalent to

$$\exists x \exists y . x \geqslant 0 \to y > 2 \tag{2}$$

Hence P is equivalent to (2), which is in prenex normal form.

THEOREM 11.   *Every formula is equivalent to a formula in prenex normal form.*

Proof.   Let P be a formula or an abbreviation of a formula in which the only logical operators that explicitly occur are $\sim$, $\to$, $\forall$, $\exists$.   The proof is by induction on the number n of occurrences of $\sim$, $\to$, $\forall$, or $\exists$ in P.

Basis.   If $n = 0$, then P is an atomic formula and is already in prenex normal form.

Induction step.   Assume that every formula with n or fewer symbols is equivalent to a formula in prenex normal form, and consider a formula P with $n + 1$ symbols.

Case 1. P is $\sim Q$ for some Q.   By the induction hypothesis, Q is equivalent to a formula Q' in prenex normal form.   Then P is equivalent to $\sim Q'$ by the equivalence theorem (or the statement calculus).   If no quantifiers appear in Q', then $\sim Q'$ is in prenex normal form.   Suppose $\sim Q'$ is $\sim Z v_1 \cdots Z v_k Q''$.   Then k applications of Theorem Schemes 7 and 14 of Section 19 (mixed as necessary) and the equivalence theorem give a formula in prenex normal form that is equivalent to P.

Case 2. P is $Q \to R$ for some Q and R. By the induction hypothesis, Q and R are equivalent to formulas Q' and R' in prenex normal form. Then P is equivalent to $Q' \to R'$. Suppose that Q' is $\forall v Q''$. Then $Q' \to R'$ is $\forall v Q'' \to R'$. Then by Theorem Scheme 36 and the equivalence theorem, P is equivalent to $\exists v(Q'' \to R')$. If v is free in R', we change the bound variable v to a variable that does not occur in $\forall v Q'' \to R'$, and then apply 36. If Q' is $\exists v Q''$, we proceed in the same way, using 23 instead of 36. k applications of 36 and 23 (mixed as necessary) move all the quantifiers in Q' to the front of the conditional. Then similarly we use 37 and 21 to move all the quantifiers in R' to the front of the conditional.

Case 3. P is $\forall v Q$ for some v and Q. By the induction hypothesis, Q is equivalent to a formula Q' in prenex normal form. Then P is equivalent to $\forall v Q'$, which is in prenex normal form.

Case 4. P is $\exists v Q$ for some v and Q. This case is similar to case 3.

EXAMPLE 12. P is $\sim\exists x(\exists x(x > 2) \to x = 3)$. First we make a change of bound variable to get $\sim\exists x(\exists y(y > 2) \to x = 3)$. Then we apply Theorem Scheme 23 to $\exists y(y > 2) \to x = 3$ to get $\forall y(y > 2 \to x = 3)$. Hence P is equivalent to $\sim\exists x \forall y(y > 2 \to x = 3)$. Then we apply Theorem Schemes 7 and 14 in turn to get $\forall x \exists y \sim(y > 2 \to x = 3)$.

If $Q \leftrightarrow R$ occurs in P, we replace it by $(Q \to R) \wedge (R \to Q)$. If $\wedge$ or $\vee$ occurs in P, we can either eliminate it and use Theorem 11, or we can leave P in abbreviated form and use Theorem Schemes 27, 28, 31, 32, 41, 42, 44, 45. Theorem Schemes 26, 35, and 43 are helpful whenever they apply.

EXAMPLE 13. P is

$$\forall x \forall y \forall z((x + y) + z = x + (y + z)) \wedge \forall x \forall y(x + y = y + x)$$

An application of Theorem Scheme 26 gives

$$\forall x . \forall y \forall z((x + y) + z = x + (y + z)) \wedge \forall y(x + y = y + x)$$

Another application of 26 gives

$$\forall x \forall y . \forall z((x + y) + z = x + (y + z)) \wedge x + y = y + x$$

Then 27 gives

$$\forall x \forall y \forall z .(x + y) + z = x + (y + z) \wedge x + y = y + x$$

1. Show that there are exactly 2^{2^n} distinct n-place truth value operations.
2. Show that $\{\wedge, \vee\}$ is not operationally complete.
3. (a) The binary connective $\downarrow$ is defined by

P	Q	$P \downarrow Q$
T	T	F
F	T	F
T	F	F
F	F	T

   Show that $\{\downarrow\}$ is operationally complete.
   (b) Find another binary connective $\uparrow$ such that $\{\uparrow\}$ is operationally complete.
4. Reduce to disjunctive and conjunctive normal form.

   (a) $P \rightarrow Q$
   (b) $P \rightarrow Q \leftrightarrow \sim R$
   (c) $xy = 0 \leftrightarrow x = 0 \vee y = 0$

5. Let P_1, P_2, P_3, be distinct prime formulas. Find the simplest formula that is equivalent to every formula whose prime constituents are P_1, P_2, P_3 and whose corresponding truth value operation is f.

p_1	p_2	p_3	$f(p_1, p_2, p_3)$
T	T	T	T
F	T	T	F
T	F	T	T
F	F	T	F
T	T	F	T
F	T	F	T
T	F	F	T
F	F	F	T

6. Reduce to prenex normal form.

   (a) $\forall x \forall y . x < y \rightarrow \exists z (x < z \wedge z < y)$
   (b) $\forall x \forall y \exists z (x + y = z)$
$$\wedge\ \forall x \forall y \forall z \forall z_1 (x + y = z \wedge x + y = z_1 \rightarrow z = z_1)$$

   (c) $\forall x.\exists y(4y = x) \to \exists y(2y = x)$

   (d) $\forall x(x = 1) .\to. \exists x(x > 2) \to \forall x(x > 3)$

   (e) $\forall x(x > 2 \to x > 1) \to \exists x(x > 2) \wedge \exists x(x > 1)$

ANSWERS

2. Hint: Show that $\sim$ is not definable.

3. (a) $\sim p = p \downarrow p$, and $p \vee q = \sim(p \downarrow q) = (p \downarrow q) \downarrow (p \downarrow q)$

   (b) Last column of truth table for $\uparrow$ is F, T, T, T

4. (a) $(P \wedge Q) \vee (\sim P \wedge Q) \vee (\sim P \wedge \sim Q); \sim P \vee Q$

   (b) $(P \wedge \sim Q \wedge R) \vee (P \wedge Q \wedge \sim R) \vee (\sim P \wedge Q \wedge \sim R)$
$$\vee (\sim P \wedge \sim Q \wedge \sim R);$$
$$(\sim P \vee \sim Q \vee \sim R) \wedge (P \vee \sim Q \vee \sim R) \wedge (P \vee Q \vee \sim R)$$
$$\wedge (\sim P \vee Q \vee R)$$

   (c) $(xy = 0 \wedge x = 0 \wedge y = 0) \vee (xy = 0 \wedge x \neq 0 \wedge y = 0)$
$$\vee (xy = 0 \wedge x = 0 \wedge y \neq 0) \vee (xy \neq 0 \wedge x \neq 0 \wedge y \neq 0);$$
$$(xy = 0 \vee x \neq 0 \vee y \neq 0) \wedge (xy = 0 \vee x = 0 \vee y \neq 0)$$
$$\wedge (xy = 0 \vee x \neq 0 \vee y = 0) \wedge (xy \neq 0 \vee x = 0 \vee y = 0)$$

5. $P_3 \to P_1$.

6. (a) $\forall x \forall y \exists z.x < y \to x < z \wedge z < y$

   (b) $\forall x \forall y \exists z \forall z_2 \forall z_1(x + y = z .\wedge. x + y = z_2$
$$\wedge\ x + y = z_1 \to z_2 = z_1)$$

   (c) $\forall x \forall y \exists z(4y = x \to 2z = x)$ or $\forall x \exists y \forall z(4z = x \to 2y = x)$

   (e) $\exists x \exists y \exists z(x > 2 \to x > 1 .\to. y > 2 \wedge z > 1)$

21   Equality

We write the first 2-place predicate symbol as $=$, and for all terms r and s, we write $(r = s)$ for $=(r, s)$ and $r \neq s$ for $\sim(r = s)$.

The *predicate calculus with equality* is the result of adjoining to the predicate calculus the following axioms, which we call the *equality axioms*.

   E1. $\forall x(x = x)$

   E2. $\forall x_1 \cdots \forall x_n \forall y_1 \cdots \forall y_n(x_1 = y_1 \wedge \cdots \wedge x_n = y_n$
$$.\to. G(x_1, \ldots, x_n) \leftrightarrow G(y_1, \ldots, y_n))$$
     (One axiom for each predicate symbol G)

   E3. $\forall x_1 \cdots \forall x_n \forall y_1 \cdots \forall y_n(x_1 = y_1 \wedge \cdots \wedge x_n = y_n$
$$\to F(x_1, \ldots, x_n) = F(y_1, \ldots, y_n)).$$
     (One axiom for each operation symbol F)

E1 is an individual axiom.   E2 and E3 are axiom schemes.

We note that

$$\forall x_1 \forall x_2 \forall y_1 \forall y_2 (x_1 = y_1 \wedge x_2 = y_2 .\rightarrow. x_1 = x_2 \leftrightarrow y_1 = y_2)$$

is an axiom, being that instance of E2 in which G is $=$.

THEOREM 1. $\vdash \forall x \forall y (x = y \rightarrow y = x)$

Proof.

1.	$\forall x_1 \forall x_2 \forall y_1 \forall y_2 (x_1 = y_1 \wedge x_2 = y_2 .\rightarrow. x_1 = x_2 \leftrightarrow y_1 = y_2)$	E2
2.	$y = y \wedge x = y .\rightarrow. y = x \leftrightarrow y = y$	spec
3.	$\forall x (x = x)$	E1
4.	$y = y$	spec
5.	$x = y \rightarrow y = x$	SC, 2, 4
6.	$\forall x \forall y (x = y \rightarrow y = x)$	gen

THEOREM 2. $\vdash \forall x \forall y \forall z (x = y \wedge y = z \rightarrow x = z)$

Proof.

1.	$\forall x_1 \forall x_2 \forall y_1 \forall y_2 (x_1 = y_1 \wedge x_2 = y_2 .\rightarrow. x_1 = x_2 \leftrightarrow y_1 = y_2)$	E2
2.	$x = y \wedge z = z .\rightarrow. x = z \leftrightarrow y = z$	spec
3.	$\forall x (x = x)$	E1
4.	$z = z$	spec
5.	$x = y \wedge y = z \rightarrow x = z$	SC, 2, 4
6.	$\forall x \forall y \forall z (x = y \wedge y = z \rightarrow x = z)$	gen

Theorems 1 and 2 enable us to collapse any chain of equalities.   In proof outlines, we indicate by " $=$ " one or more applications of E1, Theorem 1, and Theorem 2.

EXAMPLE 3.

1.	$x + y = z \wedge x + y = z_1$	
2.	$z = z_1$	$=$

The statement calculus applied to step 1 gives $x + y = z$ and $x + y = z_1$. Theorem 1 applied to $x + y = z$ gives $z = x + y$. Then Theorem 2 applied to $z = x + y$ and $x + y = z_1$ gives $z = z_1$.

EXAMPLE 4.

$$
\begin{array}{lll}
1. & 0 + 0 = 0 + 0 & = \\
2. & 0 + y = y + 0 & \\
3. & y' + 0 = y + 0' & \\
4. & y + 0' = (y + 0)' & \\
5. & y + 0' = (0 + y)' & \\
6. & 0 + y' = (0 + y)' & \\
7. & 0 + y' = y' + 0 & =, 6, 5, 3 \\
\end{array}
$$

Step 1 is an application of E1, i.e., it is the result of applying spec to E1. Step 7 comes from steps 6, 5, and 3 by Theorems 1 and 2. Theorem 1 applied to step 5 gives $(0 + y)' = y + 0'$. Then Theorem 2 applied to $0 + y' = (0 + y)'$ (step 6) and $(0 + y)' = y + 0'$ gives $0 + y' = y + 0'$. Theorem 1 applied to step 3 gives $y + 0' = y' + 0$. Then Theorem 2 applied to $0 + y' = y + 0'$ and $y + 0' = y' + 0$ gives $0 + y' = y' + 0$ (step 7). Briefly, the chain $0 + y' = (0 + y)'$, $y + 0' = (0 + y)'$, $y' + 0 = y + 0'$ of steps 6, 5, and 3 is collapsed to give $0 + y' = y + 0'$.

We now prove some substitution properties of equality.

THEOREM 5. $\vdash r = s \rightarrow t_r = t_s$, where $r, s, t_r,$ and t_s are terms, r occurs in t_r, and t_s is the result of replacing one or more specified occurrences (but not necessarily all occurrences) of r in t_r by occurrences of s.

Proof. By induction on the number n of occurrences of operation symbols in t_r.

Basis. If $n = 0$, then t_r is a variable or a constant symbol. In either case, t_r is r and t_s is s. Then $r = s \rightarrow r = s$ is a theorem because it is a tautology.

Induction step. Assume the theorem for every t_r with n or fewer symbols and consider t_r with $n + 1$ symbols. Then t_r is $F(t_1, \ldots, t_k)$, where F is an operation symbol and $t_1, \ldots, t_k$ are terms with n or fewer symbols. Then t_s is $F(t'_1, \ldots, t'_k)$, where each t'_i is the result of replacing the specified occurrences of r in t_i by occurrences of s. By the induction hypothesis, $\vdash r = s \rightarrow t_i = t'_i$ for $1 \leqslant i \leqslant k$. E3 and spec give $\vdash t_1 = t'_1 \wedge \cdots \wedge t_k = t'_k \rightarrow F(t_1, \ldots, t_k) = F(t'_1, \ldots, t'_k)$. Then the statement calculus gives $\vdash r = s \rightarrow F(t_1, \ldots, t_k) = F(t'_1, \ldots, t'_k)$.

COROLLARY 6.   *If $\Delta \vdash r = s$, then $\Delta \vdash t_r = t_s$, where r, s, t_r, and t_s are as in Theorem 5.*

Proof.   Theorem 5 and modus ponens.

By Theorem 1, we can vary Corollary 6 by replacing $\Delta \vdash r = s$ by $\Delta \vdash s = r$, or by replacing $\Delta \vdash t_r = t_s$ by $\Delta \vdash t_s = t_r$.   We indicate an application of Theorem 5 or Corollary 6 or one of its variants in proof outlines by "sub."

EXAMPLE 7.

    1. $y = z + 1$
    2. $(x(z + 1) + y) + (z + 1) = (xy + y) + y$ sub

In this example r is y, s is $z + 1$, t_y is $(xy + y) + y$, and t_{z+1} is $(x(z + 1) + y) + (z + 1)$.   Note that only two of the three occurrences of y in t_y are specified occurrences.

THEOREM 8. $\vdash r = s \mathbin{.}{\to}. P_r \leftrightarrow P_s$, *where P_r and P_s are formulas, r and s are terms, r occurs in P_r, and P_s is the result of replacing one or more specified occurrences (but not necessarily all occurrences) of r in P_r by occurrences of s, provided that no variable that occurs in r or s is a bound variable of P_r.*

Proof.   By induction on the number n of symbols in P_r, counting each occurrence of $\sim$, $\to$, or $\forall$ as a symbol.

Basis.   If $n = 0$, then P_r is an atomic formula $G(t_1, \ldots, t_k)$, where G is a predicate symbol and $t_1, \ldots, t_k$ are terms.   Then P_s is $G(t_1', \ldots, t_k')$, where each t_i' is the result of replacing the specified occurrences of r in t_i by occurrences of s.   By Theorem 5, $\vdash r = s \to t_i = t_i'$ for $1 \leqslant i \leqslant k$. E2 and spec give

$$\vdash t_1 = t_1' \wedge \cdots \wedge t_k = t_k' \mathbin{.}{\to}. G(t_1, \ldots, t_k) \leftrightarrow G(t_1', \ldots, t_k')$$

Then the statement calculus gives

$$\vdash r = s \mathbin{.}{\to}. G(t_1, \ldots, t_k) \leftrightarrow G(t_1', \ldots, t_k')$$

Induction step.   Assume the theorem for every P_r with n or fewer symbols, and consider a P_r with $n + 1$ symbols.

Case 1. P_r is $\sim Q_r$ for some Q_r. The induction hypothesis gives $\vdash r = s .\to. Q_r \leftrightarrow Q_s$. Then the statement calculus gives

$$\vdash r = s .\to. \sim Q_r \leftrightarrow \sim Q_s$$

Case 2. P_r is $Q_r \to R_r$ for some Q_r and R_r. The induction hypothesis gives $\vdash r = s .\to. Q_r \leftrightarrow Q_s$ and $\vdash r = s .\to. R_r \leftrightarrow R_s$. Then the statement calculus gives $\vdash r = s .\to. Q_r \to R_r \leftrightarrow Q_s \to R_s$.

Case 3. P_r is $\forall v Q_r$ for some v and Q_r. The induction hypothesis gives $\vdash r = s .\to. Q_r \leftrightarrow Q_s$. Then gen gives $\vdash \forall v(r = s .\to. Q_r \leftrightarrow Q_s)$. Since v is a bound variable of P_r, v is not free in $r = s$. Then Theorem Scheme 21 of Section 19 and the statement calculus give

$$\vdash r = s .\to. \forall v(Q_r \leftrightarrow Q_s)$$

Then Theorem 18.1 and the statement calculus give

$$\vdash r = s .\to. \forall v Q_r \leftrightarrow \forall v Q_s$$

COROLLARY 9.   *If* $\Delta \vdash r = s$ *and* $\Delta \vdash P_r$, *then* $\Delta \vdash P_s$, *where* r, s, P_r, *and* P_s *are as in Theorem 8.*

Proof.   Theorem 8 and the statement calculus.

By Theorem 1, we can vary Corollary 9 by replacing $\Delta \vdash r = s$ by $\Delta \vdash s = r$. We use "sub" again to indicate an application of Theorem 8 or Corollary 9 or its variant in proof outlines.

EXAMPLE 10.

6. $x < y \wedge y < 3$
    $\vdots$

9. $y = y_1 + y_2$
    $\vdots$

14. $x < y_1 + y_2 \wedge y < z$ sub, 9, 6

Here r is y, s is $y_1 + y_2$, P_y is $x < y \wedge y < z$, and $P_{y_1 + y_2}$ is $x < y_1 + y_2 \wedge y < z$. The first occurrence of y in P_y is the specified occurrence.

EXAMPLE 11.   In Corollary 9, the restriction that no variable bound in P_r may occur in r or s can be circumvented by changes of bound variables. Suppose $\Delta \vdash x = y + 7$ and $\Delta \vdash \exists y(y = x + 2)$. Let r

be x, s be $y + 7$, and P_x be $\exists y(y = x + 2)$. Corollary 9 does not apply because the variable y occurs in s and is bound in P_x. Observing that P_{y+2} is $\exists y(y = (y + 7) + 2)$, we conclude that there is good reason for the restriction. We can, however, go ahead with the substitution after changing the bound variable y in P_x to y_1. Then, from $\Delta \vdash x = y + 7$ and $\Delta \vdash \exists y_1(y_1 = x + 2)$, we can conclude $\Delta \vdash \exists y_1(y_1 = (y + 7) + 2)$.

Statements of the following forms are very common in mathematics:

> There is one and only one u such that $P(u)$
> There is exactly one u such that $P(u)$
> There is a unique u such that $P(u)$
> There is at least one u and at most one u such that $P(u)$

We translate each of them as

$$\exists u P(u) \;\wedge\; \forall u \forall v(P(u) \;\wedge\; P(v) \rightarrow u = v) \tag{1}$$

where $P(v)$ is $P(v/u)$, and v is the first variable in the alphabetic list of variables that does not occur in $P(u)$. Then we abbreviate (1) as

$$\exists! u P(u) \tag{2}$$

We have chosen v in (1) to be a specific variable to make sure that (2) has a unique unabbreviation. In practice, v can be any variable such that $P(u)$ is similar to $P(v)$. In (1), $\exists u P(u)$ says that there is at least one u such that $P(u)$, and $\forall u \forall v(P(u) \;\wedge\; P(v) \rightarrow u = v)$ says that there is at most one u such that $P(u)$.

THEOREM 12. $\vdash \forall x \exists! y(y = x)$.

Proof. $P(y)$ is $y = x$.

1.	$x = x$	$=$
2.	$\exists y(y = x)$	$\exists$
3.	$\quad y = x \wedge z = x$	as
4.	$\quad y = z$	$=, 3$
5.	$y = x \wedge z = x \rightarrow y = z$	DT, 3–4
6.	$\forall y \forall z(y = x \wedge z = x \rightarrow y = z)$	gen
7.	$\exists! y(y = x)$	SC, 2, 6
8.	$\forall x \exists! y(y = x)$	gen

A proof of $\exists! u P(u)$ breaks down into two parts, the existence part $\exists u P(u)$ and the uniqueness part $\forall u \forall v(P(u) \;\wedge\; P(v) \rightarrow u = v)$. For the uniqueness part, $u = v$ is deduced from the assumption $P(u) \land P(v)$, and then the deduction theorem and gen give

$$\forall u \forall v (P(u) \land P(v) \to u = v)$$

EXAMPLE 13.   Abelian groups. $\vdash \forall x \forall y \exists! z (x + y = z)$

Proof.

1.	$x + y = x + y$	$=$
2.	$\exists z (x + y = z)$	$\exists$
3.	$\qquad x + y = z \land x + y = z_1$	as
4.	$\qquad z = z_1$	$=, 3$
5.	$x + y = z \land x + y = z_1 \to z = z_1$	DT, 3–4
6.	$\forall z \forall z_1 (x + y = z \land x + y = z_1 \to z = z_1)$	gen
7.	$\exists! z (x + y = z)$	SC, 2, 7
8.	$\forall x \forall y \exists! z (x + y = z)$	gen

In some formulations of abelian group theory, $\forall x \forall y \exists! z (x + y = z)$ is an axiom.   There is no need for it, because informally it merely says again that $+$ is a binary operation, and formally it can be proved.

EXERCISES

1. Prove: If $P(u)$ is similar to $P(v)$, then

   (a) $\vdash \forall u . P(u) \leftrightarrow \exists v (v = u \land P(v))$
   (b) $\vdash \forall u . P(u) \leftrightarrow \forall v (v = u \to P(v))$

2. Prove (where v is the first variable that does not occur in $P(u)$):

   (a) $\vdash \exists! u P(u) \leftrightarrow \exists u \forall v (u = v \leftrightarrow P(v))$
   (b) $\vdash \exists! u P(u) \leftrightarrow \exists u (P(u) \land \forall v (P(v) \to u = v))$

3. Translate the following into symbolic form:

   (a) There exist at least two u's such that $P(u)$.
   (b) There exist at most two u's such that $P(u)$.
   (c) There exist exactly two u's such that $P(u)$.
   (d) There exist exactly three u's such that $P(u)$.

4. In number theory, prove

   $$\vdash \forall x \forall y \forall z \forall y_1 (x + y = z \land x + y_1 \neq z . \to . y \neq y_1)$$

ANSWERS

3. (a) $\exists u_1 \exists u_2 . P(u_1) \wedge P(u_2) \wedge u_1 \neq u_2.$

   (b) $\forall u_1 \forall u_2 \forall u_3 . P(u_1) \wedge P(u_2) \wedge P(u_3) \rightarrow$
       $u_1 = u_2 \vee u_1 = u_3 \vee u_2 = u_3.$

   (c) The conjunction of (a) and (b), or $\exists u_1 \exists u_2 . P(u_1) \wedge P(u_2) \wedge$
       $u_1 \neq u_2 \wedge \forall u_3 (P(u_3) \rightarrow u_3 = u_1 \vee u_3 = u_2).$

   (d) $\exists u_1 \exists u_2 \exists u_3 . P(u_1) \wedge P(u_2) \wedge P(u_3) \wedge u_1 \neq u_2 \wedge u_1 \neq u_3 \wedge$
       $u_2 \neq u_3 \wedge \forall u_4 (P(u_4) \rightarrow u_4 = u_1 \vee u_4 = u_2 \vee u_4 = u_3).$

3

FIRST ORDER
THEORIES

22 Definition and Examples

From now on *the predicate calculus* means *the predicate calculus with equality*, and ⊢ indicates a deduction in the predicate calculus. The *logical* axioms are the axioms of the predicate calculus, i.e., the instances of A1 through A6, E1 and the instances of E2 and E3, together with the additional axioms given by Ax Gen. The *proper symbols* of the predicate calculus are all the predicate, operation, and constant symbols.

A *first order theory* T is defined by a set $\mathscr{P}$ of proper symbols that contains = and a set X of statements. $\mathscr{P}$ is called the set of *proper symbols* of T; X is called the set of *proper axioms* of T. The *formulas of* T are all the formulas constructible from $\mathscr{P}$, i.e., P is a formula of T if and only if every proper symbol that occurs in P is in the set $\mathscr{P}$. X may be any set of statements of T.

Let Δ be a finite set of formulas of T, and let Q be a formula of T. Then $\Delta \vdash_T Q$ means that there is a finite sequence $S_1, \ldots, S_n$ of formulas of T such that S_n is Q, and each S_i $(1 \leqslant i \leqslant n)$ is a logical axiom or a

112

proper axiom or is inferred by modus ponens on S_j and S_k for some j and k less than i, or is in Δ.

If Δ is the empty set, we write $\vdash_T Q$ and say that Q is a *theorem of* T.

The only difference between a deduction in the predicate calculus and a deduction in T is that certain statements that would be labeled as assumptions in the predicate calculus are labeled as proper axioms in T.

THEOREM 1. *Let* T *be a first order theory.* $\vdash_T Q$ *if and only if there is a finite set* $\{P_1, \ldots, P_k\}$ *of proper axioms of* T *such that* $P_1, \ldots, P_k \vdash Q$.

Proof. Suppose $\vdash_T Q$. Let $S_1, \ldots, S_n$ be a proof of Q in T. Let $P_1, \ldots, P_k$ be the steps that are labeled as proper axioms. Relabel each P_i as an assumption. Then $S_1, \ldots, S_n$ is a deduction of Q from $\{P_1, \ldots, P_k\}$ in the predicate calculus, i.e., $P_1, \ldots, P_k \vdash Q$. Now suppose there is a finite set $\{P_1, \ldots, P_k\}$ of proper axioms of T such that $P_1, \ldots, P_k \vdash Q$. Let $S_1, \ldots, S_n$ be a deduction of Q from $\{P_1, \ldots, P_k\}$ in the predicate calculus. Relabel each P_i as a proper axiom. Then $S_1, \ldots, S_n$ is a proof of Q in T, i.e., $\vdash_T Q$.

We give some examples of first order theories. With one exception, all the examples are from modern algebra. We do not expect the reader to be an expert in modern algebra before or after he reads these examples. He should read all the examples, and return to a particular one as the need arises.

EXAMPLE 2. (Compare Example 7.1.) The set of proper symbols of the theory L of *linearly ordered sets* is $\{=, <\}$. The proper axioms of L are

L1. $\forall x \sim (x < x)$

L2. $\forall x \forall y \forall z (x < y \land y < z \rightarrow x < z)$

L3. $\forall x \forall y (x < y \lor x = y \lor y < x)$

Recall that $=$ is the first 2-place predicate symbol, i.e., $r = s$ is an abbreviation for $\alpha \# \#(r, s)$. $<$ is the second 2-place predicate symbol, i.e., $r < s$ is an abbreviation for $\alpha \# \#|(r, s)$. P is a formula of L if and only if every proper symbol that occurs in P is in $\{=, <\}$. The equality axioms of L are

E1. $\forall x (x = x)$

E2$=$. $\forall x_1 \forall x_2 \forall y_1 \forall y_2 (x_1 = y_1 \land x_2 = y_2 . \rightarrow . x_1 = x_2 \leftrightarrow y_1 = y_2)$

E2$<$. $\forall x_1 \forall x_2 \forall y_1 \forall y_2 (x_1 = y_1 \land x_2 = y_2 . \rightarrow . x_1 < x_2 \leftrightarrow y_1 < y_2)$

EXAMPLE 3.   (Compare Example 7.2.)   The set of proper symbols of the theory AG of *abelian groups* is $\{=, +, 0\}$.   The proper axioms of AG are

AG1. $\forall x \forall y \forall z((x + y) + z = x + (y + z))$
AG2. $\forall x(x + 0 = x)$
AG3. $\forall x \exists y(x + y = 0)$
AG4. $\forall x \forall y(x + y = y + x)$

$+$ is the first 2-place operation symbol, i.e., $r + s$ is an abbreviation for $\beta\#\#(r, s)$.   0 is an abbreviation for the first constant symbol γ. P is a formula of AG if and only if every proper symbol that occurs in P is in $\{=, +, 0\}$.   The equality axioms of AG are

E1. $\forall x(x = x)$
E2 =. $\forall x_1 \forall x_2 \forall y_2(x_1 = y_1 \wedge x_2 = y_2 . \rightarrow . x_1 = x_2 \leftrightarrow y_1 = y_2)$
E3 +. $\forall x_1 \forall x_2 \forall y_1 \forall y_2(x_1 = y_1 \wedge x_2 = y_2 \rightarrow x_1 + x_2 = y_1 + y_2)$

EXAMPLE 4.   The set of proper symbols of the first order theory R of *rings* is $\{=, +, \cdot, 0\}$, where $+$ is the first 2-place operation symbol, $\cdot$ is the second 2-place operation symbol, and 0 is the first constant symbol. The proper axioms of R are

R1. $\forall x \forall y \forall z((x + y) + z = x + (y + z))$
R2. $\forall x(x + 0 = x)$
R3. $\forall x \exists y(x + y = 0)$
R4. $\forall x \forall y(x + y = y + x)$
R5. $\forall x \forall y \forall z((xy)z = x(yz))$
R6. $\forall x \forall y \forall z(x(y + z) = xy + xz)$
R7. $\forall x \forall y \forall z((y + z)x = yx + zx)$

rs is an abbreviation for $r \cdot s$, and $rs + rt$ is an abbreviation for $(rs) + (rt)$.   The integers and the reals are rings with the usual meaning of $=$, $+$, $\cdot$, and 0.   Note that R1 through R4 are the same as AG1 through AG4.   Hence every ring is an abelian group.   The theory of *commutative rings* is the result of adjoining to R the proper axiom $\forall x \forall y(xy = yx)$.   The equality axioms of R are E1, E2 =, E3 +, and E3 ·.

EXAMPLE 5.   The set of proper symbols of the theory LA of *lattices* is $\{=, <, \cup, \cap\}$, where $<$ is the second 2-place predicate symbol and $\cup$

and $\cap$ are the first two 2-place operation symbols. The proper axioms of LA are

LA1. $\forall x \sim (x < x)$
LA2. $\forall x \forall y \forall z (x < y \wedge y < z \rightarrow x < z)$
LA3. $\forall x \forall y (x \leqslant x \cup y \wedge y \leqslant x \cup y)$
LA4. $\forall x \forall y (x \cap y \leqslant x \wedge x \cap y \leqslant y)$
LA5. $\forall x \forall y \forall z (x \leqslant z \wedge y \leqslant z \rightarrow x \cup y \leqslant z)$
LA6. $\forall x \forall y \forall z (z \leqslant x \wedge z \leqslant y \rightarrow z \leqslant x \cap y)$

$r \leqslant s$ is an abbreviation for $r < s \vee r = s$. $r \cup s$ is called the *least upper bound* of r and s. $r \cap s$ is called the *greatest lower bound* of r and s. The integers and the reals are lattices with the usual meaning of $=$ and $<$, with $a \cup b$ being the larger of a and b, and $a \cap b$ being the smaller of a and b.

EXAMPLE 6. The set of proper symbols of the theory G of *groups* is $\{=, \cdot, 1\}$, where $\cdot$ is the first 2-place operation symbol and 1 is the first constant symbol. The proper axioms of G are

G1. $\forall x \forall y \forall z ((xy)z = x(yz))$
G2. $\forall x (x1 = x)$
G3. $\forall x \exists y (xy = 1)$

rs is an abbreviation for $r \cdot s$. Note that G1 through G3 are *exactly* the same as AG1 through AG3 when both sets are unabbreviated. Hence every abelian group is a group. An abelian group is a group in which the operation is commutative. The mathematical practice is to reserve the additive notation $+$ and 0 for abelian groups and to use the multiplicative notation $\cdot$ and 1 for all groups, abelian or not.

EXAMPLE 7. The set of proper symbols of the theory F of *fields* is $\{=, +, \cdot, 0, 1\}$, where $+$ and $\cdot$ are the first two 2-place operation symbols and 0 and 1 are the first two constant symbols. As usual we write rs for $r \cdot s$ and $rs + rt$ for $(rs) + (rt)$. The proper axioms of F are

F1. $\forall x \forall y \forall z ((x + y) + z = x + (y + z))$
F2. $\forall x (x + 0 = x)$
F3. $\forall x \exists y (x + y = 0)$
F4. $\forall x \forall y (x + y = y + x)$
F5. $\forall x \forall y \forall z ((xy)z = x(yz))$
F6. $\forall x (x1 = x)$

F7. $\forall x(x \neq 0 \rightarrow \exists z(xz = 1))$
F8. $\forall x \forall y(xy = yx)$
F9. $\forall x \forall y \forall z(x(y + z) = xy + xz)$
F10. $0 \neq 1$

The rationals, the reals, and the complex numbers are fields with the usual meaning of $=$, $+$, $\cdot$, 0, and 1. The integers do not form a field because F7 fails. F1 through F4 state that a field is an abelian group with $+$ and 0. F5 through F8 state that the nonzero elements of a field are an abelian group with $\cdot$ and 1. The theory of *division rings* is the result of replacing F8 by $\forall x \forall y \forall z((y + z)x = yx + zx)$.

EXAMPLE 8. In the theory F of fields, let n be an abbreviation for the term $\underbrace{1 + 1 + \cdots + 1}_{n \text{ times}}$. In the familiar fields, $n \neq 0$ for every positive integer n. Such fields are said to be of *characteristic zero*. In algebra it is proved that if a field is not of characteristic zero, then there is a prime p such that $n = 0$ if and only if n is a multiple of p. Such a field is said to be of *characteristic p*. There exist fields of characteristic p for every prime p. The theory F^p of *fields of characteristic p* is the result of adjoining to F the proper axiom $p = 0$. The theory F^0 of *fields of characteristic zero* is the result of adjoining to F as proper axioms all the statements $p \neq 0$:

$$1 + 1 \neq 0, \quad 1 + 1 + 1 \neq 0, \quad 1 + 1 + 1 + 1 + 1 \neq 0, \quad \cdots$$

EXAMPLE 9. The theory ACF of *algebraically closed fields* is the result of adjoining to the theory of fields one proper axiom for each positive integer n that says that every polynomial of degree n has a root. For $n = 3$, the axiom is

$$\forall y \forall y_1 \forall y_2 \forall y_3(y_3 \neq 0 \rightarrow \exists x(y + y_1 x + y_2 x^2 + y_3 x^3 = 0))$$

where x^k is an abbreviation for $\underbrace{x \cdot x \cdots x}_{k \text{ times}}$.

The field of complex numbers is algebraically closed. The fields of rational and real numbers are not algebraically closed. The field of algebraic numbers is algebraically closed. An algebraic number is a complex number that is a root of a polynomial with rational coefficients. For example, $\sqrt{2}$ and i are algebraic numbers because $\sqrt{2}$ is a root of $x^2 - 2$ and i is a root of $x^2 + 1$. The set of complex numbers is uncountable because it includes the set of real numbers. The set of algebraic numbers is countable. The idea of the proof is that the set of all polynomials with rational coefficients is countable because the set of rational numbers is countable, and every polynomial has only a finite number of roots.

EXAMPLE 10. The theory OF of *ordered fields* is the result of adjoining to the theory of fields the 2-place predicate symbol $<$, the proper axioms L1 through L3 of the theory of linearly ordered sets, and the following proper axioms:

OF1. $\forall x \forall y \forall z (x < y \rightarrow x + z < y + z)$

OF2. $\forall x \forall y \forall z (x < y \wedge 0 < z \rightarrow xy < xz)$

The rationals and reals are ordered fields with the usual meaning of $<$. The field of complex numbers is not ordered because there is no way of defining $<$ so that all the proper axioms of OF hold. We sketch the proof. *x is positive* means $0 < x$. In an ordered field, the square of every nonzero element is positive, and the sum of two positive elements is positive. Suppose for contradication that the field of complex numbers is ordered. Then 1 and -1 are positive because 1 is the square of 1 and -1 is the square of i. Then $1 + (-1)$ is positive, i.e., $0 < 0$. But $\sim(0 < 0)$ by L1.

EXAMPLE 11. The theory RCF of *real closed fields* is the result of adjoining to the theory of ordered fields the following proper axiom:

RCF1. $\forall x (0 < x \rightarrow \exists y (y^2 = x))$

which says that every positive element has a square root, and adjoining for each *odd* positive integer n, the proper axiom that says that every polynomial of degree n has a root. (See Example 9.) The field of real numbers is a real closed field. The theory of real closed fields is roughly that part of the theory of real numbers that is studied in high-school algebra. The field of complex numbers is not a real closed field because it is not ordered, and the field of rational numbers is not a real closed field because RCF1 fails. For example, the rational number 2 has no rational square root.

EXAMPLE 12. The theory DL of *dense linearly ordered sets with neither first nor last element* is the result of adjoining to the proper axioms of L (Example 2)

L4. $\forall x \forall y (x < y \rightarrow \exists z (x < z \wedge z < y))$

L5. $\forall x \exists y (y < x)$

L6. $\forall x \exists y (x < y)$

The rationals and the reals with the usual meaning of $=$ and $<$ are dense linearly ordered sets with neither first nor last element.

EXAMPLE 13.   The predicate calculus is a first order theory. Its proper symbols are all the proper symbols, and it has no proper axioms.

EXAMPLE 14.   The set of proper symbols of the theory BA of *Boolean algebras* is $\{=, \cup, \cap, ', 0, 1\}$, where $\cup$ and $\cap$ are the first two 2-place operation symbols, $'$ is the first 1-place operation symbol, and 0 and 1 are the first two constant symbols.   The proper axioms of BA are

BA1. $\forall x \forall y \forall z((x \cup y) \cup z = x \cup (y \cup z))$
BA2. $\forall x \forall y \forall z((x \cap y) \cap z = x \cap (y \cap z))$
BA3. $\forall x \forall y(x \cup y = y \cup x)$
BA4. $\forall x \forall y(x \cap y = y \cap x)$
BA5. $\forall x \forall y \forall z(x \cup (y \cap z) = (x \cup y) \cap (x \cup z))$
BA6. $\forall x \forall y \forall z(x \cap (y \cup z) = (x \cap y) \cup (x \cap z))$
BA7. $\forall x(x \cup 0 = x)$
BA8. $\forall x(x \cap 1 = x)$
BA9. $\forall x(x \cup x' = 1)$
BA10. $\forall x(x \cap x' = 0)$
BA11. $0 \neq 1$

Let A be any nonempty set, and let D be the set of all subsets of A. Then D is a Boolean algebra with the following interpretations of $=$, $\cup$, $\cap$, $'$, 0, and 1. $=$ is equality of sets, $\cup$ and $\cap$ are union and intersection, B' is $\{x \in A \mid x \notin B\}$, 0 is the empty set $\varnothing$, and 1 is A.

A first order theory is *finitely axiomatized* if and only if its set of proper axioms is finite.

A set X of statements is *decidable* if and only if there is an effective procedure for deciding whether or not any given statement is in X. Every finite set is decidable, and some infinite sets are decidable.   For example, the set of proper axioms of the theory of algebraically closed fields is decidable.

A first order theory is *formal* if and only if its set of proper axioms is decidable.   All the examples above are formal theories.   We are really interested only in formal theories, because the notion of proof is effective for a first order theory if and only if the theory is formal.   We need to consider theories that are not formal because they enter into the proofs of the main theorems about first order theories.

What distinguishes a first order theory from a theory of higher order is that in the intended interpretation, all the variables range over the elements of a given domain. An example of a second order formula is the following statement of mathematical induction:

$$\forall M . 0 \in M \;\wedge\; \forall x(x \in M \to x + 1 \in M) \to \forall x(x \in M)$$

Here the variable M ranges over *sets* of numbers. In practice, the theory of groups for example deals not only with elements of a group, but with sets of elements and sets of sets of elements. The formal counterpart is a third order theory.

We restrict our attention to first order theories for three reasons. First, more is known about first order theories than about higher order theories. Second, higher order logic is essentially the same as first order logic. That is, the fundamental procedure remains the removal and insertion of quantifiers and the use of the statement calculus. Third, anything that can be done in any mathematical theory can be done in set theory, and set theory can be formulated as a first order theory. Every mathematical entity (function, space, sequence, number, etc.) can be construed in one way or another to be a set. Therefore only one kind of variable is necessary, for a set of sets is itself a set. Not only can set theory be formulated as a first order theory, but as a finitely axiomatized theory. We give no details because the formulation is meaningless without a lengthy development which would take us too far afield.

Every n-place operation symbol of a first order theory can be replaced by an $n + 1$-place predicate symbol, and every constant symbol by a 1-place predicate symbol. We illustrate the procedure with AG. Let G be the first 3-place predicate symbol and H be the first 1-place predicate symbol. We replace $+$ by G and 0 by H. $G(r, s, t)$ is interpreted as $r + s = t$, and $H(r)$ is interpreted as $r = 0$. We need the additional axioms

$$\forall x \forall y \exists ! z G(x, y, z)$$
$$\exists ! x H(x)$$

Axioms AG2 and AG3 translate into

AG2′. $\forall x \forall y (H(y) \to G(x, y, x))$
AG3′. $\forall x \forall z (H(z) \to \exists y G(x, y, z))$

The translations of AG1 and AG4 are left as exercises. The structure of the predicate calculus and first order theories can be greatly simplified by discarding all the operation and constant symbols. However, the resulting formulations of first order theories are rather removed from the familiar formulations.

EXERCISES

1. Give the equality axioms for the theories R, F, LA, and BA.
2. Give axioms AG1' and AG4' corresponding to AG1 and AG4, using the predicate symbols G and H in place of $+$ and 0.
3. Give a formulation of R using the predicate symbols G, H, and K in place of $+$, $\cdot$, and 0.
4. We give below three definitions of "group" that appear in the literature. Two are correct, and one is nonsense. State which is nonsense and why, and formulate the other two as first order theories.

   (a) A group is a nonempty set D together with a binary operation on D (for which we use the language of multiplication) such that
      1. For all x, y, z in D, $(xy)z = x(yz)$.
      2. There is an element z of D such that
         (i) $xz = x$ for every x in D,
         (ii) For every x in D there is a y in D such that $xy = z$.
   (b) Same as (a) except that 2 is replaced by
      2'. There is an element z of D such that $xz = x$ for every x in D.
      2''. For every x in D there is a y in D such that $xy = z$.
   (c) Same as (a) except that 2 is replaced by
      2*. For every x and y in D there is a z in D such that $xz = y$.
      2**. For every x and y in D there is a z in D such that $zx = y$.

5. Prove that if a field is not of characteristic zero, then it is of characteristic p for some prime p.
6. Let the first order theory T be finitely axiomatized, and let $P_1, \ldots, P_k$ be the proper axioms of T. Prove that $\vdash_T Q$ if and only if $\vdash P_1 \wedge \cdots \wedge P_k \to Q$.

23   Deduction

In this section we show how the deduction techniques of the predicate calculus carry over to first order theories. We begin with some theorems of AG. We recall that the proper axioms of AG are

AG1. $\forall x \forall y \forall z ((x + y) + z = x + (y + z))$
AG2. $\forall x (x + 0 = x)$
AG3. $\forall x \exists y (x + y = 0)$
AG4. $\forall x \forall y (x + y = y + x)$

THEOREM 1. $\vdash_{AG} \exists! y \forall x (x + y = x)$

Proof. First we give an intuitive proof. By AG2 there is a y, namely 0, such that $\forall x (x + y = x)$. Suppose $\forall x (x + y = x)$ and $\forall x (x + y_1 = x)$. Then, in particular, $y_1 + y = y_1$ and $y + y_1 = y$. Then by the commutative law (AG4) we have $y = y_1$. We transform this intuitive proof into the following proof outline.

1.	$\forall x (x + 0 = x)$	AG2
2.	$\exists y \forall x (x + y = x)$	$\exists$
3.	$\quad \forall x (x + y = x) \wedge \forall x (x + y_1 = x)$	as
4.	$\quad \forall x (x + y = x)$	SC
5.	$\quad y_1 + y = y_1$	spec
6.	$\quad \forall x (x + y_1 = x)$	SC, 3
7.	$\quad y + y_1 = y$	spec
8.	$\quad \forall x \forall y (x + y = y + x)$	AG4
9.	$\quad y_1 + y = y + y_1$	spec
10.	$\quad y = y_1$	=, 7, 9, 5
11.	$\forall y \forall y_1 . \forall x (x + y = x)$ $\wedge \forall x (x + y_1 = x) \rightarrow y = y_1$	DT, 3–10, and gen
12.	$\exists! y \forall x (x + y = x)$	SC, 2, 11

THEOREM 2. $\vdash_{AG} \forall x \forall z \forall z_1 (x + z = x + z_1 \rightarrow z = z_1)$

Proof. Suppose $x + z = x + z_1$. Then $z + x = z_1 + x$ by the commutative law. By AG3 there is a y such that $x + y = 0$. Adding y to both sides and using the associative law (AG1), we have $z + (x + y) = z_1 + (x + y)$. Then $z + 0 = z_1 + 0$, since $x + y = 0$. Then $z = z_1$ by AG2.

1.	$x + z = x + z_1$	as
2.	$\forall x \forall y (x + y = y + x)$	AG4
3.	$x + z = z + x$	spec
4.	$x + z_1 = z_1 + x$	spec, 2

5.	$z + x = z_1 + x$	$=, 3, 1, 4$
6.	$\forall x \exists y(x + y = 0)$	AG3
7.	$\exists y(x + y = 0)$	spec
8.	$x + y = 0$	Cy
9.	$(z + x) + y = (z_1 + x) + y$	sub, 5
10.	$\forall x \forall y \forall z((x + y) + z$	
	$\qquad = x + (y + z))$	AG1
11.	$(z + x) + y = z + (x + y)$	spec
12.	$(z_1 + x) + y = z_1 + (x + y)$	spec, 10
13.	$z + (x + y) = z_1 + (x + y)$	$=, 11, 9, 12$
14.	$z + 0 = z_1 + 0$	sub, 8, 13
15.	$\forall x(x + 0 = x)$	AG2
16.	$z + 0 = z$	spec
17.	$z_1 + 0 = z_1$	spec, 15
18.	$z = z_1$	$=, 16, 14, 17$
19.	$z = z_1$	C, 8
20.	$\forall x \forall z \forall z_1(x + z = x + z_1 \to z = z_1)$	DT, 1–19, and gen

THEOREM 3. $\vdash_{AG} \forall x \exists! y(x + y = 0)$

Proof.   Let x be fixed but arbitrary.   By AG3 there is a y such that $x + y = 0$.   Suppose $x + y = 0$ and $x + y_1 = 0$.   Then $x + y = x + y_1$, and Theorem 2 gives $y = y_1$.

1.	$\forall x \exists y(x + y = 0)$	AG3
2.	$\exists y(x + y = 0)$	spec
3.	$x + y = 0 \land x + y_1 = 0$	as
4.	$x + y = x + y_1$	$=, 3$
5.	$\forall x \forall z \forall z_1(x + z = x + z_1 \to z = z_1)$	T2
6.	$x + y = x + y_1 \to y = y_1$	spec
7.	$y = y_1$	MP, 6, 4
8.	$\forall y \forall y_1(x + y = 0 \land x + y_1 = 0 \to y = y_1)$	DT, 3–7, and gen
9.	$\exists! y(x + y = 0)$	SC, 2, 8
10.	$\forall x \exists! y(x + y = 0)$	gen

THEOREM 4. $\vdash_{AG} \forall x \forall y \exists! z(x + z = y)$

Proof.   Let x and y be fixed but arbitrary.   By AG3 there is a y_1 such that $x + y_1 = 0$.   Then $x + (y_1 + y) = (x + y_1) + y = 0 + y = y + 0 = y$.   Hence there is a z, namely $y_1 + y$, such that

$x + z = y$. Suppose $x + z = y$ and $x + z_1 = y$. Then $z = z_1$ by Theorem 2.

1.	$\forall x \exists y(x + y = 0)$	AG3
2.	$\exists y(x + y = 0)$	spec
3.	$x + y_1 = 0$	Cy_1
4.	$\forall x \forall y \forall z((x + y) + z = x + (y + z))$	AG1
5.	$(x + y_1) + y = x + (y_1 + y)$	spec
6.	$0 + y = x + (y_1 + y)$	sub, 3, 5
7.	$\forall x \forall y(x + y = y + x)$	AG4
8.	$0 + y = y + 0$	spec
9.	$\forall x(x + 0 = x)$	AG2
10.	$y + 0 = y$	spec
11.	$x + (y_1 + y) = y$	=, 6, 8, 10
12.	$\exists z(x + z = y)$	$\exists$
13.	$\exists z(x + z = y)$	C, 3
14.	$x + z = y \land x + z_1 = y$	as
15.	$x + z = x + z_1$	=, 14
16.	$\forall x \forall z \forall z_1(x + z = x + z_1 \rightarrow z = z_1)$	T2
17.	$x + z = x + z_1 \rightarrow z = z_1$	spec
18.	$z = z_1$	MP, 17, 15
19.	$\forall z \forall z_1 . x + z = y \land x + z_1 = y \rightarrow z = z_1$	DT, 14–18, and gen
20.	$\forall x \forall y \exists! z(x + z = y)$	SC, 13, 19, and gen

Next we prove in L the *trichotomy law*

$$\forall x \forall y(x < y \;\bar{\vee}\; x = y \;\bar{\vee}\; y < x)$$

First we define $\bar{\vee}$.

$P \;\bar{\vee}\; Q$ is an abbreviation for $(P \vee Q) \land \sim(P \land Q)$. $\bar{\vee}$ has the same rank as $\vee$ and $\land$ in the abbreviation of formulas, and the convention of association to the left is extended to $\bar{\vee}$. For example, $P \;\bar{\vee}\; Q \;\bar{\vee}\; R$ is an abbreviation for $(P \;\bar{\vee}\; Q) \;\bar{\vee}\; R$. We note that $P \;\bar{\vee}\; Q$ is a stronger statement than $P \vee Q$, i.e., $P \;\bar{\vee}\; Q \rightarrow P \vee Q$ is a tautology, but the converse is not. The proper axioms of L are

L1. $\forall x \sim (x < x)$
L2. $\forall x \forall y \forall z(x < y \land y < z \rightarrow x < z)$
L3. $\forall x \forall y(x < y \vee x = y \vee y < x)$

The reason that L3 is taken as an axiom rather than the stronger trichotomy law is that the latter can be proved from L1 through L3.

THEOREM 5. $\vdash_L \forall x \forall y (x < y \bar{\vee} x = y \bar{\vee} y < x)$

Proof. Let x and y be fixed but arbitrary. By L3, at least one of $x < y$, $x = y$, $y < x$ holds. To show that at most one holds, we show that any two together give a contradiction. From $x < y$ and $x = y$ we get $x < x$ (or $y < y$) by sub, contradicting L1. From $x < y$ and $y < x$ we get $x < x$ (or $y < y$) by L2, contradicting L1. From $x = y$ and $y < x$ we again get $x < x$ (or $y < y$) by sub, contradicting L1. Hence $x < y \bar{\vee} x = y \bar{\vee} y < x$.

1.	$\forall x \forall y (x < y \vee x = y \vee y < x)$	L3
2.	$x < y \vee x = y \vee y < x$	spec
3.	$x < y \wedge x = y$	as
4.	$x < y$	SC
5.	$x = y$	SC, 3
6.	$x < x$	sub, 5, 4
7.	$x < y \wedge x = y \rightarrow x < x$	DT, 3–6
8.	$\forall x {\sim} (x < x)$	L1
9.	${\sim}(x < x)$	spec
10.	${\sim}(x < y \wedge x = y)$	SC, 7, 9
11.	$\forall x \forall y \forall z (x < y \wedge y < z \rightarrow x < z)$	L2
12.	$x < y \wedge y < x \rightarrow x < x$	spec
13.	${\sim}(x < y \wedge y < x)$	SC, 12, 9
14.	${\sim}(x = y \wedge y < x)$	similar to 3–10
15.	$x < y \bar{\vee} x = y \bar{\vee} y < x$	SC, 2, 10, 13, 14
16.	$\forall x \forall y (x < y \bar{\vee} x = y \bar{\vee} y < x)$	gen

Next is a theorem of ring theory. The proper axioms of R are

R1.	$\forall x \forall y \forall z ((x + y) + z = x + (y + z))$
R2.	$\forall x (x + 0 = x)$
R3.	$\forall x \exists y (x + y = 0)$
R4.	$\forall x \forall y (x + y = y + x)$
R5.	$\forall x \forall y \forall z ((xy)z = x(yz))$
R6.	$\forall x \forall y \forall z (x(y + z) = xy + xz)$
R7.	$\forall x \forall y \forall z ((y + z)x = yx + zx)$

Because R1 through R4 are the same as AG1 through AG4, every theorem of AG is also a theorem of R. Hence Theorems 1 through 4 are theorems of R.

THEOREM 6. $\vdash_R \forall x (x0 = 0)$

Proof. $x0 + 0 = x0 = x(0 + 0) = x0 + x0$ by R2, R2, and R6. Then Theorem 2 applied to $x0 + x0 = x0 + 0$ gives $x0 = 0$.

1.	$\forall x(x + 0 = x)$	R2
2.	$x0 + 0 = x0$	spec
3.	$\forall x \forall y \forall z(x(y + z) = xy + xz)$	R6
4.	$x(0 + 0) = x0 + x0$	spec
5.	$0 + 0 = 0$	spec, 1
6.	$x0 = x0 + x0$	sub, 5, 4
7.	$x0 + x0 = x0 + 0$	=, 6, 2
8.	$\forall x \forall z \forall z_1(x + z = x + z_1 \to z = z_1)$	T2
9.	$x0 + x0 = x0 + 0 \to x0 = 0$	spec
10.	$x0 = 0$	MP, 9, 7
11.	$\forall x(x0 = 0)$	gen

Finally we have some theorems of field theory. The proper axioms of F are

F1.	$\forall x \forall y \forall z((x + y) + z = x + (y + z))$
F2.	$\forall x(x + 0 = x)$
F3.	$\forall x \exists y(x + y = 0)$
F4.	$\forall x \forall y(x + y = y + x)$
F5.	$\forall x \forall y \forall z((xy)z = x(yz))$
F6.	$\forall x(x1 = x)$
F7.	$\forall x(x \neq 0 \to \exists z(xz = 1))$
F8.	$\forall x \forall y(xy = yx)$
F9.	$\forall x \forall y \forall z(x(y + z) = xy + xz)$
F10.	$0 \neq 1$

THEOREM 7. $\vdash_F \forall x \forall y \forall z((y + z)x = yx + zx)$

Proof. $(y + z)x = x(y + z) = xy + xz = yx + zx$ by F8, F9, and F8.

1.	$\forall x \forall y(xy = yx)$	F8
2.	$(y + z)x = x(y + z)$	spec
3.	$\forall x \forall y \forall z(x(y + z) = xy + xz)$	F9
4.	$x(y + z) = xy + xz$	spec
5.	$(y + z)x = xy + xz$	=, 2, 4
6.	$xy = yx$	spec, 1
7.	$(y + z)x = yx + xz$	sub, 6, 5
8.	$xz = zx$	spec, 1

| 9. | $(y + z)x = yx + zx$ | sub, 8, 7 |
| 10. | $\forall x \forall y \forall z ((y + z)x = yx + yz)$ | gen |

We observe that every axiom of R is a theorem of F. Hence every theorem of R is a theorem of F, i.e., every field is a ring.

THEOREM 8. $\vdash_F \forall x \forall y (xy = 0 \rightarrow x = 0 \lor y = 0)$

Proof. Suppose $xy = 0$ and $y \neq 0$. Then by F7 there is a z such that $yz = 1$. Then $x = x \cdot 1 = x(yz) = (xy)z = 0z = z0 = 0$ by F6, sub, F5, sub, F8, and Theorem 6.

1.	$xy = 0 \land y \neq 0$	as
2.	$xy = 0$	SC
3.	$y \neq 0$	SC, 1
4.	$\forall x(x \neq 0 \rightarrow \exists z(xz = 1))$	F7
5.	$y \neq 0 \rightarrow \exists z(yz = 1)$	spec
6.	$\exists z(yz = 1)$	MP, 5, 3
7.	$\quad yz = 1$	Cz
8.	$\quad \forall x(x1 = x)$	F6
9.	$\quad x1 = x$	spec
10.	$\quad x(yz) = x$	sub, 7, 9
11.	$\quad \forall x \forall y \forall z((xy)z = x(yz))$	F5
12.	$\quad (xy)z = x(yz)$	spec
13.	$\quad 0z = x(yz)$	sub, 2, 12
14.	$\quad \forall x \forall y(xy = yx)$	F8
15.	$\quad 0z = z0$	spec
16.	$\quad \forall x(x0 = 0)$	T6
17.	$\quad z0 = 0$	spec
18.	$\quad x = 0$	=, 10, 13, 15, 17
19.	$\quad x = 0$	C, 7
20.	$xy = 0 \land y \neq 0 \rightarrow x = 0$	DT, 1–19
21.	$xy = 0 \rightarrow x = 0 \lor y = 0$	SC
22.	$\forall x \forall y(xy = 0 \rightarrow x = 0 \lor y = 0)$	gen

Some verification is necessary in transferring a metatheorem of the predicate calculus to a first order theory. For example, suppose that $\Delta, P \vdash_T Q$, where T is a first order theory, P and Q are formulas of T, and Δ is a finite set of formulas of T. Then $\Delta \vdash_T P \rightarrow Q$ by the deduction theorem. The possibility arises that the deduction theorem does not apply because some of the steps in the deduction of $P \rightarrow Q$

from Δ are not formulas of T.   There is no real problem, because it is easy to verify that in the proof of the deduction theorem, each step in the deduction of $P \to Q$ from Δ is actually a formula of T.

Similarly, the possibility arises that a theorem of the predicate calculus that is a formula of T may not be a theorem of T because a step in its proof is not a formula of T. We show in Section 27 that this never happens.   In the meantime we justify the use of the theorem schemes already proved in the predicate calculus by the observation that no proof of a formula P introduces a proper symbol that is not in P, and hence each step of the proof of P is a formula of T whenever P is a formula of T.

EXERCISES

1. Prove: $\vdash_{AG} \forall z.z = 0 \leftrightarrow \forall x(x + z = x \wedge \exists y(x + y = z))$
2. Prove: (a) $\vdash_R \forall x(0x = 0)$
   (b) $\vdash_R \forall x \forall y(x(y + y) = (x + x)y)$
3. Prove: (a) $\vdash_F \exists! y \forall x(xy = x)$
   (b) $\vdash_F \forall x \forall z \forall z_1(x \neq 0 .\to. xz = xz_1 \to z = z_1)$
   (c) $\vdash_F \forall x(x \neq 0 \to \exists! y(xy = 1))$
   (d) $\vdash_F \forall x \forall y(x \neq 0 \to \exists! z(xz = y))$
   (e) $\vdash_F \forall x \forall y(x^2 = y^2 \to x = y \vee x + y = 0)$ (r^2 is an abbreviation for $r \cdot r$.)
4. Let AG' be the result of adjoining to AG the 1-place operation symbol $-$, and replacing axiom AG3 by AG3': $\forall x(x + (-x) = 0)$. Prove $\vdash_{AG'} \forall x \forall y(-x = y \leftrightarrow x + y = 0)$
5. Prove
   (a) $\vdash_{LA} \forall x \forall y \forall z(x \cup y = z \leftrightarrow x \leqslant z \wedge y \leqslant z$
   $\wedge\ \forall z_1(x \leqslant z_1 \wedge y \leqslant z_1 \to z \leqslant z_1))$
   (b) $\vdash_{LA} \forall x \forall y \exists! z(x \leqslant z \wedge y \leqslant z \wedge \forall z_1(x \leqslant z_1 \wedge y \leqslant z_1 \to z \leqslant z_1))$

24   Number Theory

In this section we give a formulation N of formal number theory. The set of proper symbols of N is $\{=, ', +, \cdot, 0\}$, where $'$ is the first 1-place operation symbol, $+$ and $\cdot$ are the first two 2-place operation symbols, and 0 is the first constant symbol. r' is called the successor of r; intuitively, r' is the number that immediately follows r, i.e., $r + 1$. In stating the proper axioms and theorems of N, we omit the sign $\cdot$ of multiplication and many parentheses in accordance with the usual conventions of number theory.

The proper axioms of N are

N1. $\forall x \forall y (x' = y' \rightarrow x = y)$
N2. $\forall x (x' \neq 0)$
N3. $\forall x (x + 0 = x)$
N4. $\forall x \forall y (x + y' = (x + y)')$
N5. $\forall x (x0 = 0)$
N6. $\forall x \forall y (xy' = xy + x)$
N7. For each formula $P(v)$, the closure of

$$P(0/v) \;\wedge\; \forall v(P(v) \rightarrow P(v'/v)) \rightarrow \forall v P(v)$$

N1 and N2 state the fundamental properties of the successor operation. N3 and N4 serve to define addition in terms of the successor operation. N5 and N6 serve to define multiplication in terms of addition. N7 is the axiom scheme of mathematical induction. The equality axioms of N are E1, E2$=$, E3$'$, and E3$+$, and E3$\cdot$.

In using the axioms and theorems of N in proof outlines, we shall omit the spec steps. For example, we justify the step $(x + y)' \neq 0$ by N2. We shall omit some gen steps at the end of proof outlines. We shall use N7 as a derived rule of inference in the following way: If step j is $P(0/v)$ and step k is $\forall v(P(v) \rightarrow P(v'/v))$, we write the step $\forall v P(v)$ (or sometimes $P(v)$) with analysis "ind, j, k." We shall write $\vdash$ instead of $\vdash_N$. 1 is an abbreviation for $0'$.

We begin with some properties of addition.

THEOREM 1. $\vdash \forall x (x + 1 = x')$

Proof.

1.	$x + 0' = (x + 0)'$	N4
2.	$x + 0 = x$	N3
3.	$x + 0' = x'$	sub, 2, 1
4.	$x + 1 = x'$	same as 3

THEOREM 2. $\vdash \forall x \forall y \forall z .(x + y) + z = x + (y + z)$

Proof. Induction on z. $P(z)$ is $(x + y) + z = x + (y + z)$.

1.	$(x + y) + 0 = x + y$	N3
2.	$y + 0 = y$	N3
3.	$(x + y) + 0 = x + (y + 0)$	sub, 2, 1

4.	$(x + y) + z = x + (y + z)$	as (ind. hyp.)
5.	$((x + y) + z)' = (x + (y + z))'$	sub, 4
6.	$(x + y) + z' = ((x + y) + z)'$	N4
7.	$x + (y + z)' = (x + (y + z))'$	N4
8.	$(x + y) + z' = x + (y + z)'$	=, 6, 5, 7
9.	$y + z' = (y + z)'$	N4
10.	$(x + y) + z' = x + (y + z')$	sub, 9, 8
11.	$\forall z.(x + y) + z = x + (y + z) \rightarrow$	
	$(x + y) + z' = x + (y + z')$	DT, 4–10, and gen
12.	$\forall z.(x + y) + z = x + (y + z)$	ind, 3, 11

Step 4 above is the induction hypothesis for use with N7. Theorem 2 is the associative law of addition. Theorem 3 prepares the way for the commutative law of addition which is Theorem 4.

THEOREM 3. $\vdash \forall x \forall y.x' + y = x + y'$

Proof. Induction on y. $P(y)$ is $x' + y = x + y'$

1.	$x' + 0 = x'$	N3
2.	$x + 0 = x$	N3
3.	$(x + 0)' = x'$	sub, 2
4.	$x + 0' = (x + 0)'$	N4
5.	$x' + 0 = x + 0'$	=, 1, 3, 4
6.	$x' + y = x + y'$	as (ind. hyp.)
7.	$x' + y' = (x' + y)'$	N4
8.	$x' + y' = (x + y')'$	sub, 6, 7
9.	$x + (y')' = (x + y')'$	N4
10.	$x' + y' = x + (y')'$	=, 8, 9
11.	$\forall y.x' + y = x + y' \rightarrow x' + y' = x + (y')'$	DT, 6–10, and gen
12.	$\forall y.x' + y = x + y'$	ind, 5, 11

THEOREM 4. $\vdash \forall x \forall y.x + y = y + x$

Proof. Induction on x. $P(x)$ is $x + y = y + x$. First we prove $0 + y = y + 0$ by induction on y.

1.	$0 + 0 = 0 + 0$	=
2.	$0 + y = y + 0$	as (ind. hyp.)
3.	$y' + 0 = y + 0'$	T3

4.	$y + 0' = (y + 0)'$	N4
5.	$y + 0' = (0 + y)'$	sub, 2, 4
6.	$0 + y' = (0 + y)'$	N4
7.	$0 + y' = y' + 0$	$=$, 6, 5, 3
8.	$\forall y . 0 + y = y + 0 \to 0 + y' = y' + 0$	DT, 2–7, and gen
9.	$0 + y = y + 0$	ind, 1, 8
10.	$x + y = y + x$	as (ind. hyp.)
11.	$x' + y = x + y'$	T3
12.	$x + y' = (x + y)'$	N4
13.	$x + y' = (y + x)'$	sub, 10, 12
14.	$y + x' = (y + x)'$	N4
15.	$x' + y = y + x'$	$=$, 11, 13, 14
16.	$\forall x . x + y = y + x \to x' + y = y + x'$	DT, 10–15, and gen
17.	$x + y = y + x$	ind, 9, 16

THEOREM 5. $\vdash \forall x \forall y \forall z . x + y = x + z \to y = z$

Proof.   Induction on x. $P(x)$ is $x + y = x + z \to y = z$

1.	$0 + y = 0 + z$	as
2.	$y + 0 = 0 + y$	T4
3.	$0 + z = z + 0$	T4
4.	$y + 0 = y$	N3
5.	$z + 0 = z$	N3
6.	$y = z$	$=$, 4, 2, 1, 3, 5
7.	$0 + y = 0 + z \to y = z$	DT, 1–6
8.	$x + y = x + z \to y = z$	as (ind. hyp.)
9.	$x' + y = x' + z$	as
10.	$x' + y = x + y'$	T3
11.	$x' + z = x + z'$	T3
12.	$x + y' = (x + y)'$	N4
13.	$x + z' = (x + z)'$	N4
14.	$(x + y)' = (x + z)'$	$=$, 12, 10, 9, 11, 13
15.	$(x + y)' = (x + z)' \to$ $x + y = x + z$	N1
16.	$y = z$	SC, 15, 14, 8
17.	$x' + y = x' + z \to y = z$	DT, 9–16
18.	$\forall x (x + y = x + z \to y = z . \to .$ $x' + y = x' + z \to y = z)$	DT, 8–17, and gen
19.	$x + y = x + z \to y = z$	ind, 7, 18

THEOREM 6. $\vdash \forall x . x = 0 \lor \exists y (x = y')$

Proof. Induction on x. $P(x)$ is $x = 0 \lor \exists y (x = y')$

1. $0 = 0$ $=$
2. $0 = 0 \lor \exists y (0 = y')$ SC
3. $x' = x'$ $=$
4. $\exists y (x' = y')$ $\exists$
5. $x = 0 \lor \exists y (x = y') \to x' = 0 \lor \exists y (x' = y')$ SC
6. $\forall x . x = 0 \lor \exists y (x = y') \to x' = 0 \lor \exists y (x' = y')$ gen
7. $\forall x . x = 0 \lor \exists y (x = y')$ ind, 2, 6

Order is defined in terms of addition. $r \leqslant s$ is an abbreviation for $\exists v (r + v = s)$, where r and s are terms and v is the first variable that does not occur in r or s.   (v is chosen in this way to make $r \leqslant s$ have a unique unabbreviation.   In practice any variable u such that $r + v = s$ is similar to $r + u = s$ may be used.)

THEOREM 7. $\vdash \forall x (x \leqslant x)$

Proof.

1. $x + 0 = x$ N3
2. $\exists y (x + y = x)$ $\exists$
3. $x \leqslant x$ same as 2

THEOREM 8. $\vdash \forall x . 0 \leqslant x$

Proof.

1. $x + 0 = x$ N3
2. $0 + x = x + 0$ T4
3. $0 + x = x$ $=$, 2, 1
4. $\exists y (0 + y = x)$ $\exists$
5. $0 \leqslant x$ same as 4

THEOREM 9. $\vdash \forall x . x \leqslant x'$

Proof.

1. $x + 1 = x'$ T1
2. $\exists y (x + y = x')$ $\exists$
3. $x \leqslant x'$ same as 2

THEOREM 10. $\vdash \forall x \forall y \forall z . x \leqslant y \wedge y \leqslant z \rightarrow x \leqslant z$

Proof.

1.	$x \leqslant y \wedge y \leqslant z$	as
2.	$x \leqslant y$	SC
3.	$y \leqslant z$	SC, 1
4.	$\exists z(x + z = y)$	same as 2
5.	$\exists x_1(y + x_1 = z)$	same as 3
6.	$x + z_1 = y$	Cz_1, 4
7.	$y + x_1 = z$	Cx_1, 5
8.	$(x + z_1) + x_1 = z$	sub, 6, 7
9.	$(x + z_1) + x_1 = x + (z_1 + x_1)$	T2
10.	$x + (z_1 + x_1) = z$	=, 9, 8
11.	$\exists x_1(x + x_1 = z)$	$\exists$
12.	$x \leqslant z$	same as 11
13.	$x \leqslant z$	C, 7
14.	$x \leqslant z$	C, 6
15.	$x \leqslant y \wedge y \leqslant z \rightarrow x \leqslant z$	DT, 1–14

THEOREM 11. $\vdash \forall x \forall y . x \leqslant y \vee y' \leqslant x$

Proof. Induction on x. $P(x)$ is $x \leqslant y \vee y' \leqslant x$. The induction step is proved by cases. We prove $y' \leqslant x \rightarrow y' \leqslant x'$, $x = y \rightarrow y' \leqslant x'$, and $x \leqslant y \wedge x \neq y \rightarrow x' \leqslant y$. Then the statement calculus gives $x \leqslant y \vee y' \leqslant x \rightarrow x' \leqslant y \vee y' \leqslant x'$.

1.	$0 \leqslant y$	T8
2.	$0 \leqslant y \vee y' \leqslant 0$	SC
3.	$x \leqslant x'$	T9
4.	$y' \leqslant x \wedge x \leqslant x' \rightarrow y' \leqslant x'$	T10
5.	$y' \leqslant x \rightarrow y' \leqslant x'$	SC, 3, 4
6.	$x = y . \rightarrow . x' \leqslant x' \leftrightarrow y' \leqslant x'$	sub
7.	$x' \leqslant x'$	T7
8.	$x = y \rightarrow y' \leqslant x'$	SC, 6, 7
9.	$x \leqslant y \wedge x \neq y$	as
10.	$x \leqslant y$	SC
11.	$x \neq y$	SC, 9
12.	$\exists z(x + z = y)$	same as 10
13.	$x + z = y$	Cz
14.	$z = 0 . \rightarrow . x + z = y \leftrightarrow x + 0 = y$	sub

15.	$z = 0 \to x + 0 = y$	SC, 13, 14
16.	$x + 0 = x$	N3
17.	$z = 0 \to x = y$	sub, 16, 15
18.	$z \neq 0$	SC, 11, 17
19.	$z = 0 \lor \exists y(z = y')$	T6
20.	$\exists y(z = y')$	SC, 18, 19
21.	$z = x_1'$	Cx_1
22.	$x + x_1' = y$	sub, 21, 13
23.	$x' + x_1 = x + x_1'$	T3
24.	$x' + x_1 = y$	$=$, 23, 22
25.	$\exists z(x' + z = y)$	$\exists$
26.	$x' \leqslant y$	same as 25
27.	$x' \leqslant y$	C, 21
28.	$x' \leqslant y$	C, 13
29.	$x \leqslant y \land x \neq y \to x' \leqslant y$	DT, 9–28
30.	$\forall x.x \leqslant y \lor y' \leqslant x \to x' \leqslant y \lor y' \leqslant x'$	SC, 5, 8, 29, and gen
31.	$x \leqslant y \lor y' \leqslant x$	ind, 2, 30

THEOREM 12. $\vdash \forall x \forall y.x + y = 0 \to x = 0$

Proof.   Induction on y. $P(y)$ is $x + y = 0 \to x = 0$

1.	$x + 0 = 0 \to x + 0 = 0$	taut
2.	$x + 0 = x$	N3
3.	$x + 0 = 0 \to x = 0$	sub, 2, 1
4.	$x + y' = (x + y)'$	N4
5.	$(x + y)' \neq 0$	N2
6.	$x + y' \neq 0$	sub, 4, 5
7.	$\forall y(x + y = 0 \to x = 0 .\to. x + y' = 0 \to x = 0)$	SC and gen
8.	$\forall y.x + y = 0 \to x = 0$	ind, 3, 7

THEOREM 13. $\vdash \forall x \forall y.x \leqslant y \land y \leqslant x \to x = y$

Proof.

1.	$x \leqslant y \land y \leqslant x$	as
2.	$x \leqslant y$	SC
3.	$\exists z(x + z = y)$	same as 2
4.	$y \leqslant x$	SC, 1
5.	$\exists z(y + z = x)$	same as 4
6.	$x + z = y$	Cz, 3
7.	$y + z_1 = x$	Cz_1, 5

8.	$(x + z) + z_1 = x$	sub, 6, 7
9.	$(x + z) + z_1 = x + (z + z_1)$	T2
10.	$x + 0 = x$	N3
11.	$x + (z + z_1) = x + 0$	$=$, 9, 8, 10
12.	$x + (z + z_1) = x + 0 \to z + z_1 = 0$	T5
13.	$z + z_1 = 0$	MP, 12, 11
14.	$z + z_1 = 0 \to z = 0$	T12
15.	$z = 0$	MP, 14, 13
16.	$x + 0 = y$	sub, 15, 6
17.	$x = y$	$=$, 10, 16
18.	$x = y$	C, 7
19.	$x = y$	C, 6
20.	$x \leqslant y \land y \leqslant x \to x = y$	DT, 1–19

THEOREM 14. $\vdash \forall x \forall y . y \leqslant x' \to y \leqslant x \lor y = x'$

Proof.

1.	$y \leqslant x' \land \sim(y \leqslant x)$	as
2.	$y \leqslant x'$	SC
3.	$\sim(y \leqslant x)$	SC, 1
4.	$y \leqslant x \lor x' \leqslant y$	T11
5.	$x' \leqslant y$	SC, 3, 4
6.	$y \leqslant x' \land x' \leqslant y \to y = x'$	T13
7.	$y = x'$	SC, 2, 5, 6
8.	$y \leqslant x' \land \sim(y \leqslant x) \to y = x'$	DT, 1–7
9.	$y \leqslant x' \to y \leqslant x \lor y = x'$	SC

THEOREM 15. $\vdash \forall x \forall y \forall z . y \leqslant z \leftrightarrow x + y \leqslant x + z$

Proof.

1.	$y + x_1 = z \to x + (y + x_1) = x + z$	sub
2.	$x + (y + x_1) = x + z \to y + x_1 = z$	T5
3.	$y + x_1 = z \leftrightarrow x + (y + x_1) = x + z$	SC, 1, 2
4.	$(x + y) + x_1 = x + (y + x_1)$	T2
5.	$y + x_1 = z \leftrightarrow (x + y) + x_1 = x + z$	sub, 4, 3
6.	$\exists x_1(y + x_1 = z) \leftrightarrow \exists x_1((x + y) + x_1 = x + z)$	equiv, 5
7.	$y \leqslant z \leftrightarrow x + y \leqslant x + z$	same as 6

$r < s$ is an abbreviation for $\exists v((r + v)' = s)$, where r and s are terms and v is the first variable that does not occur in r or s.

THEOREM 16. $\vdash \forall x \sim (x < 0)$

1.	$x < 0$	as
2.	$\exists y((x + y)' = 0)$	same as 1
3.	$(x + y)' = 0$	Cy
4.	$(x + y)' \neq 0$	N2
5.	$\sim(x < 0)$	SC, 3, 4
6.	$\sim(x < 0)$	C, 3
7.	$x < 0 \rightarrow \sim(x < 0)$	DT, 1–6
8.	$\sim(x < 0)$	SC

THEOREM 17. $\vdash \forall x \forall y . x < y' \leftrightarrow x \leqslant y$

Proof.

1.	$x + z = y \rightarrow (x + z)' = y'$	sub
2.	$(x + z)' = y' \rightarrow x + z = y$	N1
3.	$(x + z)' = y' \leftrightarrow x + z = y$	SC, 1, 2
4.	$\exists z((x + z)' = y') \leftrightarrow \exists z(x + z = y)$	equiv, 3
5.	$x < y' \leftrightarrow x \leqslant y$	same as 4

THEOREM 18. $\vdash \forall x(x < x')$

Proof.

1.	$x < x' \leftrightarrow x \leqslant x$	T17
2.	$x \leqslant x$	T7
3.	$x < x'$	SC, 1, 2

THEOREM 19. $\vdash \forall x \forall y . x' \leqslant y \leftrightarrow x < y$

Proof.

1.	$x' + z = x + z'$	T3
2.	$x + z' = (x + z)'$	N4
3.	$x' + z = (x + z)'$	=, 1, 2
4.	$x' \leqslant y \leftrightarrow x' \leqslant y$	taut
5.	$x' \leqslant y \leftrightarrow \exists z(x' + z = y)$	same as 4
6.	$x' \leqslant y \leftrightarrow \exists z((x + z)' = y)$	sub, 3, 5
7.	$x' \leqslant y \leftrightarrow x < y$	same as 6

THEOREM 20. $\vdash \forall x \forall y . y \leqslant x \bar{\vee} x < y$

Proof.

1.	$y \leqslant x \vee x' \leqslant y$	T11
2.	$x' \leqslant y \leftrightarrow x < y$	T19
3.	$y \leqslant x \vee x < y$	SC, 1, 2
4.	$\quad y \leqslant x \wedge x < y$	as
5.	$\quad y \leqslant x$	SC
6.	$\quad x' \leqslant y \wedge y \leqslant x \to x' \leqslant x$	T10
7.	$\quad x' \leqslant x$	SC, 2, 4, 6
8.	$\quad \exists y (x' + y = x)$	same as 7
9.	$\quad\quad x' + z = x$	Cz
10.	$\quad\quad x' + z = x + z'$	T3
11.	$\quad\quad x + 0 = x$	N3
12.	$\quad\quad x + z' = x + 0$	$=$, 10, 9, 11
13.	$\quad\quad x + z' = x + 0 \to z' = 0$	T5
14.	$\quad\quad z' = 0$	MP, 13, 12
15.	$\quad\quad z' \neq 0$	N2
16.	$\quad\quad 0 \neq 0$	SC, 14, 15
17.	$\quad 0 \neq 0$	C, 9
18.	$y \leqslant x \wedge x < y \to 0 \neq 0$	DT, 4–17
19.	$0 = 0$	$=$
20.	$\sim (y \leqslant x \wedge x < y)$	SC, 18, 19
21.	$y \leqslant x \bar{\vee} x < y$	SC, 3, 20

THEOREM 21. $\vdash \forall x \forall y \forall z . y < z \leftrightarrow x + y < x + z$

Proof.

1.	$z \leqslant y \leftrightarrow x + z \leqslant x + y$	T15
2.	$z \leqslant y \bar{\vee} y < z$	T20
3.	$x + z \leqslant x + y \bar{\vee} x + y < x + z$	T20
4.	$y < z \leftrightarrow x + y < x + z$	SC, 1–3

THEOREM 22. $\vdash \forall x \forall y . x \leqslant y \vee y \leqslant x$

Proof.

1.	$x \leqslant y \vee y' \leqslant x$	T11
2.	$y \leqslant y'$	T9
3.	$y \leqslant y' \wedge y' \leqslant x \to y \leqslant x$	T10
4.	$x \leqslant y \vee y \leqslant x$	SC, 1–3

THEOREM 23. $\vdash \forall x . x \leqslant 0 \rightarrow x = 0$

Proof.

1.	$x \leqslant 0$	as
2.	$0 \leqslant x$	T8
3.	$x \leqslant 0 \wedge 0 \leqslant x \rightarrow x = 0$	T13
4.	$x = 0$	SC, 1–3
5.	$x \leqslant 0 \rightarrow x = 0$	DT, 1–4

For the next theorem we write $\bar{k}$ for the term consisting of 0 followed by k primes with appropriate parentheses. For example, $\bar{3}$ is an abbreviation for $((0')')'$. Note that $\overline{k + 1}$ is $(\bar{k})'$, which we write as $\bar{k}'$. We also write $Q(\bar{k})$ for $Q(\bar{k}/v)$.

THEOREM 24.   *For every number k,*

$$\vdash Q(\bar{0}) \wedge Q(\bar{1}) \wedge \cdots \wedge Q(\bar{k}) \rightarrow \forall z (z \leqslant \bar{k} \rightarrow Q(z)) \tag{1}$$

Proof. Let $Q(z)$ be a fixed but arbitrary formula. Then (1) is a theorem scheme because it makes one assertion for each number k. The proof is by induction on k in the metalanguage. We cannot use induction *in* N because no single formula of N encompasses all the instances of (1).

Basis. $\vdash Q(\bar{0}) \rightarrow \forall z (z \leqslant \bar{0} \rightarrow Q(z))$

1.	$Q(\bar{0})$	as
2.	$z \leqslant \bar{0}$	as
3.	$z \leqslant \bar{0} \rightarrow z = \bar{0}$	T23
4.	$z = \bar{0}$	MP, 3, 2
5.	$Q(z)$	sub, 4, 1
6.	$z \leqslant \bar{0} \rightarrow Q(z)$	DT, 1–5
7.	$\forall z (z \leqslant \bar{0} \rightarrow Q(z))$	gen
8.	$Q(\bar{0}) \rightarrow \forall z (z \leqslant \bar{0} \rightarrow Q(z))$	DT, 1–7

Induction step.   We assume (1) and (recalling that $\overline{k + 1}$ is $\bar{k}'$) show that

$$\vdash Q(\bar{0}) \wedge Q(\bar{1}) \wedge \cdots \wedge Q(\bar{k}) \wedge Q(\bar{k}') \rightarrow \forall z (z \leqslant \bar{k}' \rightarrow Q(z))$$

1.	$\forall z (z \leqslant \bar{k} \rightarrow Q(z)) \wedge Q(\bar{k}')$	as
2.	$\forall z (z \leqslant \bar{k} \rightarrow Q(z))$	SC
3.	$z \leqslant \bar{k} \rightarrow Q(z)$	spec

4.	$Q(\bar{k}')$	SC, 1
5.	$z \leqslant \bar{k}' \to z \leqslant \bar{k} \vee z = \bar{k}'$	T14
6.	$z = \bar{k}' \to . Q(z) \leftrightarrow Q(\bar{k}')$	sub
7.	$z \leqslant \bar{k}' \to Q(z)$	SC, 3–6
8.	$\forall z(z \leqslant \bar{k}' \to Q(z))$	gen
9.	$\forall z(z \leqslant \bar{k} \to Q(z)) \wedge Q(\bar{k}') \to \forall z(z \leqslant \bar{k}' \to Q(z))$	DT, 1–8
10.	$Q(\bar{0}) \wedge Q(\bar{1}) \wedge \cdots \wedge Q(\bar{k}) \to \forall z(z \leqslant \bar{k} \to Q(z))$	(1)
11.	$Q(\bar{0}) \wedge Q(\bar{1}) \wedge \cdots \wedge Q(\bar{k}) \wedge Q(\bar{k}') \to \forall z(z \leqslant \bar{k}' \to Q(z))$	SC, 9, 10

We move on to multiplication.   The first theorem is the distributive law.

THEOREM 25. $\vdash \forall x \forall y \forall z . x(y + z) = xy + xz$

Proof. Induction on z. $P(z)$ is $x(y + z) = xy + xz$.

1.	$y + 0 = y$	N3
2.	$x(y + 0) = xy$	sub, 1
3.	$xy + 0 = xy$	N3
4.	$x(y + 0) = xy + 0$	=, 2, 3
5.	$x0 = 0$	N5
6.	$x(y + 0) = xy + x0$	sub, 5, 4
7.	$\quad x(y + z) = xy + xz$	as (ind. hyp.)
8.	$\quad y + z' = (y + z)'$	N4
9.	$\quad x(y + z') = x(y + z)'$	sub, 8
10.	$\quad x(y + z)' = x(y + z) + x$	N6
11.	$\quad x(y + z') = x(y + z) + x$	=, 9, 10
12.	$\quad x(y + z') = (xy + xz) + x$	sub, 7, 11
13.	$\quad (xy + xz) + x = xy + (xz + x)$	T2
14.	$\quad x(y + z') = xy + (xz + x)$	=, 12, 13
15.	$\quad xz' = xz + x$	N6
16.	$\quad x(y + z') = xy + xz'$	sub, 15, 14
17.	$\forall z . x(y + z) = xy + xz \to$	
	$\qquad x(y + z') = xy + xz'$	DT, 7–16, and gen
18.	$\forall z . x(y + z) = xy + xz$	ind, 6, 17

THEOREM 26. $\vdash \forall x \forall y . x'y = xy + y$

Proof. Induction on y. $P(y)$ is $x'y = xy + y$.

1.	$x'0 = 0$	N5
2.	$x0 = 0$	N5

3.	$x0 + 0 = x0$	N3
4.	$x'0 = x0 + 0$	=, 1–3
5.	$x'y = xy + y$	as (ind. hyp.)
6.	$x'y' = x'y + x'$	N6
7.	$x'y' = (xy + y) + x'$	sub, 5, 6
8.	$(xy + y) + x' = xy + (y + x')$	T2
9.	$x'y' = xy + (y + x')$	=, 7, 8
10.	$y' + x = y + x'$	T3
11.	$x + y' = y' + x$	T4
12.	$y + x' = x + y'$	=, 10, 11
13.	$x'y' = xy + (x + y')$	sub, 12, 9
14.	$(xy + x) + y' = xy + (x + y')$	T2
15.	$x'y' = (xy + x) + y'$	=, 13, 14
16.	$xy' = xy + x$	N6
17.	$x'y' = xy' + y'$	sub, 16, 15
18.	$\forall y . x'y = xy + y \to x'y' = xy' + y'$	DT, 5–17, and gen
19.	$\forall y . x'y = xy + y$	ind, 4, 18

EXERCISES

1. Prove

   (a) $\vdash 1 \neq 0$
   (b) $\vdash \forall x(x \neq x')$

2. Prove

   (a) $\vdash \overline{2} + \overline{2} = \overline{4}$
   (b) $\vdash \overline{2} \cdot \overline{2} = \overline{4}$

3. Without using Theorem 3, prove $\vdash \forall x . x + 1 = 1 + x$, and then prove Theorem 4.

4. Prove

   (a) $\vdash \forall x \forall y . x \leqslant y \leftrightarrow x < y \lor x = y$
   (b) $\vdash \forall x \forall y . x < y \leftrightarrow x \leqslant y \land x \neq y$

5. Prove in any order:

   (a) $\vdash \forall x . x = 0 \; \bar{\lor} \; \exists y(x = y')$
   (b) $\vdash \forall x \sim (x < x)$
   (c) $\vdash \forall x \forall y \forall z . x < y \land y < z \to x < z$
   (d) $\vdash \forall x \forall y . x < y \lor x = y \lor y < x$

(e) $\vdash \forall x (x < 1 \leftrightarrow x = 0)$

(f) $\vdash \forall x \forall y . x + y = 1 \rightarrow x = 1 \vee y = 1$

(g) $\vdash 0 < 1$

6. Prove in any order:

(a) $\vdash \forall x \forall y \forall z . (xy)z = x(yz)$

(b) $\vdash \forall x \forall y . xy = yx$

(c) $\vdash \forall x (1x = x)$

(d) $\vdash \forall x \forall y . xy = 0 \rightarrow x = 0 \vee y = 0$

(e) $\vdash \forall x \forall y \forall z . x \neq 0 \wedge xy = xz \rightarrow y = z$

(f) $\vdash \forall x \forall y \forall z (x \neq 0 . \rightarrow . y \leqslant z \leftrightarrow xy \leqslant xz)$

(g) $\vdash \forall x \forall y \forall z (x \neq 0 . \rightarrow . y < z \leftrightarrow xy < xz)$

(h) $\vdash \forall x \forall y . y \neq 0 \rightarrow \exists z (x < yz)$

(i) $\vdash \forall x \forall y \forall z . x < yz \rightarrow z \neq 0$

7. $r|s$ (r divides s) is an abbreviation for $\exists v(rv = s)$, where r and s are terms and v is the first variable that does not occur in r or s.   Prove in any order:

(a) $\vdash \forall x . x | x$

(b) $\vdash \forall x . x | 0$

(c) $\vdash \forall x \forall y . x | xy$

(d) $\vdash \forall x . 0 | x \leftrightarrow x = 0$

(e) $\vdash \forall x \forall y \forall z . x | y \wedge y | z \rightarrow x | z$

(f) $\vdash \forall x \forall y . y \neq 0 \wedge x | y \rightarrow x \leqslant y \wedge x \neq 0$

(g) $\vdash \forall x \forall y . 1 < x \wedge x | y' \rightarrow \sim x | y$

8. $\mathrm{pr}(s)$ (s is a prime) is an abbreviation for

$$1 < s \wedge \forall v(v | s \rightarrow v = 1 \vee v = s)$$

where s is a term and v is the first variable that does not occur in s. Prove the following:

(a) $\vdash \forall x . 1 < x \wedge \forall y (1 < y \wedge y | x \rightarrow x \leqslant y) \rightarrow \mathrm{pr}(x)$

(b) $\vdash \mathrm{pr}(\bar{2})$

9. Prove that for every number k,

$$\vdash \forall x (x = \bar{0} \vee x = \bar{1} \vee \cdots \vee x = \bar{k} \leftrightarrow x \leqslant \bar{k})$$

25   Consistency and Completeness

A first order theory T is *negation consistent* if and only if there is no formula Q such that both Q and $\sim Q$ are theorems of T.

A first order theory T is *absolutely consistent* if and only if there is at least one formula of T that is not a theorem of T.

THEOREM 1. *A first order theory is negation consistent if and only if it is absolutely consistent.*

Proof. We proceed by contraposition. Suppose the theory T is negation inconsistent; i.e., there is a formula Q of T such that both Q and $\sim Q$ are theorems of T. Let P be any formula of T. $\sim Q .\rightarrow. Q \rightarrow P$ is a theorem of T since it is a tautology. Then by two applications of modus ponens, P is a theorem of T. Since P is arbitrary, every formula of T is a theorem; i.e., T is absolutely inconsistent. Now suppose that T is absolutely inconsistent. Let Q be any formula of T. $\sim Q$ is also a formula of T. Since every formula of T is a theorem, both Q and $\sim Q$ are theorems of T; i.e., T is negation inconsistent.

Theorem 1 allows us to say *consistent* or *inconsistent* without qualification for first order theories.

Consistency makes sense and Theorem 1 holds for the statement calculus.

THEOREM 2. *The statement calculus is consistent.*

Proof. The formula $A(x)$ is not a theorem of the statement calculus because it is not a tautology.

THEOREM 3. *The predicate calculus is consistent.*

Proof. To each formula P we assign a formula P', called the *transform* of P, as follows. First, every occurrence of $\forall v$, for every variable v, is deleted. Then each occurrence of every term is replaced by an occurrence of x. Finally each occurrence of $x = x$ is replaced by an occurrence of $x = x \rightarrow x = x$. We show below that the transform of every axiom of the predicate calculus is a tautology. Since modus ponens applied to two tautologies always gives a tautology, the transform of every theorem of the predicate calculus is a tautology. $A(x)$ is its own transform and is not a tautology. Hence $A(x)$ is not a theorem of the predicate calculus, and the predicate calculus is consistent. Every axiom has one of the following forms, preceded by a finite number of universal quantifiers given by Ax Gen.

A1. $P \to . Q \to P$

A2. $S \to . P \to Q :\to: S \to P .\to. S \to Q$

A3. $\sim Q \to \sim P .\to. P \to Q$

A4. $\forall v(P \to Q) .\to. \forall v P \to \forall v Q$

A5. $\forall v P \to P(t/v)$ if P admits t for v

A6. $P \to \forall v P$ if v is not free in P

E1. $\forall x(x = x)$

E2. $\forall x_1 \cdots \forall x_n \forall y_1 \cdots \forall y_n (x_1 = y_1 \wedge \cdots \wedge$
$$x_n = y_n .\to. G(x_1, \ldots, x_n) \leftrightarrow G(y_1, \ldots, y_n))$$

E3. $\forall x_1 \cdots \forall x_n \forall y_1 \cdots \forall y_n (x_1 = y_1 \wedge \cdots \wedge$
$$x_n = y_n \to F(x_1, \ldots, x_n) = F(y_1, \ldots, y_n))$$

The transforms are as follows:

A1'. $P' \to . Q' \to P'$

A2'. $S' \to . P' \to Q' :\to: S' \to P' .\to. S' \to Q'$

A3'. $\sim(Q') \to \sim(P') .\to. P' \to Q'$

A4'. $P' \to Q' .\to. P' \to Q'$

A5'. $P' \to P'$

A6'. $P' \to P'$

E1'. $x = x \to x = x$

E2'. $(x = x \to x = x) \wedge \cdots \wedge (x = x \to x = x)$
$$.\to. G(x, \ldots, x) \leftrightarrow G(x, \ldots, x)$$

E3'. $(x = x \to x = x) \wedge \cdots \wedge (x = x \to x = x)$
$$\to (x = x \to x = x)$$

We shall use the next three theorems frequently.

THEOREM 4. *A first order* T *is consistent if and only if there is no formula Q such that* $Q \wedge \sim Q$ *is a theorem of* T.

Proof. Suppose that $Q \wedge \sim Q$ is a theorem of T. Let P be any formula of T. $Q \wedge \sim Q \to P$ is a theorem of T because it is a tautology. Then P is a theorem of T by modus ponens. Hence T is inconsistent. Now suppose that T is inconsistent. Let Q be a formula of T. Then $Q \wedge \sim Q$ is also a formula of T, and hence a theorem of T.

THEOREM 5. *Let* T *be a first order theory, and let* P *be a statement of* T. *Let* T' *be the result of adjoining* P *to* T *as a proper axiom. If* T' *is inconsistent, then* $\sim P$ *is a theorem of* T.

Proof. Suppose that T' is inconsistent. Then $\vdash_{T'} \sim P$. Let $S_1, \ldots, S_n$ be a proof of $\sim P$ in T'. Label each step that is P as an assumption. Then $S_1, \ldots, S_n$ is a deduction in T of $\sim P$ from P, i.e., $P \vdash_T \sim P$. Then $\vdash_T P \to \sim P$ by the deduction theorem. $(P \to \sim P) \to \sim P$ is a tautology of T and hence a theorem of T. Then modus ponens gives $\vdash_T \sim P$.

THEOREM 6. *Let* T *be a first order theory. Let* P *be a formula of* T, *and let* P^* *be the closure of* P. *Then* $\vdash_T P$ *if and only if* $\vdash_T P^*$.

Proof. If $\vdash_T P$, then $\vdash_T P^*$ by gen. If $\vdash_T P^*$, then $\vdash_T P$ by spec.

A first order theory T is *negation complete* if and only if for every statement S of T, either S or $\sim S$ is a theorem of T.

In the definition above, "statement" cannot be replaced by "formula." Suppose, for example, that we demand of number theory that either $x < 2$ or $\sim(x < 2)$ be a theorem. Then by gen, either $\forall x(x < 2)$ or $\forall x \sim(x < 2)$ should be a theorem. But since $\forall x(x < 2)$ and $\forall x \sim(x < 2)$ are both false, we do not desire or expect either of them to be provable.

A first order theory T is *absolutely complete* if and only if for every statement S of T that is not a theorem of T, the result of adjoining S to T as a proper axiom is inconsistent.

An absolutely complete theory is like a balloon filled to capacity: any attempt to enlarge it causes it to explode.

We note that an inconsistent theory is trivially negation complete and vacuously absolutely complete.

THEOREM 7. *A first order theory is negation complete if and only if it is absolutely complete.*

Proof. Let T be a first order theory. If T is inconsistent, then T is both negation complete and absolutely complete. So suppose that T is consistent. Suppose that T is negation complete. Let S be any statement of T that is not a theorem of T, and let T' be the result of adjoining S as a proper axiom to T. $\sim S$ is a theorem of T because T is negation complete and S is not a theorem of T. Then $\sim S$ is a theorem of T' since every theorem of T is a theorem of T'. Hence T' is inconsistent since S is also a theorem of T'. Therefore T is absolutely complete. For the converse, suppose that T is absolutely complete, and let S be any statement of T. We show that S or $\sim S$ is a theorem of T. If S is a theorem of T, we are done. So suppose that S is not a theorem of T. Since T is absolutely complete, the result of adjoining

S as a proper axiom to T is inconsistent.   Hence $\sim S$ is a theorem of T by Theorem 5.   Therefore T is negation complete.

Theorem 7 allows us to say *complete* or *incomplete* without qualification for first order theories.

We observe that a theory is consistent if it does not have too many theorems, and it is complete if it does not have too few theorems. There are other useful definitions of consistency and completeness besides the ones given above.   The following definition is especially applicable to the statement calculus and the predicate calculus.

Let T be a theory (first order or not).   Let X be a set of formulas of T.   T is *consistent relative to* X if and only if every theorem of T is in X. T is *complete relative to* X if and only if every formula in X is a theorem of T.   For example, the statement calculus is consistent and complete relative to the set of tautologies.   Later we shall define *valid formula* and prove that the predicate calculus is consistent and complete relative to the set of valid formulas.

EXERCISES

1. Let T be a first order theory, and let P be a statement of T.   Let T′ be the result of adjoining $\sim P$ to T as a proper axiom.   Prove that T′ is inconsistent if and only if P is a theorem of T.

2. For the formal theory of Exercise 3.4, suppose that the only logical operators are $\to$ and $\forall$.   Discuss the consistency of this theory.

3. Prove that a first order theory T is consistent and complete if and only if for every statement S of T, exactly one of the pair $\{S,\ \sim S\}$ is a theorem of T.

4. A certain theory has as its theorems precisely those formulas of the predicate calculus that are neither tautologies nor contradictions.

   (a) Is this theory negation consistent?   Why?
   (b) Is it absolutely consistent?   Why?

5. Let T be a first order theory whose proper axioms are an infinite sequence $P_1, P_2, \ldots$ of statements such that $\vdash P_n \to P_m$ if and only if $n \geqslant m$.   Prove that T is consistent.

6. Prove that neither the statement calculus nor the predicate calculus is negation complete or absolutely complete.

7. Prove that a first order theory T is complete if and only if for all statements P and Q of T, if $\vdash_T P \vee Q$, then $\vdash_T P$ or $\vdash_T Q$.

2. This theory is absolutely inconsistent but vacuously negation
   consistent.   There is no conflict with Theorem 1 because this theory
   is not a first order theory.
4. This theory is negation inconsistent because $A(x)$ and $\sim A(x)$ are
   theorems, but it is absolutely consistent because $A(x) \rightarrow A(x)$ is not
   a theorem.

26   Truth

A *domain* is any nonempty set.   An *interpretation* for a set X of
formulas is a domain D together with a rule that (i) assigns to each
n-place predicate symbol (that occurs in a formula) of X an n-place
predicate in D; (ii) assigns to each n-place operation symbol of X an
n-place operation in D; (iii) assigns to each constant symbol of X an
element of D; and (iv) assigns to = the identity predicate = in D,
defined by: $a = b$ is true if and only if a and b are the same.

A *model* for a set X of formulas is an interpretation M for X such that
every formula of X is true in M.

The notion of the truth of a formula in an interpretation is highly
intuitive.   We illustrate with two examples.

EXAMPLE 1.   We exhibit a model M for the set of proper axioms of AG:

AG1. $\forall x \forall y ((x + y) + z = x + (y + z))$
AG2. $\forall x (x + 0 = 0)$
AG3. $\forall x \exists y (x + y = 0)$
AG4. $\forall x \forall y (x + y = y + x)$

The domain of M consists of the two elements a and b. M assigns to
+ the operation $\circ$ in D defined below, and M assigns a to 0.

$\circ$	a	b
a	a	b
b	b	a

The statement $(a \circ b) \circ a = a \circ (b \circ a)$ is true in M because $(a \circ b) \circ a =$
$b \circ a = b$ and $a \circ (b \circ a) = a \circ b = b$.   In the same way all eight
statements of the form $(x \circ y) \circ z = x \circ (y \circ z)$ are true in M.   Hence

$\forall x \forall y \forall z((x \circ y) \circ z = x \circ (y \circ z))$ is true in M. Hence AG1 is true in M. $a \circ a = a$ and $b \circ a = b$ are true in M. Since a and b are the only elements of D, $\forall x(x \circ a = x)$ is true in M. Hence AG2 is true in M. Because $a \circ a = a$ and $b \circ b = a$ are true in M, $\exists y(a \circ y = a)$ and $\exists y(b \circ y = a)$ are true in M. Because a and b are the only elements of D, $\forall x \exists y(x \circ y = a)$ is true in M. Hence AG3 is true in M. $\forall x \forall y(x \circ y = y \circ x)$ is true in M because all 4 statements $a \circ a = a \circ a$, $a \circ b = b \circ a$, $b \circ a = a \circ b$, $b \circ b = b \circ b$ are true in M. Hence AG4 is true in M.

EXAMPLE 2. We exhibit a model M for the set of proper axioms of L:

L1. $\forall x \sim (x < x)$
L2. $\forall x \forall y \forall z(x < y \wedge y < z \to x < z)$
L3. $\forall x \forall y(x < y \vee x = y \vee y < x)$

Again the domain of M is $\{a, b\}$, and M assigns to $<$ the predicate $\lhd$ in D, defined by

$\lhd$	a	b
a	F	T
b	F	F

Since $a \lhd a$ and $b \lhd b$ are false in M, $\sim(a \lhd a)$ and $\sim(b \lhd b)$ are true in M. Hence $\forall x \sim (x \lhd x)$ is true in M. Hence L1 is true in M. $a \lhd b \wedge b \lhd b \to a \lhd b$ is true in M because $b \lhd b$ is false in M. In the same way, all eight statements of the form $x \lhd y \wedge y \lhd z \to x \lhd z$ are true in M. Hence $\forall x \forall y \forall z(x \lhd y \wedge y \lhd z \to x \lhd z)$ is true in M. Hence L2 is true in M. $a \lhd a \vee a = a \vee a \lhd a$ and $b \lhd b \vee b = b \vee b \lhd b$ are true in M, because $a = a$ and $b = b$ are true in M. $a \lhd b \vee a = b \vee b \lhd a$ and $b \lhd a \vee b = a \vee a \lhd b$ are true in M, because $a \lhd b$ is true in M. Hence $\forall x \forall y(x \lhd y \vee x = y \vee x \lhd y)$ is true in M. Hence L3 is true in M.

The intuitive notion of truth is satisfactory for many purposes, but for the development of a theory of truth, a precise definition is essential. We offer two examples to illustrate the ideas underlying the precise definition.

EXAMPLE 3. Let P be the formula $\forall x \forall y(x < y \to \exists z(x < z \wedge z < y))$. Let I be the interpretation for P whose domain is the set R of real

numbers, and which assigns to $<$ the usual meaning of $<$ in R.
Paralleling the construction of P, we assign to each subformula of P a
set of points in R^3. We use R^3 because the three variables x, y, z occur
free in one or more subformulas of P. To the atomic formula $x < z$
we assign the set of all points (a_1, a_2, a_3) such that $a_1 < a_3$. This is
precisely what is called in analytic geometry the graph of $x < z$ in
three-dimensional space. To the atomic formula $z < y$ we assign the
set of all points (a_1, a_2, a_3) such that $a_3 < a_2$. To the formula
$x < z \wedge z < y$ we assign the intersection of the sets assigned to $x < z$
and $z < y$, i.e., the set of all points (a_1, a_2, a_3) such that $a_1 < a_3$ and
$a_3 < a_2$. To the formula $\exists z(x < z \wedge z < y)$ we assign the set of
all points (a_1, a_2, a_3) such that (a_1, a_2, d) is in the set assigned to
$x < z \wedge z < y$ for some real number d. Hence (a_1, a_2, a_3) is in the set
assigned to $\exists z(x < z \wedge z < y)$ if and only if there is a real number d
such that $a_1 < d$ and $d < a_2$. Thus $(1, 2, 3)$ is in this set because there
is a real number 1.5 such that $1 < 1.5$ and $1.5 < 2$. To the atomic
formula $x < y$ we assign the set of all points (a_1, a_2, a_3) such that
$a_1 < a_2$. Recall that to a formula $Q \wedge R$ we assigned the intersection
of the sets assigned to Q and R. To a formula $Q \vee R$ we assign the
union of the sets assigned to Q and R. To a formula $\sim Q$ we assign the
complement of the set assigned to Q, i.e., the set of all points that are
not assigned to Q. Since $Q \rightarrow R$ is equivalent to $\sim Q \vee R$, we assign
to $Q \rightarrow R$ the complement of the set assigned to Q union the set
assigned to R. Hence a point is in the set assigned to $Q \rightarrow R$ if and
only if it is not in the set assigned to Q or is in the set assigned to R.
Hence to the formula $x < y \rightarrow \exists z(x < z \wedge z < y)$ we assign the set of
all points (a_1, a_2, a_3) such that (a_1, a_2, a_3) is not in the set assigned to
$x < y$ or is in the set assigned to $\exists z(x < z \wedge z < y)$. Hence (a_1, a_2, a_3)
is in the set assigned to $x < y \rightarrow \exists z(x < z \wedge z < y)$ if and only if
$a_1 < a_2$ is false or there is a d such that $a_1 < d$ and $d < a_2$. Let
(a_1, a_2, a_3) be a point. Either $a_2 \leqslant a_1$ or $a_1 < a_2$. If $a_2 \leqslant a_1$, then
$a_1 < a_2$ is false. If $a_1 < a_2$, then there is a real number d, namely
$(a_1 + a_2)/2$ such that $a_1 < d$ and $d < a_2$. Hence every point is in the set
assigned to $x < y \rightarrow \exists z(x < z \wedge z < y)$. To the formula $\forall y(x < y \rightarrow$
$\exists z(x < z \wedge z < y))$ we assign the set of all points (a_1, a_2, a_3) such that $(a_1,$
$d, a_3)$ is in the set assigned to $x < y \rightarrow \exists z(x < z \wedge z < y)$ for every real
number d. Every point is in the set assigned to $\forall y(x < y \rightarrow \exists z(x < z \wedge$
$z < y))$ because every point is in the set assigned to $x < y \rightarrow \exists z(x < z \wedge$
$z < y)$. Finally, to the formula $\forall x \forall y(x < y \rightarrow \exists z(x < z \wedge z < y))$ we
assign the set of all points (a_1, a_2, a_3) such that (d, a_2, a_3) is in the set

assigned to $\forall y(x < y \rightarrow \exists z(x < z \wedge z < y))$ for every real number d. Again this is the set of all points. Thus all points are assigned to P. This is our criterion for truth. We conclude that P is true in this interpretation.

EXAMPLE 4. Again let P be the formula $\forall x \forall y(x < y \rightarrow \exists z(x < z \wedge z < y))$. Let I be the interpretation for P whose domain D is the set of integers, and which assigns to $<$ the usual meaning of $<$ in D. Again we assign to each subformula Q a set of points in D^3, but we change the wording a little. Instead of talking about the set assigned to Q, we speak now of whether or not a point is in this set. Let $p = (a_1, a_2, a_3)$ be an arbitrary point in D^3. p *satisfies* Q means p is in the set assigned to Q. p satisfies $x < z$ if and only if $a_1 < a_3$. p satisfies $z < y$ if and only if $a_3 < a_2$. Then p satisfies $x < z \wedge z < y$ if and only if p satisfies $x < z$ and $z < y$, i.e., $a_1 < a_3$ and $a_3 < a_2$. p satisfies $\exists z(x < z \wedge z < y)$ if and only if there is an integer d such that (a_1, a_2, d) satisfies $x < z \wedge z < y$, i.e., there is an integer d such that $a_1 < d$ and $d < a_2$. p satisfies $x < y$ if and only if $a_1 < a_2$. Then p satisfies $x < y \rightarrow \exists z(x < z \wedge z < y)$ if and only if p does not satisfy $x < y$ or p satisfies $\exists z(x < z \wedge z < y)$, i.e., $a_1 < a_2$ is false or there is a d such that $a_1 < d$ and $d < a_2$. Thus $(1, 2, 3)$ does not satisfy $x < y \rightarrow \exists z(x < z \wedge z < y)$ because $1 < 2$, and there is no integer d such that $1 < d$ and $d < 2$. In the integers, $a_1 < a_2$ is false if and only if $a_1 \geqslant a_2$. Hence p satisfies $x < y \rightarrow \exists z(x < z \wedge z < y)$ if and only if $a_1 \geqslant a_2$ or there is an integer d such that $a_1 < d$ and $d < a_2$. p satisfies $\forall y(x < y \rightarrow \exists z(x < z \wedge z < y))$ if and only if (a_1, d, a_3) satisfies $x < y \rightarrow \exists z(x < z \wedge z < y)$ for every integer d. We know that (a_1, d, a_3) satisfies $x < y \rightarrow \exists z(x < z \wedge z < y)$ if and only if $a_1 \geqslant d$ or there is an integer e such that $a_1 < e$ and $e < d$. Hence p satisfies $\forall y(x < y \rightarrow \exists z(x < z \wedge z < y))$ if and only if for every d, $a_1 \geqslant d$ or there is an e such that $a_1 < e$ and $e < d$. No p satisfies $\forall y(x < y \rightarrow \exists z(x < z \wedge z < y))$, for if $d = a_1 + 1$, then $a_1 \geqslant d$ is false, and there is no integer e such that $a_1 < e$ and $e < a_1 + 1$. Finally, p satisfies $\forall x \forall y(x < y \rightarrow \exists z(x < z \wedge z < y))$ if and only if (d, a_2, a_3) satisfies $\forall y(x < y \rightarrow \exists z(x < z \wedge z < y))$ for every integer d. No point satisfies $\forall x \forall y(x < y \rightarrow \exists z(x < z \wedge z < y))$ because no point satisfies $\forall y(x < y \rightarrow \exists z(x < z \wedge z < y))$. Hence the empty set is assigned to P. This is our criterion for falsehood. We conclude that P is false in this interpretation.

We shall show that every statement is assigned all points or no points, i.e., is true or false. A formula with free variables may be neither true nor false. For example, in the standard interpretation in R, the formula $x < y$ is assigned the set of all points (a_1, a_2) such that $a_1 < a_2$. This set is neither all of R^2 nor the empty set. Note that in dealing with the formula $x < y$ alone we work in R^2, but in dealing with $x < y$ as a subformula of $\forall x \forall y (x < y \rightarrow \exists z (x < z \land z < y))$, we work in R^3 because we know that we have to contend with a z-coordinate eventually.

When interpreting a set of formulas simultaneously, the simplest procedure is to work in the infinite dimensional space D^∞ consisting of all infinite sequences $(a_1, a_2, \ldots)$ of elements of D. We write the variables in alphabetic order as

$$x_1 \quad x_2 \quad x_3 \quad \cdots$$

and correlate x_i with the ith coordinate a_i of the point $(a_1, a_2, \ldots, a_i, \ldots)$. Each formula imposes a restriction only on those coordinates corresponding to the free variables of the formula. For example, the point $(a_1, a_2, \ldots)$ satisfies $x_7 < x_2 \lor x_2 < x_4$ if and only if $a_7 < a_2$ or $a_2 < a_4$.

We now start in on the precise definition of truth. Let P be a formula, and let I be an interpretation with domain D for P. From now on p is the point $(a_1, a_2, \ldots)$ of D^∞, and q is the point $(b_1, b_2, \ldots)$ of D^∞. Let d be an element of D. Then $p(d/k)$ is the result of replacing the kth coordinate of p by d, i.e.,

$$p(d/k) = (a_1, \ldots, a_{k-1}, d, a_{k+1}, \ldots)$$

To each term t that occurs in P, p assigns an element $p(t)$ of D as follows. If t is the variable x_i, then $p(x_i) = a_i$. If t is the constant symbol c, then $p(t) = d$, where d is the element of D assigned to c by I. Suppose that $p(t_1), \ldots, p(t_m)$ have been defined, and t is $F(t_1, \ldots, t_m)$, where F is an m-place operation symbol. Let f be the operation assigned to F by I. Then $p(F(t_1, \ldots, t_m)) = f(p(t_1), \ldots, p(t_m))$.

EXAMPLE 5. t is $(x_7 + 0) \cdot x_2 + x_3$, and I assigns in the domain R the usual meaning of $+$, $\cdot$, and 0. Then $p(t) = (a_7 + 0) \cdot a_2 + a_3$. Thus if $p = (1, 3, 5, \ldots, 2n - 1, \ldots)$, then $p(t) = (13 + 0) \cdot 3 + 5 = 44$.

We define *p satisfies P in I*.

Case 1. P is an atomic formula $G(t_1, \ldots, t_m)$, where G is an m-place predicate symbol and $t_1, \ldots, t_m$ are terms. Let g be the predicate assigned to G by I. Then p satisfies P if and only if $g(p(t_1), \ldots, p(t_m))$ is true.

Suppose that *p satisfies Q* and *p satisfies R* have been defined.

Case 2. P is $\sim Q$. Then p satisfies P if and only if p does not satisfy Q.

Case 3. P is $Q \to R$. Then p satisfies P if and only if p does not satisfy Q or p satisfies R.

Case 4. P is $\forall x_k Q$. Then p satisfies P if and only if $p(d/k)$ satisfies Q for every element d of D.

From the definitions of $\wedge$, $\vee$, $\leftrightarrow$, and $\exists$ we have immediately: p satisfies $Q \wedge R$ if and only if p satisfies Q and p satisfies R; p satisfies $Q \vee R$ if and only if p satisfies Q or p satisfies R; p satisfies $Q \leftrightarrow R$ if and only if p satisfies both Q and R or p satisfies neither Q nor R; p satisfies $\exists x_k Q$ if and only if $p(d/k)$ satisfies Q for some d in D.

The formula P is *true* in the interpretation I if and only if every point satisfies P. P is *false* in I if and only if no point satisfies P.

We shall use the following theorem often, sometimes without explicit mention.

THEOREM 6.   *Let I be an interpretation for the formulas P and Q.*

(a) If p satisfies $P \to Q$ and p satisfies P, then p satisfies Q.

(b) If $P \to Q$ is true in I and P is true in I, then Q is true in I.

(c) P is true in I if and only if $\forall x_k P$ is true in I.

(d) P is true in I if and only if the closure of P is true in I.

(e) $\sim P$ is true in I if and only if P is false in I.

(f) P is not both true and false in I.

(g) If P is a statement, then exactly one of the pair $\{P, \sim P\}$ is true in I and the other is false in I.

(h) If P and Q are statements, then $P \to Q$ is true in I if and only if P is false in I or Q is true in I.

(i) If P and Q are statements, then $P \to Q$ is false in I if and only if P is true in I and Q is false in I.

Proof.

(a) If p satisfies $P \to Q$, then p does not satisfy P or p satisfies Q. Hence if p satisfies P, then p satisfies Q.

(b) Let p be a point. Suppose $P \to Q$ and P are true in I. Then p satisfies $P \to Q$ and p satisfies P. Hence p satisfies Q by (a). Since p is arbitrary, Q is true in I.

(c) Suppose $\forall x_k P$ is true in I. Then every point p satisfies $\forall x_k P$. Then $p(d/k)$ satisfies P for every d in the domain. In particular $p = p(a_k/k)$ satisfies P. Hence every point satisfies P, and P is true in I. Now suppose that P is true in I. Then every point satisfies P. Hence $p(d/k)$ satisfies P for every point p and every element d. Hence every point p satisfies $\forall x_k P$. Hence $\forall x_k P$ is true in I.

(d) Let $\forall x_{i_1} \cdots \forall x_{i_n} P$ be the closure of P. Then P is true in I if and only if $\forall x_{i_1} \cdots \forall x_{i_n} P$ is true in I by n applications of (c).

(e) $\sim P$ is true in I if and only if every point satisfies $\sim P$. Every point satisfies $\sim P$ if and only if no point satisfies P. No point satisfies P if and only if P is false.

(f) Suppose P is both true and false in I. Then every point satisfies P and no point satisfies P. But this is impossible because the domain is not empty and hence there is at least one point.

(g) Suppose P is a statement. Then P has no free variables. In Lemma 7 below, let $\{x_{i_1}, \ldots, x_{i_k}\}$ be the empty set. Then all points p and q satisfy the hypotheses of Lemma 7. Hence by Lemma 7, all points satisfy P or no points satisfy P, i.e., P is true in I or P is false in I. Then use (e) and (f).

(h) Suppose P and Q are statements. Suppose $P \to Q$ is true in I. Let p be a point. Then p satisfies $P \to Q$. Hence p does not satisfy P or p satisfies Q. If p does not satisfy P, then P is not true in I, and hence P is false in I by (g). If p satisfies Q, then Q is not false in I, and hence Q is true in I by (g). Now suppose that P is false in I or Q is true in I. If P is false in I, then no point satisfies P, and hence every point satisfies $P \to Q$. If Q is true in I, then every point satisfies Q, and hence every point satisfies $P \to Q$. Hence $P \to Q$ is true in I.

(i) Suppose that P and Q are statements. Then $P \to Q$ is also a statement. Hence by (g), $P \to Q$ is false in I if and only if $P \to Q$ is not true in I. By (g) and (h), $P \to Q$ is not true in I if and only if P is true in I and Q is false in I.

We shall try to take the mystery out of the next lemma with an example. Let P be the formula $x_1 + x_2 < x_3$. Let I be the interpretation for P whose domain is R, and which assigns the usual meaning to $+$ and $<$. Let $p = (1, 3, 5, \ldots, 2n - 1, \ldots)$. p assigns to the term $x_1 + x_2$ the real number 4 ($= 1 + 3$), and assigns to x_3 the real number 5. Hence p acting on P determines the statement $4 < 5$ of real numbers. Now let q be any point whose first three coordinates are 1, 3, 5. Then q acting on P determines the same statement $4 < 5$.

LEMMA 7.   *Let I be an interpretation for the formula P. Let every variable free in P occur in the list $x_{i_1}, \ldots, x_{i_k}$. Let p and q be points such that $a_{i_j} = b_{i_j}$ for $1 \leqslant j \leqslant k$. Then p satisfies P if and only if q satisfies P.*

Proof.   First we show that if P is an atomic formula, then $p(t) = q(t)$ for every term t of P. If t is a variable, then t is x_{i_j} with $i \leqslant j \leqslant k$. Then $p(t) = p(x_{i_j}) = a_{i_j} = b_{i_j} = q(x_{i_j}) = q(t)$. If t is a constant symbol c, then $p(t) = p(c) = d = q(c) = q(t)$, where d is the element of the domain assigned to c by I. Suppose that $p(t_1) = q(t_1), \ldots, p(t_m) = q(t_m)$, and t is $F(t_1, \ldots, t_m)$ where F is an m-place operation symbol. Let f be the operation assigned to F by I. Then

$$p(t) = p(F(t_1, \ldots, t_m)) = f(p(t_1), \ldots, p(t_m))$$
$$= f(q(t_1), \ldots, q(t_m)) = q(F(t_1, \ldots, t_m)) = q(t)$$

Now we prove the lemma by induction on the number n of symbols in P, counting each occurrence of $\sim$, $\rightarrow$, or $\forall$ as a symbol.

Basis.   If $n = 0$, then P is an atomic formula $G(t_1, \ldots, t_m)$, where G is an m-place predicate symbol and $t_1, \ldots, t_m$ are terms. Let g be the predicate assigned to G by I. p satisfies P if and only if $g(p(t_1), \ldots, p(t_m))$ is true, and q satisfies P if and only if $g(q(t_1), \ldots, q(t_m))$ is true. Since $p(t_1) = q(t_1), \ldots, p(t_m) = q(t_m)$, p satisfies P if and only if q satisfies P.

Induction step.   Assume the lemma holds for every formula with n or fewer symbols, and consider P with $n + 1$ symbols. In cases 2 and 3 the proof is immediate by the induction hypothesis and the definition of satisfaction.

Case 2. P is $\sim Q$ for some Q.

Case 3. P is $Q \rightarrow R$ for some Q and R.

Case 4. P is $\forall x_m Q$ for some m and Q. Suppose p satisfies P. Let d be an element of the domain. Then $p(d/m)$ satisfies Q. Then whether or not x_m is one of $x_{i_1}, \ldots, x_{i_k}$, the i_jth coordinate of $q(d/m)$ is the same as the i_jth coordinate of $p(d/m)$, since $a_{i_j} = b_{i_j}$ for $i \leqslant j \leqslant k$.

Hence $q(d/m)$ satisfies Q by the induction hypothesis.   Then q satisfies P because d is arbitrary.   Similarly, if q satisfies P, then p satisfies P.

An interpretation I with domain D is *finite* (or *countable*) if and only if D is finite (or countable).

If the interpretation I for the formula P is finite, then there is an effective procedure for deciding if P is true in I, based on the following two observations.   First, every predicate and operation in D is defined by a finite table.   Second, if exactly n variables occur in P, then we can just as well use n-tuples for points instead of infinite sequences, and the number of n-tuples in a finite domain is finite.

EXAMPLE 8.   Let P be the formula $\forall x_1(x_1 \neq 0 \to \exists x_2(x_1 \cdot x_2 = 1))$. Let the domain of the interpretation I be $\{0, 1, 2\}$.   Let I assign 0 to 0, 1 to 1, and the operation $\cdot$ to $\cdot$ as defined below.

	0	1	2
0	0	0	0
1	0	1	2
2	0	2	1

Let p be a point.   There are infinitely many points, but only nine distinct cases to consider, because only a_1 and a_2 enter into the analysis, and D has exactly three elements.   In this example, the nine cases collapse to three.   Let Q be the subformula $x_1 \neq 0 \to \exists x_2(x_1 \cdot x_2 = 1)$. If a_1 is 0, then p does not satisfy $x_1 \neq 0$, and hence satisfies Q.   If a_1 is 1, then p satisfies $\exists x_2(x_1 \cdot x_2 = 1)$ and hence Q, because the point $(1, 1, a_3, a_4, \ldots)$ satisfies $x_1 \cdot x_2 = 1$.   If a_1 is 2, then again p satisfies $\exists x_2(x_1 \cdot x_2 = 1)$ and hence Q, because the point $(2, 2, a_3, a_4, \ldots)$ satisfies $x_1 \cdot x_2 = 1$.   Hence every point satisfies Q, i.e., Q is true in I. Hence P is true in I by Theorem 6(c).

A formula P is *valid* if and only if P is true in every interpretation. A valid formula is logically true, i.e., the way that $\sim$, $\to$, $\forall$, and $=$ enter into its construction makes it true regardless of how its proper symbols are interpreted.

We show that every theorem of the predicate calculus is valid.

LEMMA 9.   *Every tautology is valid.*

Proof. Let $P_1, \ldots, P_n$ be the distinct prime constituents of P. Let p be a point. Then for each i, p satisfies P_i or p does not satisfy P_i. We make out the truth table for P, but instead of T and F, we write *Yes* for p *satisfies* and *No* for p *does not satisfy*. By the definition of satisfaction, this table is exactly like the truth table for P except that T and F are replaced throughout by *Yes* and *No*. If P is a tautology, then only *Yes* appears in the column for P, i.e., p always satisfies P.

EXAMPLE 10

$(\sim$	Q	$\rightarrow$	$\sim$	$P)$	$\rightarrow$	$(P$	$\rightarrow$	$Q)$
No	Yes	Yes	No	Yes	Yes	Yes	Yes	Yes
No	Yes	Yes	Yes	No	Yes	No	Yes	Yes
Yes	No	No	No	Yes	Yes	Yes	No	No
Yes	No	Yes	Yes	No	Yes	No	Yes	No

LEMMA 11. $\forall x_k(P \rightarrow Q) . \rightarrow . \forall x_k P \rightarrow \forall x_k Q$ *is valid.*

Proof. Let p be a point. It suffices to show that if p satisfies $\forall x_k(P \rightarrow Q)$ and p satisfies $\forall x_k P$, then p satisfies $\forall x_k Q$, for in all other cases p satisfies $\forall x_k(P \rightarrow Q) . \rightarrow . \forall x_k P \rightarrow \forall x_k Q$ by the definition of satisfaction. Suppose p satisfies $\forall x_k(P \rightarrow Q)$ and p satisfies $\forall x_k P$. Let d be an element of the domain. Then $p(d/k)$ satisfies $P \rightarrow Q$ and $p(d/k)$ satisfies P. Then $p(d/k)$ satisfies Q by Theorem 6(a). Since d is arbitrary, p satisfies $\forall x_k Q$.

LEMMA 12. $P \rightarrow \forall x_k P$ *is valid if x_k is not free in P.*

Proof. Let p be a point. It suffices to show that if p satisfies P, then p satisfies $\forall x_k P$. Suppose p satisfies P, and x_k is not free in P. Let $x_{i_1}, \ldots, x_{i_n}$ be the free variables of P. x_k is not one of them. Let d be an element of the domain. Then $p(d/k)$ agrees with p in the coordinates $i_1, \ldots, i_n$. Hence $p(d/k)$ satisfies P by Lemma 7. Since d is arbitrary, P satisfies $\forall x_k P$.

Lemmas 9, 11, and 12 show that every instance of Axiom Schemes A1 through A4 and A6 is valid. For A5 we need two preliminary lemmas.

LEMMA 13. *Let s and t be terms. Let s' be the result of replacing each occurrence of x_k in s by an occurrence of t. Let p be a point, and let $p' = p(p(t)/k)$. Then $p(s') = p'(s)$.*

Proof. Suppose s is x_i, with $i \neq k$. Then $s' = s = x_i$. Hence $p(s') = p(x_i) = a_i$, and $p'(s) = p'(x_i) = a_i$. Suppose s is x_k. Then $s' = t$. Hence $p(s') = p(t)$, and $p'(s) = p'(x_k) = p(t)$, since the kth coordinate of p' is $p(t)$. Suppose s is the constant symbol c. Then $s' = s = c$. Let d be the element of the domain assigned to c by the interpretation. Then $p(s') = p(c) = d$, and $p'(s) = p'(c) = d$. Now suppose the lemma holds for $s_1, \ldots, s_m$, and s is $F(s_1, \ldots, s_m)$, where F is an m-place operation symbol. Let f be the operation assigned to F. s' is $F(s'_1, \ldots, s'_m)$. Hence

$$p(s') = p(F(s'_1, \ldots, s'_m)) = f(p(s'_1), \ldots, p(s'_m))$$
$$= f(p'(s_1), \ldots, p'(s_m)) = p'(F(s_1, \ldots, s_m)) = p'(s)$$

LEMMA 14. *Let P admit the term t for x_k. Let p be a point, and let $p' = p(p(t)/k)$. Then p satisfies $P(t/x_k)$ if and only if p' satisfies P.*

Proof. The proof is by induction on the number n of symbols in P, counting each occurrence of $\sim$, $\rightarrow$, or $\forall$ as a symbol.

Basis. If $n = 0$, then P is an atomic formula $G(s_1, \ldots, s_m)$, where G is an m-place predicate symbol and $s_1, \ldots, s_m$ are terms. Let s'_i ($1 \leqslant i \leqslant m$) be the result of replacing each occurrence of x_k in s_i by an occurrence of t. Then $P(t/x_k)$ is $G(s'_1, \ldots, s'_m)$. Let g be predicate assigned to G by the interpretation. p satisfies $P(t/x_k)$ if and only if $g(p(s'_1), \ldots, p(s'_m))$ is true. p' satisfies P if and only if $g(p'(s_1), \ldots, p'(s_m))$ is true. By Lemma 13, $p(s'_i) = p'(s_i)$ for $1 \leqslant i \leqslant m$. Hence p satisfies $p(t/x_k)$ if and only if p' satisfies P.

Induction step. Assume the lemma holds for every formula with n or fewer symbols, and consider P with $n + 1$ symbols.

Case 1. P is $\sim Q$ for some Q. Then $P(t/x_k)$ is $\sim Q(t/x_k)$, and Q admits t for x_k. p satisfies $P(t/x_k)$ if and only if p does not satisfy $Q(t/x_k)$. By the induction hypothesis, p does not satisfy $Q(t/x_k)$ if and only if p' does not satisfy Q. p' does not satisfy Q if and only if p' satisfies P.

Case 2. P is $Q \rightarrow R$ for some Q and R. Then $P(t/x_k)$ is $Q(t/x_k) \rightarrow R(t/x_k)$, and Q and R admit t for x_k. As in case 1, the proof is immediate by the induction hypothesis and the definition of satisfaction.

Case 3. P is $\forall x_j Q$ for some j and Q. Then $P(t/x_k)$ is $\forall x_j Q(t/x_k)$, and Q admits t for x_k. Let $(p(d/j))'$ be the result of replacing the kth term of $p(d/j)$ by the element of D assigned to t by $p(d/j)$, and let $p'(d/j)$ be the result of replacing the jth term of p' by d. Suppose x_k is free in P and $j \neq k$. p satisfies $P(t/x_k)$ if and only if $p(d/j)$ satisfies $Q(t/x_k)$ for every element d of the domain.   By the induction hypothesis, $p(d/j)$ satisfies $Q(t/x_k)$ if and only if $(p(d/j))'$ satisfies Q.   Since P admits t for x_k, x_j does not occur in t.   Therefore the element assigned to t by a point does not depend on the jth coordinate of the point.   Hence $(p(d/j))' = p'(d/j)$ for every d. p' satisfies P if and only if $p'(d/j)$ satisfies Q for every d.   Hence p satisfies $P(t/x_k)$ if and only if p' satisfies P. If x_k is not free in P, then $P(t/x_k)$ is P.   By Lemma 7, p satisfies P if and only if p' satisfies P, since p' differs from p only in the kth coordinate.   In particular, if $j = k$, then x_k is not free in P.

LEMMA 15. $\forall x_k P \to P(t/x_k)$ *is valid if P admits the term t for x_k.*

Proof.   It suffices to show that if p satisfies $\forall x_k P$, then p satisfies $P(t/x_k)$.   Suppose p satisfies $\forall x_k P$.   Then $p(d/k)$ satisfies P for every d in the domain.   In particular $p(p(t)/k)$ satisfies P.   Then p satisfies $P(t/x_k)$ by Lemma 14.

LEMMA 16.   *Every equality axiom is valid.*

Proof.   Let I be an interpretation, and let p be a point.   E1 is $\forall x_1(x_1 = x_1)$. p satisfies $x_1 = x_1$ because $a_1 = a_1$ (is true).   Since p is arbitrary, $x_1 = x_1$ is true in I.   Then E1 is true in I by Theorem 6(c). Let $\forall x_1 \cdots \forall x_n \forall x_{n+1} \cdots \forall x_{n+n} Q$ be an instance of E2, where Q is

$$x_1 = x_{n+1} \wedge \cdots \wedge x_i = x_{n+i} \wedge \cdots \wedge$$
$$x_n = x_{n+n} .\to . \, G(x_1, \ldots, x_n) \leftrightarrow G(x_{n+1}, \ldots, x_{n+n}).$$

Let g be the predicate assigned to G by I.   If $a_i \neq a_{n+i}$ for some i, then p does not satisfy $x_i = x_{n+i}$, and hence p satisfies Q.   If $a_i = a_{n+i}$ for every i, then $g(a_1, \ldots, a_n)$ is the same as $g(a_{n+1}, \ldots, a_{n+n})$.   Then p satisfies $G(x_1, \ldots, x_n) \leftrightarrow G(x_{n+1}, \ldots, x_{n+n})$, and hence p satisfies Q. Since p is arbitrary, Q is true in I.   Then $\forall x_1 \cdots \forall x_n \forall x_{n+1} \cdots \forall x_{n+n} Q$ is true in I by Theorem 6(c).   Similarly, every instance of E3 is true in I. Since I is arbitrary, every equality axiom is valid.

THEOREM 17.   *Every theorem of the predicate calculus is valid.*

Proof.   Every instance of A1 through A6 is valid by Lemmas 9, 11, 12, and 15.   Every equality axiom is valid by Lemma 16.   Every

axiom that is given by Ax Gen is valid by Theorem 6(c).   Therefore
every axiom of the predicate calculus is valid.   If $P \to Q$ and P are
valid, then Q is valid by Theorem 6(b).   Hence every theorem of the
predicate calculus is valid.   (Compare the proof of Theorem 15.5.)

EXERCISES

1. Let I be the interpretation for AG whose domain consists of the
   single element a, and which assigns to $+$ the operation $\circ$ defined by
   $a \circ a = a$, and assigns a to 0.   Show that I is a model for the proper
   axioms of AG.
2. Let I be the interpretation for the theory F of fields whose domain is
   $\{0, 1\}$, and which assigns 0 to 0 and 1 to 1, and the operations $+$
   and $\cdot$ to $+$ and $\cdot$.

+	0	1			0	1
0	0	1		0	0	0
1	1	0		1	0	1

   Show that I is a model for the proper axioms of F.
3. Show that p satisfies $\exists x_k P$ if and only if $p(d/k)$ satisfies P for some
   element d of the domain.
4. Disprove the following: If I is an interpretation for the formulas P
   and Q, then $P \to Q$ is true in I if and only if P is false in I or Q is true
   in I.
5. A formula P is *satisfiable* if and only if there is a point that satisfies
   P.   Let $v_1, \ldots, v_n$ be the free variables of P.   Show that P is
   satisfiable if and only if $\exists v_1 \cdots \exists v_n P$ is satisfiable.
6. Prove that each of the following formulas is valid or give a counter-
   example to show that it is invalid.   Do not use Theorem 17 or its
   lemmas.

   (a) $\forall x_1 A(x_1) \lor \forall x_1 B(x_1) \to \forall x_1(A(x_1) \lor B(x_1))$
   (b) $\exists x_1 A(x_1) \land \exists x_1 B(x_1) \to \exists x_1(A(x_1) \land B(x_1))$
   (c) $\forall x_1 A(x_1) \to A(x_2)$
   (d) $A(x_2) \to \forall x_1 A(x_1)$
   (e) $\exists x_2 \forall x_1 A(x_1, x_2) \to \forall x_1 \exists x_2 A(x_1, x_2)$
   (f) $\forall x_1 \exists x_2 B(x_1, x_2) \to \exists x_2 \forall x_1 B(x_1, x_2)$
   (g) $\forall x_1 A(x_1) \to \forall x_2 A(x_2)$
   (h) $A(x_1) \to A(x_2)$

(i) $A(x_2) \to \exists x_1 A(x_1)$

(j) $\exists x_1 A(x_1) \to A(x_2)$

(k) $\forall x_k (P \to Q) \;.\to.\; \exists x_k P \to \exists x_k Q$

(l) $\forall x_k P \to \forall x_k Q \;.\to.\; \forall x_k (P \to Q)$

(m) $\exists x_k (P \to Q) \;.\to.\; \forall x_k P \to Q$ if x_k is not free in Q

(n) $\forall x_k (P \to Q) \;.\to.\; P \to \forall x_k Q$ if x_k is not free in P

(o) $P(t/x_k) \to \exists x_k P$ if P admits t for x_k

7. Show that no proper axiom of AG is valid.

8. Show that $P \wedge Q$ is true in I if and only if P is true in I and Q is true in I.

27   The Completeness Theorem

From now on T (perhaps with subscripts or primes) stands for a first order theory.

A *model* for T is a model for the set of theorems of T.

THEOREM 1.   *M is a model for* T *if and only if every proper axiom of* T *is true in M.*

Proof. Suppose every proper axiom of T is true in M. Every logical axiom of T is true in M because every logical axiom is valid by Theorem 26.17. Hence every axiom of T is true in M. Then every theorem of T is true in M because modus ponens preserves truth by Theorem 26.6(b). Conversely, if M is a model for T, then every theorem of T is true in M and hence every proper axiom of T is true in M.

THEOREM 2.   *If* T *has a model, then* T *is consistent.*

Proof. Suppose M is a model for T. Suppose for contradiction that T is inconsistent. Let S be a statement of T. Then both S and $\sim S$ are theorems of T. Then both S and $\sim S$ are true in M, contradicting Theorem 26.6(g).

We now begin the proof of the completeness theorem: *Every consistent first order theory has a countable model.*

T' is an *extension* of T if and only if every theorem of T is a theorem of T'.

We note that if T′ is an extension of T, then every model for T′ is also a model for T.   For example, F is an extension of AG, and hence every field is an abelian group.

A term is *closed* if and only if no variables occur in it.

THEOREM 3.   The following sets are countable: the set of formulas of T, the set of statements of T, the set of statements of T that begin with a universal quantifier, and the set of closed terms of T.

Proof.   The formal symbols of the predicate calculus are

$$\sim \quad \rightarrow \quad \forall \quad (\ ; \ ) \quad \alpha \quad \beta \quad \gamma \quad x \quad | \quad \#$$

(We temporarily replace the comma by the semicolon to prevent confusion with commas in the metalanguage.)   We regard these symbols as the letters of an alphabet, with the order above being the alphabetic order.   Thus $\sim$ is the first letter of the alphabet, $\rightarrow$ is the second letter, etc.   We regard each string as a word.   We enumerate the strings as follows.   First we enumerate all the 1-letter words in dictionary order: $\sim, \rightarrow, \forall, \ldots, \#$; then all the 2-letter words in dictionary order

$$\sim\sim, \ \sim\rightarrow, \ldots, \ \sim\#, \ \rightarrow\sim, \ \rightarrow\rightarrow, \ \rightarrow\forall, \ldots, \ \rightarrow\#, \ \forall\sim, \ldots, \ \#\#$$

then all the 3-letter words in dictionary order, and so on, with all the n-letter words following in dictionary order all the words with fewer than n letters.   Every string has a definite position in this sequence. Hence the set of all strings of the predicate calculus is countable. Every formula of T is a string of the predicate calculus.   Then by Theorem 2.4, the set of all formulas of T is countable.   Similarly, the statements of T, the statements of T that begin with a universal quantifier, and the closed terms of T are all countable sets.

THEOREM 4.   *Let T be consistent.   Then T has a consistent and complete extension with the same formulas as T.*

Proof.   Let $P_1, P_2, P_3, \ldots$ be an enumeration of the statements of T.   We define by induction an infinite sequence $T_0, T_1, T_2, \ldots$ of first order theories. T_0 is T.   Suppose that $T_0, T_1, \ldots, T_{n-1}$ have been defined.   Then T_n is the result of adjoining P_n to T_{n-1} as a proper axiom if the result is consistent; otherwise, T_n is T_{n-1}.   Thus for every n, T_n is a consistent extension of T_{n-1}.   Let T′ be the first order theory whose proper axioms are all the proper axioms of all the T_n's. That is, P is a proper axiom of T' if and only if P is a proper axiom of some T_n. T' is an extension of every T_n, and T' has the same formulas as T and every T_n. We show that T' is consistent and complete. Suppose, for contradiction, that T' is not consistent. Then $\vdash_{T'} Q \wedge \sim Q$ for some formula Q. Let $S_1, \ldots, S_m$ be a proof of $Q \wedge \sim Q$ in T', and let $P_1, \ldots, P_j$ be all the distinct steps in the proof that are labeled as proper axioms. By the definition of T', each P_i is a proper axiom of some T_{k_i}. Let n be the largest of the numbers $k_1, k_2, \ldots, k_j$. By the construction of the sequence $T_0, T_1, T_2, \ldots$, each P_i is a proper axiom of T_n. Hence $S_1, \ldots, S_m$ is a proof of $Q \wedge \sim Q$ in T_n, contradicting the consistency of T_n. Now let S be a statement of T'. We show that S or $\sim S$ is a theorem of T'. Since S is a statement of T, S is P_n for some n. Suppose T_n is the result of adjoining P_n to T_{n-1} as a proper axiom. Then P_n is a proper axiom of T', and hence a theorem of T'. Suppose T_n is T_{n-1}. Then the result of adjoining P_n to T_{n-1} is inconsistent. Then by Theorem 25.5, $\vdash_{T_{n-1}} \sim P_n$. Then $\vdash_{T'} \sim P_n$, since T' is an extension of T_{n-1}.

The reason we must contend with first order theories that are not formal is that the proof of Theorem 4 is not constructive: The set of proper axioms of the consistent and complete extension is not effectively given. The set may or may not be decidable.

We may assume that there are infinitely many constant symbols that are not proper symbols of T. For even if T requires an infinite list of constant symbols, we may use the odd-numbered ones, so that the even-numbered ones are not proper symbols of T.

LEMMA 5.   Let $b_1, b_2, \ldots$ be an infinite sequence of constant symbols that are not proper symbols of T. Let T' be the result of adjoining $b_1, b_2, \ldots$ to the set of proper symbols of T. If T is consistent, then so is T'.

Proof.   We proceed by contraposition. Suppose T' is inconsistent. Then by Theorem 25.4 there is a formula Q such that $\vdash_{T'} Q \wedge \sim Q$. Let $S_1, \ldots, S_n$ be a proof of $Q \wedge \sim Q$ in T'. Let $b^1, \ldots, b^m$ be all the distinct new constant symbols that occur in this proof. Let $u_1, \ldots, u_m$ be distinct variables that do not occur in this proof. Let S_i' be the result of replacing each occurrence of b^j in S_i by an occurrence of u_j ($1 \leqslant i \leqslant n$ and $1 \leqslant j \leqslant m$). We show below that $S'_1, \ldots, S'_n$ is a proof in T. Since S'_n is $Q' \wedge \sim Q'$, and Q' is a formula of T, T is inconsistent by Theorem 25.4.

We show that $S'_1, \ldots, S'_n$ is a proof in T by induction on n, but we omit the induction framework and give only the various cases that arise.

Case 1. S_i is a logical axiom that is not an equality axiom. Then S'_i is also a logical axiom, because axiom schemes A1 through A6 are not sensitive to replacing a constant symbol by a new variable.

Case 2. S_i is a proper axiom or an equality axiom. Then S'_i is S_i, because the proper and equality axioms of T' are exactly those of T.

Case 3. S_i is inferred from S_j and $S_j \to S_i$ by modus ponens. Then S'_i is inferred from S'_j and $(S_j \to S_i)'$ by modus ponens, because $(S_j \to S_i)'$ is $S'_j \to S'_i$.

LEMMA 6. *Let $\forall v Q$ be a statement of* T, *and let c be a constant symbol that does not occur in a proper axiom of* T. *Let* T' *be the result of adjoining $Q(c/v) \to \forall v Q$ as a proper axiom to* T. *If* T *is consistent, then so is* T'.

Proof. We proceed by contraposition. Suppose that T' is inconsistent. Then by Theorem 25.5, $\vdash_T \sim(Q(c/v) \to \forall v Q)$. Then by the statement calculus, $\vdash_T Q(c/v)$ and $\vdash_T \sim \forall v Q$. Let $S_1, \ldots, S_n$ be a proof of $Q(c/v)$ in T. Let u be a variable other than v that does not occur in this proof. Then $Q(u/v)$ is similar to Q. For $1 \leqslant i \leqslant n$, let S'_i be the result of replacing each occurrence of c in S_i by an occurrence of u. Then as in the proof of Lemma 5, $S'_1, \ldots, S'_n$ is a proof of $Q(u/v)$ in T. Then gen gives $\vdash_T \forall u Q(u/v)$, and a change of bound variable gives $\vdash_T \forall v Q$. Since $\vdash_T \sim \forall v Q$, T is inconsistent.

T is *closed* if and only if (i) T has at least one closed term, and (ii) for every statement $\forall v Q$ of T that begins with a universal quantifier, $\forall v Q$ is a theorem of T whenever $Q(t/v)$ is a theorem of T for every closed term t of T.

THEOREM 7. *Every consistent first order theory has a consistent, complete, and closed extension.*

Proof. Let T be consistent. Let T_0 be the result of adjoining to T an infinite sequence $b_1, b_2, \ldots$ of new constant symbols. T_0 is consistent by Lemma 5. Let $(\forall v Q)_1, (\forall v Q)_2, \ldots$ be the enumeration given by Theorem 3 of the statements of T_0 that begin with a universal quantifier. For each n, only a finite number of new constant symbols occur in the set $\{(\forall vQ)_1, (\forall vQ)_2, \ldots, (\forall vQ)_n\}$. Hence there is a new constant symbol, call it b^n, that does not occur in this set. We define by induction an infinite sequence $T_0, T_1, \ldots$ of first order theories with the same formulas as T_0. Assuming that T_{n-1} has been defined, then T_n is the result of adjoining $Q(b^n/v) \rightarrow (\forall vQ)_n$ as a proper axiom to T_{n-1}. Then by induction each T_n is consistent, for T_0 is consistent, and if T_{n-1} is consistent, then T_n is consistent by Lemma 6.

Let T' be the theory whose proper axioms are all the proper axioms of all the T_n's. Then exactly as in the proof of Theorem 4, T' is consistent. Then by Theorem 4, T' has a consistent and complete extension T'' with the same formulas as T'. We note that T'', T', and each T_n have exactly the same formulas. We show that T'' is closed. Let $\forall vQ$ be a statement of T'' that begins with a universal quantifier, and suppose that $Q(t/v)$ is a theorem of T'' for every closed term t. $\forall vQ$ is $(\forall vQ)_n$ for some n. $Q(b^n/v) \rightarrow (\forall vQ)_n$ is an axiom of T'' because it is an axiom of T_n and hence of T'. Since b^n is a closed term, $Q(b^n/v)$ is a theorem of T'' by hypothesis. Then $(\forall vQ)_n$ is a theorem of T'' by modus ponens. Hence T'' is a consistent, complete, and closed extension of T.

THEOREM 8.   *Every consistent, complete, and closed first order theory has a countable model.*

Proof. Let T be consistent, complete, and closed. Let a be a closed term of T. Let $[a]$ be the set of all closed terms b of T such that $\vdash_T a = b$. Let M be the interpretation for T defined as follows. The domain D of M consists of all the sets $[a]$. M is countable, for by Theorem 3, the closed terms of T can be enumerated $a_1, a_2, \ldots$. Then the elements of D can be enumerated $[a_1], [a_2], \ldots$. M assigns to the m-place predicate symbol G of T the predicate g, defined by:

$$g([a_1], \ldots, [a_m]) \quad \text{is true if and only if} \quad \vdash_T G(a_1, \ldots, a_m)$$

M assigns to the m-place operation symbol F of T the operation f, defined by: $f([a_1], \ldots, [a_m])$ is $[F(a_1, \ldots, a_m)]$. M assigns to the constant symbol c of T the element $[c]$ of D. Before we go on, we must show that the definitions of g and f make sense. Consider g. Suppose that $[a_i] = [b_i]$ for $1 \leqslant i \leqslant m$. Then $g([a_1], \ldots, [a_m])$ is the same as $g([b_1], \ldots, [b_m])$. Then we must show that $\vdash_T G(a_1, \ldots, a_m)$ if and only if $\vdash_T G(b_1, \ldots, b_m)$. b_i is in $[b_i]$ because $\vdash_T b_i = b_i$. Then b_i is in $[a_i]$

since $[a_i] = [b_i]$. Hence $\vdash_T a_i = b_i$. E2 gives $\vdash_T a_1 = b_1 \wedge \cdots \wedge a_m = b_m \cdot \rightarrow . \, G(a_1, \ldots, a_m) \leftrightarrow G(b_1, \ldots, b_m)$. Then the statement calculus gives $\vdash_T G(a_1, \ldots, a_m) \leftrightarrow G(b_1, \ldots, b_m)$. Then by the statement calculus again, $\vdash_T G(a_1, \ldots, a_m)$ if and only if $\vdash_T G(b_1, \ldots, b_m)$. Hence the definition of g makes sense. Similarly, using E3 in place of E2, the definition of f makes sense.

Let P be a statement of T, and let n be the number of symbols in P, counting each occurrence of $\sim$, $\rightarrow$, or $\forall$ as a symbol. We prove by induction on n that P is true in M if and only if $\vdash_T P$. Then M is a model for T. For if Q is a theorem of T, then so is its closure, and Q is true in M if and only if its closure is true in M.

Basis. If $n = 0$, then P is an atomic statement $G(a_1, \ldots, a_m)$ where G is an m-place predicate symbol and $a_1, \ldots, a_m$ are closed terms. First we show that $p(a) = [a]$ for every point p and every closed term a. If a is a constant symbol, then $p(a) = [a]$ by the definition of M. Suppose $p(a_1) = [a_1], \ldots, p(a_k) = [a_k]$, and a is $F(a_1, \ldots, a_k)$, where F is an operation symbol. Then

$$p(a) = p(F(a_1, \ldots, a_k)) = f(p(a_1), \ldots, p(a_k))$$
$$= f([a_1], \ldots, [a_k]) = (\text{by the definition of } M) \, [F(a_1, \ldots, a_k)] = [a]$$

We prove the basis step. Suppose $\vdash_T P$. Then $g([a_1], \ldots, [a_m])$ is true by the definition of M. Let p be a point. p satisfies P if and only if $g(p(a_1), \ldots, p(a_m)) = g([a_1], \ldots, [a_m])$ is true. Hence every point satisfies P, and P is true in M. If P is not a theorem of T, then $g([a_1], \ldots, [a_m])$ is false, and hence no point satisfies P, i.e., P is false in M.

Induction step. Assume that P is true in M if and only if $\vdash_T P$ for every statement P with n or fewer symbols, and consider a statement P with $n + 1$ symbols.

Case 1. P is $\sim Q$ for some Q. Suppose P is true in M. Then Q is false in M. Then Q is not a theorem of T by the induction hypothesis. Then $\vdash_T \sim Q$ because T is complete. Suppose that P is false in M. Then Q is true in M. Then $\vdash_T Q$ by the induction hypothesis. Then $\sim Q$ is not a theorem of T because T is consistent.

Case 2. P is $Q \rightarrow R$ for some Q and R. Suppose that P is true in M. Then Q is false in M or R is true in M. By the induction hypothesis, Q is not a theorem of T or R is a theorem of T. Suppose that Q is not a theorem of T. Then $\vdash_T \sim Q$ because T is complete. $\sim Q \rightarrow (Q \rightarrow R)$ is a theorem of T because it is a tautology. Then $\vdash_T Q \rightarrow R$ by modus ponens. Suppose that R is a theorem of T. $R \rightarrow (Q \rightarrow R)$ is a theorem of T because it is a tautology. Then $\vdash_T Q \to R$ by modus ponens. Hence if P is true in M, then $\vdash_T P$. Now suppose that P is false in M. Then Q is true in M and R is false in M. By the induction hypothesis, Q is a theorem of T and R is not a theorem of T. Then $\sim R$ is a theorem of T because T is complete. $Q \to . \sim R \to \sim (Q \to R)$ is a theorem of T because it is a tautology. Then two applications of modus ponens give $\vdash_T \sim (Q \to R)$. Then $Q \to R$ is not a theorem of T because T is consistent.

Case 3. P is $\forall x_k Q$ for some k and Q. Let a be a closed term of T. Q admits a for x_k. Suppose P is true in M. $\forall x_k Q \to Q(a/x_k)$ is true in M because it is valid by Lemma 25.15. Then $Q(a/x_k)$ is true in M because modus ponens preserves truth. Then $\vdash_T Q(a/x_k)$ by the induction hypothesis. Then $\vdash_T \forall x_k Q$ because T is closed and a is arbitrary. Suppose $\vdash_T P$. Then $\vdash_T Q(a/x_k)$ by spec. Then $Q(a/x_k)$ is true in M by the induction hypothesis. Let p be a point. Then p satisfies $Q(a/x_k)$. Let $p' = p(p(a)/k)$. Then p' satisfies Q by Lemma 26.14. We have shown that $p(a) = [a]$. Hence $p' = p([a]/k)$. Therefore $p([a]/k)$ satisfies Q. Since $[a]$ is an arbitrary element of the domain, p satisfies $\forall x_k Q$. Since p is arbitrary, $\forall x_k Q$ is true in M.

THEOREM 9. (*The completeness theorem.*) *Every consistent first order theory has a countable model.*

Proof. Let T be consistent. Then T has a consistent, complete, and closed extension T′ by Theorem 7. T′ has a countable model M by Theorem 8. M is a model for T because T′ is an extension of T.

THEOREM 10. *A first order theory is consistent if and only if it has a model.*

Proof. Theorem 2 and the completeness theorem.

Recall that T is complete relative to the set X of formulas of T if and only if every formula of X is in T. A significant choice of X is the set of formulas true in every model for T. For example, if Q is a formula of AG that is true in every abelian group, then we expect Q to be a theorem of AG. Indeed, if Q were not a theorem of AG, we would be compelled to strengthen the predicate calculus to make it a theorem of AG. The theorem below states that the predicate calculus is strong enough: Every first order theory is complete relative to its set of formulas true in every model.

THEOREM 11. *Let Q be a formula of* T. *If Q is true in every model for* T, *then Q is a theorem of* T.

Proof. Suppose that Q is true in every model for T. First suppose Q is a statement. Let T′ be the result of adjoining $\sim Q$ to T as a proper axiom. If M is a model for T′, then both Q and $\sim Q$ are true in M, which is impossible. Therefore T′ has no model. Then T′ is inconsistent by the completeness theorem. Hence $\vdash_T \sim\sim Q$ by Theorem 25.5 Then $\vdash_T Q$ by the statement calculus. If Q is not a statement, then the closure Q^* of Q is true in every model for T by Theorem 26.6(c). Hence $\vdash_T Q^*$ since Q^* is a statement. Therefore $\vdash_T Q$ by spec.

THEOREM 12. *Every valid formula is a theorem of the predicate calculus.*

Proof. Suppose Q is valid. Then Q is true in every model for the predicate calculus. The predicate calculus is a first order theory. Hence $\vdash Q$ by Theorem 11.

Theorem 12 says that the predicate calculus is complete relative to the set of valid formulas. The completeness theorem, which apparently says nothing about completeness, bears that name because Theorems 11 and 12, which are completeness theorems, follow immediately from it.

THEOREM 13. *A formula is valid if and only if it is a theorem of the predicate calculus.*

Proof. Theorem 12 and Theorem 26.17.

THEOREM 14. *If Q is a formula of* T *that is a theorem of the predicate calculus, then Q is a theorem of* T.

Proof. Suppose Q is a formula of T that is a theorem of the predicate calculus. Then Q is valid by Theorem 13. Hence Q is true in every model for T. Then Q is a theorem of T by Theorem 11.

Theorem 14 says that every first order theory is self-contained with respect to the predicate calculus.

THEOREM 15 (*The Löwenheim–Skolem theorem*).   *If* T *has a model, then* T *has a countable model.*

Proof.   Theorem 2 and the completeness theorem.

THEOREM 16 (*The compactness theorem*).   *If every finite set of proper axioms of* T *has a model, then* T *has a model.*

Proof.   The proof is by contraposition.   Suppose T has no model. Then T is inconsistent by the completeness theorem.   Hence there is a formula Q such that $\vdash_T Q \wedge \sim Q$.   By Theorem 22.1 there is a finite set $\{P_1, \ldots, P_k\}$ of proper axioms of T such that $P_1, \ldots, P_k \vdash Q \wedge \sim Q$. Let $\{P_1, \ldots, P_k\}$ be the set of proper axioms of T'.   Then $\vdash_{T'} Q \wedge \sim Q$ by Theorem 22.1.   Hence T' is inconsistent.   Therefore T' has no model by Theorem 2.   Hence $\{P_1, \ldots, P_k\}$ has no model by Theorem 1.

For each positive integer $n \geqslant 2$, let $\exists n$ be the statement

$$\exists x_1 \exists x_2 \cdots \exists x_n (x_1 \neq x_2 \wedge x_1 \neq x_3 \wedge \cdots \wedge$$
$$x_1 \neq x_n \wedge x_2 \neq x_3 \wedge \cdots \wedge x_2 \neq x_n \wedge \cdots \wedge x_{n-1} \neq x_n)$$

For example, $\exists 3$ is $\exists x_1 \exists x_2 \exists x_3 (x_1 \neq x_2 \wedge x_1 \neq x_3 \wedge x_2 \neq x_3)$. $\exists n$ is true in an interpretation I if and only if the domain of I has at least n elements.   If $n \geqslant k$, then $\vdash \exists n \rightarrow \exists k$.

THEOREM 17.   *Suppose that for every positive integer* n, T *has a model with at least* n *elements.   Then* T *has an infinite model.*

Proof.   Let T' be the result of adjoining all the $\exists n$ statements as proper axioms to T.   Let X be any finite set of proper axioms of T'. Because X is finite, there is a greatest positive integer n such that $\exists n$ is in X.   Let M be a model for T with at least n elements.   Then M is a model for X.   Then T' has a model M' by the compactness theorem. M' is a model for T, and M' is infinite because every statement $\exists n$ is true in M'.

EXERCISES

1. Use Theorems 1 and 2 to show that AG, L, and F are consistent.
2. The ordering in the proof of Theorem 3 is not exactly the usual dictionary ordering, because, e.g., it would place *be* before *ask*.

State why the usual dictionary ordering does not yield a proof of Theorem 3.

3. Let M be a model for T.   Let the theorems of T′ be precisely the formulas of T that are true in M.   Show that T′ is a consistent and complete extension of T.

4. Prove that a formula Q of T is a theorem of T if and only if Q is a theorem of every consistent and complete extension of T.

5. Let T be consistent and complete, and let M be a model for T. Without using the completeness theorem, prove that a formula Q of T is a theorem of T if and only if it is true in M.

6. Show that AG is not closed.

7. Prove that if a formula Q of T is true in every countable model for T, then $\vdash_{\mathrm{T}} Q$.

8. Derive the completeness theorem from Theorem 11 and the Löwenheim–Skolem theorem.

9. Derive the completeness theorem for finitely axiomatized theories from Theorems 12 and 14 and the Löwenheim–Skolem theorem.

10. Derive the completeness theorem from the compactness theorem, the Löwenheim–Skolem theorem, and the completeness theorem for finitely axiomatized theories.

11. Let T be finitely axiomatized, and let $P_1, \ldots, P_k$ be the proper axioms of T.   Prove that $\vdash_{\mathrm{T}} Q$ if and only if $P_1 \wedge \cdots \wedge P_k \to Q$ is valid.

12. Prove that $\vdash_{\mathrm{T}} Q$ if and only if there is a finite set $\{P_1, \ldots, P_j\}$ of proper axioms of T such that $P_1 \wedge \cdots \wedge P_j \to Q$ is valid.

13. Let $P_1, P_2, \ldots$ be an infinite sequence of statements of T.   Let T′ be the result of adjoining all the P_i's as proper axioms to T.   Prove that Q is true in every model for T′ if and only if there is a finite set $\{P_{i_1}, \ldots, P_{i_j}\}$ of P_i's such that $P_{i_1} \wedge \cdots \wedge P_{i_j} \to Q$ is true in every model for T.

14. Prove that if Q is a formula of the theory of fields that is true in every field of characteristic zero, then there is a prime p (depending on Q) such that Q is true in every field of characteristic greater than p.

28   Independence

A proper axiom S of T is *independent* if and only if S is not provable from the other axioms of T.

From previous theorems it follows immediately that if T is consistent, then S is independent if and only if there is a model for the other proper axioms of T in which S is false.

EXAMPLE 1.   L1 is an independent proper axiom of L.   Let the domain of M consist of a alone, and let $<$ be defined in M by $a < a = T$. Then L2 and L3 are true in M, but L1 is false in M.

EXAMPLE 2.   In the theory F of fields, the commutative law of addition $\forall x \forall y(x + y = y + x)$ is dependent (i.e., not independent).   We sketch an informal proof of $\forall x \forall y(x + y = y + x)$, using some theorems of F which can be proved from the other axioms of F.

$$(x + y)(1 + 1) = (x + y)1 + (x + y)1 = x + y + x + y$$

Distributing in another way,

$$(x + y)(1 + 1) = x(1 + 1) + y(1 + 1)$$
$$= x1 + x1 + y1 + y1 = x + x + y + y$$

Hence $x + x + y + y = x + y + x + y$.   The cancellation law applied on the left gives $x + y + y = y + x + y$.   Then the cancellation law applied on the right gives $x + y = y + x$.

Independence of all the proper axioms is a matter of elegance, not necessity.   A dependent axiom does no real harm; it is merely superfluous.

EXAMPLE 3.   The two distributive laws for the theory R of rings are

  R6. $\forall x \forall y \forall z(x(y + z) = xy + xz)$
  R7. $\forall x \forall y \forall z((y + z)x = yx + zx)$

It is customary to define a commutative ring to be a ring that satisfies the additional property

  R8. $\forall x \forall y(xy = yx)$

In the theory of commutative rings, R6 and R7 are dependent because each can be proved from the other by R8.   (See Theorem 23.7.)   But as soon as R6 or R7 is omitted, the other one becomes independent. An axiom is not dependent or independent by itself, but relative to a set of axioms.

Independence makes sense for all axiomatic theories.   The classic example of an independent axiom is Euclid's fifth postulate.   A non-Euclidean geometry is a model for geometry in which the fifth postulate is false and all the other axioms are true.

The preceding discussion is concerned with a statement that is already an axiom. Now suppose a statement is not an axiom but is being considered as a possible axiom.

The statement S of T is *consistent with* T if and only if the result of adjoining S to T as a proper axiom is consistent. For example, the statement $\forall x \forall y (xy = yx)$ of the theory G of groups is consistent with G because there is an abelian group.

The statement S of T is *independent of* T if and only if both S and $\sim S$ are consistent with T. For example, the statement $\forall x \forall y (x = y)$ of AG is independent of AG because there is an abelian group with exactly one element, and there is an abelian group with more than one element.

An important example of an independent statement is the statement of set theory called *the axiom of choice*. The axiom of choice states that for every nonempty set $\mathscr{A}$ of nonempty sets, there is a function that assigns to each set A in $\mathscr{A}$ an element of A. Because the consistency of set theory has not been proved, a more precise statement of this result is: If set theory is consistent, then the axiom of choice is independent. A famous independent statement of number theory is discussed in Section 31.

A proper symbol may be dependent.

An n-place predicate symbol G of T is *dependent* if and only if there is a formula $P(x_1, \ldots, x_n)$ of T whose free variables are exactly $x_1, \ldots, x_n$, such that G does not occur in P and

$$\vdash_T \forall x_1 \cdots \forall x_n (G(x_1, \ldots, x_n) \leftrightarrow P(x_1, \ldots, x_n))$$

EXAMPLE 4.   BA* is the result of adjoining to BA the 2-place predicate symbol $\leqslant$ and the following proper axioms:

BA12. $\forall x \forall y \forall z (x \leqslant y \wedge y \leqslant z \to x \leqslant z)$
BA13. $\forall x \forall y (x \leqslant y \wedge y \leqslant x \to x = y)$
BA14. $\forall x \forall y \forall z (x \leqslant y \to x \cup z \leqslant y \cup z)$
BA15. $\forall x \forall y \forall z (x \leqslant y \to x \cap z \leqslant y \cap z)$
BA16. $\forall x \forall y (x \leqslant y \to y' \leqslant x')$

The predicate symbol $\leqslant$ is dependent because

$$\vdash_{BA*} \forall x_1 \forall x_2 (x_1 \leqslant x_2 \leftrightarrow x_1 \cup x_2 = x_2)$$

An n-place operation symbol F of T is *dependent* if and only if there is a formula $P(x_1, \ldots, x_n, x_{n+1})$ of T whose free variables are exactly $x_1, \ldots, x_n, x_{n+1}$ such that F does not occur in P and

$$\vdash_T \forall x_1 \cdots \forall x_{n+1}(F(x_1, \ldots, x_n) = x_{n+1} \leftrightarrow P(x_1, \ldots, x_n, x_{n+1}))$$

EXAMPLE 5.   AG′ is the result of adjoining to AG the 1-place operation symbol $-$ and replacing AG3 by

AG3′. $\forall x(x + (-x) = 0)$

The operation symbol $-$ is dependent because

$$\vdash_{AG'} \forall x_1 \forall x_2(-x_1 = x_2 \leftrightarrow x_1 + x_2 = 0)$$

EXAMPLE 6.   In the theory LA of lattices, $\cup$ is dependent because

$$\vdash_{LA} \forall x_1 \forall x_2 \forall x_3(x_1 \cup x_2 = x_3 \leftrightarrow x_1 \leqslant x_3 \wedge x_2 \leqslant x_3$$
$$\wedge \ \forall x_4(x_1 \leqslant x_4 \wedge x_2 \leqslant x_4 \rightarrow x_3 \leqslant x_4))$$

Similarly, $\cap$ is dependent in LA.

EXAMPLE 7.   In the theory R of rings, the operation symbol $\cdot$ is independent.   Let M_1 be the interpretation for R in the integers with the usual meaning of $+$, $\cdot$, and 0.   Let M_2 be the same as M_1 except that M_2 assigns to $\cdot$ the operation $\circ$ defined by $a \circ b = 0$ for all integers a and b. M_1 and M_2 are models for R.   Suppose for contradiction that $\cdot$ is dependent.   Then there is a formula $P(x_1, x_2, x_3)$ of R such that $\cdot$ does not occur in P and $\vdash_R \forall x_1 \forall x_2 \forall x_3(x_1 \cdot x_2 = x_3 \leftrightarrow P(x_1, x_2, x_3))$. Then $x_1 \cdot x_2 = x_3 \leftrightarrow P(x_1, x_2, x_3)$ is true in both M_1 and M_2.   Let $p = (2, 3, 6, \ldots)$ be a point whose first three coordinates are 2, 3, 6. Then p satisfies $x_1 \cdot x_2 = x_3 \leftrightarrow P(x_1, x_2, x_3)$. p satisfies $x_1 \cdot x_2 = x_3$ in M_1 because $2 \cdot 3 = 6$ in the ring of integers.   Hence p satisfies $P(x_1, x_2, x_3)$ in M_1. p does not satisfy $x_1 \cdot x_2 = x_3$ in M_2 because $2 \circ 3 \neq 6$.   Hence p does not satisfy $P(x_1, x_2, x_3)$ in M_2.   But $\cdot$ does not occur in $P(x_1, x_2, x_3)$, and M_1 and M_2 are identical except for $\cdot$. Therefore p satisfies $P(x_1, x_2, x_3)$ in M_1 if and only if p satisfies $P(x_1, x_2, x_3)$ in M_2.   This contradiction shows that $\cdot$ is independent in R, i.e., it cannot be defined from the other proper symbols of R.

A constant symbol c of T is *dependent* if and only if there is a formula $P(x_1)$ of T with exactly one free variable x_1 such that c does not occur in P and $\vdash_T \forall x_1(c = x_1 \leftrightarrow P(x_1))$.

EXAMPLE 8. The constant symbol 0 of AG is dependent because

$$\vdash_{AG} \forall x_1(0 = x_1 \leftrightarrow \forall x_2(x_2 + x_1 = x_2))$$

Many theories have dependent operation and constant symbols because it is more intuitive to work with the operation or constant symbol than with a formula. For example, a theorem of AG is

$$\forall x \exists! y(x + y = 0) \tag{1}$$

Let AG* be the result of adjoining to AG the 1-place operation symbol − and the proper axiom

$$\forall x(x + (-x) = 0) \tag{2}$$

In working with AG informally, it is customary after proving (1) to introduce the notation $-x$ and to note (2). The formal counterpart is to extend AG to AG*. Similarly, in other first order theories it is customary to adjoin new operation symbols and proper axioms after justifying theorems of the form (1) have been proved. This is especially true in number theory, where there are many familiar operations (e.g., $n!$ and n^m) for which no operation symbol occurs in the axioms. This procedure is justified because all the successive extensions are essentially the same theory. As an example we show exactly how AG* is related to AG.

First, − is dependent in AG* because

$$\vdash_{AG*} \forall x_1 \forall x_2(-x_1 = x_2 \leftrightarrow x_1 + x_2 = 0)$$

Second, (2) cannot be proved in AG (even if − is adjoined) because − does not occur in any proper axiom. Third, AG and AG* have essentially the same models. More precisely, every model for AG* is a model for AG because AG* is an extension of AG, and every model for AG can be extended to a model for AG* as follows. Let M be a model for AG with domain D, and let M assign a to 0. Because (1) is true in M, for every element d of D there is a unique element d' of D such that $d + d' = a$. Define the 1-place operation − in D by $-d = d'$. Let M^* be the same as M, except that M^* assigns − to the operation symbol − of AG*. Then M^* is a model for AG*. We conclude that for practical purposes AG and AG* are two formulations of the same theory.

EXERCISES

1. Prove that if T is consistent, then the proper axiom S of T is independent if and only if there is a model for the other proper axioms of T in which S is false.

2. Show that all the proper axioms of AG are independent.

3. Show that all the proper axioms of L are independent.

4. Show that the proper axiom $0 \neq 1$ of the theory F of fields is independent.

5. Let T be finitely axiomatized with at least one proper axiom. Show that there is a theory T′ with the same formulas and theorems as T which has only one proper axiom.

6. Prove that the statement S of T is consistent with T if and only if $\sim S$ is not a theorem of T.

7. Prove that T is complete if and only if there is no statement of T that is independent of T.

8. Prove that the statement S of T is independent of T if and only if there exist models M_1 and M_2 for T such that S is true in M_1 and false in M_2.

9. Let p and q be distinct primes. Show that $p = 0 \land q = 0$ is not consistent with F.

10. Show that the statement $1 + 1 = 0$ is independent of F.

11. The theory OAG of ordered abelian groups has the proper symbols $=$, $+$, 0, and $<$, and the proper axioms AG1 through AG4, L1 through L3, and

   OAG8. $\forall x \forall y \forall z(x < y \to x + z < y + z)$

   Show that $<$ is independent in OAG.

12. Give without proof a theorem of BA that shows that the operation symbol $\cap$ is dependent.

13. Let F* be the result of adjoining to F the 1-place operation symbol ′ and the proper axiom

   F11. $\forall x(x \neq 0 \to x \cdot x' = 1)$

   Show that every model for F can be extended to a model for F*. Discuss $0'$.

14. Formulate the theory of fields, using only the proper symbols $=$, $+$, and $\cdot$.

29   Completeness and Categoricity

THEOREM 1.   T *is complete if and only if every statement of* T *that is true in one model for* T *is true in every model for* T.

Proof.   Suppose T is complete, and S is a statement of T that is true in the model M for T.   We show that S is true in every model for T. Suppose for contradiction that S is not true in the model M' for T. Then S is not a theorem of T by Theorem 27.11.   Similarly, $\sim S$ is not a theorem of T because $\sim S$ is not true in M.   Hence neither S nor $\sim S$ is a theorem of T, contradicting the completeness of T.   Now suppose that every statement of T that is true in one model for T is true in every model for T.   If T is inconsistent, then T is complete.   So suppose that T is consistent.   Let S be a statement of T.   Since T is consistent, T has a model M by the completeness theorem. S or $\sim S$ is true in M.   By hypothesis, S or $\sim S$ is true in every model for T.   Hence S or $\sim S$ is a theorem of T by Theorem 27.11.   Since S is arbitrary, T is complete.

EXAMPLE 2.   AG is not complete because the statement $\forall x \forall y (x = y)$ is true in a model with exactly one element and is false in a model with more than one element.

Let M and M' be models for T with domains D and D'.   For each predicate symbol G of T, let g and g' be the predicates assigned to G by M and M'.   For each operation symbol F of T, let f and f' be the operations assigned to F by M and M'. M is *isomorphic* to M' if and only if there is a 1–1 correspondence between D and D' (say d is paired off with d') such that for every n-tuple $(d_1, \ldots, d_n)$ of elements of D and every predicate symbol G of T and every operation symbol F of T and every constant symbol c of T and every element d of D, $g(d_1, \ldots, d_n) = T$ if and only if $g'(d'_1, \ldots, d'_n) = T$, and $f(d_1, \ldots, d_n) = d$ if and only if $f'(d'_1, \ldots, d'_n) = d'$, and M assigns d to c if and only if M' assigns d' to c.

If M is isomorphic to M', then for practical purposes M and M' are the same.   In particular, a formula of T is true in M if and only if it is true in M'.   (See Exercise 8.)   When we say that all models of a given set of models are isomorphic, we mean that for every M and M' in the set, M is isomorphic to M'.

T is *categorical* if and only if all models for T are isomorphic.

The familiar algebraic theories are not categorical because they have models with different numbers of elements. One advantage of the axiomatic approach in algebra is that one theorem establishes a true formula in each of many different models.

The obvious way to make a theory categorical is to pile on axioms until only one model remains. (This must be done with some care to avoid reducing the number of models to zero.) Axioms fixing the number of elements in a model sometimes make a theory categorical.

Let $\exists!n$ be the statement

$$\exists x_1 \cdots \exists x_n (x_1 \neq x_2 \wedge \cdots \wedge x_1 \neq x_n \wedge x_2 \neq x_3 \wedge \cdots \wedge x_2 \neq x_n$$
$$\wedge \cdots \wedge x_{n-1} \neq x_n \wedge \forall y(y = x_1 \vee y = x_2 \vee \cdots \vee y = x_n))$$

Thus $\exists!3$ is

$$\exists x_1 \exists x_2 \exists x_3 (x_1 \neq x_2 \wedge x_1 \neq x_3 \wedge x_2 \neq x_3$$
$$\wedge \forall y(y = x_1 \vee y = x_2 \vee y = x_3))$$

Every model for $\exists!n$ has exactly n elements.

EXAMPLE 3.   Let AG_2 be the result of adjoining $\exists!2$ to AG as a proper axiom, and let AG_4 be the result of adjoining $\exists!4$ to AG as a proper axiom.   Then AG_2 is categorical, and AG_4 is not categorical.

Proof.   Let M_1 be the model for AG_2 defined below.

+	0	1
0	0	1
1	1	0

Let M_2 be a model for AG_2 with elements a and b, and let M_2 assign a to 0.   Then $a + a = a$ and $b + a = b$, because AG2 is true in M_2. Then $a + b = b$, because AG4 is true in M_2.   We assert that $b + b = a$, for if $b + b = b$, then there is no y such that $b + y = a$, contradicting the fact that AG3 is true in M_2.   Therefore M_2 is defined by

+	a	b
a	a	b
b	b	a

If a is paired off with 0, and b is paired off with 1, the tables for M_1 and

M_2 correspond entry by entry, showing that M_1 and M_2 are isomorphic. Since M_2 is arbitrary, every model for AG_2 is isomorphic to M_1. Hence AG_2 is categorical.

Straightforward computation shows that M_3 and M_4 are models for AG_4, where M_3 assigns 0 to 0, and M_4 assigns a to 0.

M_3				
+	0	1	2	3
0	0	1	2	3
1	1	2	3	0
2	2	3	0	1
3	3	0	1	2

M_4				
+	a	b	c	d
a	a	b	c	d
b	b	a	d	c
c	c	d	a	b
d	d	c	b	a

M_3 is not isomorphic to M_4 because the statement $\forall x(x + x = 0)$ is true in M_4 and is false in M_3.

THEOREM 4.   *If* T *is categorical, then* T *is complete.*

Proof.   Suppose T is categorical.   Then every statement of T that is true in one model for T is true in every model for T.   Then T is complete by Theorem 1.

EXAMPLE 5.   The theory DL (Example 22.12) is complete but not categorical.   Axiom L4 (in conjunction with L1 through L3) forces every model for DL to be infinite.   The rationals and the reals with the usual meaning of < are models for DL.   Since the rationals are countable and the reals are uncountable, DL is not categorical. By a theorem of Cantor, all countable infinite models for DL are isomorphic to the rationals.   We use Cantor's theorem to show that DL is complete.   Let S be a statement of DL.   Let T_1 be the result of adjoining S as a proper axiom to DL, and let T_2 be the result of adjoining $\sim S$ as a proper axiom to DL.   We assert that T_1 or T_2 is inconsistent.   Then $\vdash_{DL}\sim S$ or $\vdash_{DL}\sim\sim S$ by Theorem 25.5.   Hence $\vdash_{DL}\sim S$ or $\vdash_{DL}S$ by the statement calculus, and DL is complete. Suppose to the contrary that T_1 and T_2 are consistent.   Then T_1 and T_2 have countable models M_1 and M_2 by the completeness theorem. M_1 and M_2 are models for DL since T_1 and T_2 are extensions of DL. M_1 and M_2 are countable infinite because all models for DL are infinite. S is true in M_1 and false in M_2. This is impossible because M_1 and M_2 are isomorphic by Cantor's theorem. Hence DL is complete.

Some of the most interesting results about completeness and categoricity require some knowledge of cardinal numbers and transfinite methods. Intuitively, the cardinal number of a set is the number of elements in the set. The cardinal number of a finite set is a nonnegative integer. The cardinal number of an infinite set is called a *transfinite cardinal number*. Every set A has a unique cardinal number $\bar{\bar{A}}$. $\bar{\bar{A}} = \bar{\bar{B}}$ if and only if there is a 1–1 correspondence between A and B. $\bar{\bar{A}} \leqslant \bar{\bar{B}}$ if and only if there is a 1–1 correspondence between A and a subset of B. $\bar{\bar{A}} < \bar{\bar{B}}$ if and only if $\bar{\bar{A}} \leqslant \bar{\bar{B}}$ and $\bar{\bar{A}} \neq \bar{\bar{B}}$. The Schröder–Bernstein theorem: if $\bar{\bar{A}} \leqslant \bar{\bar{B}}$ and $\bar{\bar{B}} \leqslant \bar{\bar{A}}$, then $\bar{\bar{A}} = \bar{\bar{B}}$. All countable infinite sets have the same cardinal number ω.

Shortly we shall discuss theories with uncountable sets of proper symbols. For the moment we assume without proof that the compactness theorem applies to such theories.

THEOREM 6.   *Let* T *have an infinite model* M. *Then for every transfinite cardinal number* $\mathscr{C}$, T *has a model with at least* $\mathscr{C}$ *elements.*

Proof. Let A be a set with cardinal number $\mathscr{C}$. Let T′ be the result of adjoining to T one new constant symbol for each element of A, and adjoining to T one new proper axiom $a \neq b$ for each pair $\{a, b\}$ of distinct new constant symbols. Let X be any finite subset of the proper axioms of T′. Let $a_1, \ldots, a_n$ be all the distinct new constant symbols that occur in X. Let $M′$ be the same as M except that $M′$ assigns a different element of the domain to each a_i. This is always possible because M is infinite. Then $M′$ is a model for X. Hence T′ has a model M_1 by the compactness theorem. M_1 is a model for T because T′ is an extension of T. The cardinal number of M_1 is at least $\mathscr{C}$, because each new proper axiom $a \neq b$ is true in M_1.

Theorem 6 applies to many theories, including AG, L, R, and F.

THEOREM 7.   *If first order number theory is consistent, then it is not categorical.*

Proof. Suppose N is consistent. Then N has a countable model M by the completeness theorem. The proper axioms of N force every model to be infinite. Then by Theorem 6, N has a model M' whose cardinal number is at least the cardinal number of the reals. Hence N is not categorical, since M is countable and M' is uncountable.

First order number theory is intended to be categorical. We want the nonnegative integers, with the usual meaning of $+$, $\cdot$, $'$, and 0, to be the one and only model (except for isomorphic copies). But no matter how many axioms are adjoined to N, Theorem 7 still applies, and the resulting theory is not categorical if it is consistent.

A set is *well-ordered* if and only if it is linearly ordered and every nonempty subset has a smallest element, i.e., has an element a such that $a \leqslant b$ for every b in the subset. If A is well-ordered, and B is a subset of A such that for every x in A, x is in B whenever every y less than x is in B, then $B = A$ (*transfinite induction*). For every cardinal number $\mathscr{C}$, there is a well-ordered set of cardinal number $\mathscr{C}$. (The proof of this statement uses the axiom of choice.)

A *generalized first order theory* is like a first order theory except that it may have an uncountable set of proper symbols. A generalized first order theory with an uncountable set of proper symbols is not formal because the notion of formula is not effective. The theory T$'$ in the proof of Theorem 6 is such a theory. The next theorem extends the completeness theorem to generalized first order theories. We restrict our attention to theories whose sets of proper symbols are well-ordered. For such theories, all the sets of Theorem 27.3 are well-ordered.

THEOREM 8. *Let* T *be a generalized first order theory, and let* $\mathscr{C}$ *be the cardinal number of the set of proper symbols of* T. *Then* T *has a model with at most* $\mathscr{C}$ *elements if* $\mathscr{C}$ *is transfinite.*

Proof. The proofs of Theorems and Lemmas 3 through 7 in Section 27 go as before, replacing infinite sequences by well-ordered sets of cardinal number $\mathscr{C}$, and ordinary induction by transfinite induction. For example, in the proof of Theorem 7 in Section 27, the infinite sequence of new constant symbols is replaced by a well-ordered set of cardinal number $\mathscr{C}$ of new constant symbols, and the theorem is proved by transfinite induction. The proof of Theorem 8 in Section 27 is the same as before (ordinary induction), but now the model M has at most $\mathscr{C}$ elements instead of at most ω elements.

Because of Theorem 8, all the theorems that follow from the completeness theorem extend to generalized first order theories with exactly the same proofs. In the generalized Löwenheim–Skolem theorem, countable (i.e., $\leqslant \omega$) is replaced by $\leqslant \mathscr{C}$, where $\mathscr{C}$ is the cardinal number of the set of proper symbols of the theory if $\mathscr{C}$ is transfinite.

THEOREM 9. *If* T *has an infinite model, then for every transfinite cardinal number* $\mathscr{C}$, T *has a model with exactly* $\mathscr{C}$ *elements.*

Proof. Suppose T has an infinite model M. Let A be a well-ordered set of cardinal number $\mathscr{C}$. Define T′ as in the proof of Theorem 6. Then exactly as in the proof of Theorem 6, T′ has a model M_1. By the generalized Löwenheim–Skolem theorem, T′ has a model M_2 with at most $\mathscr{C}$ elements. M_2 has at least $\mathscr{C}$ elements because each new proper axiom $a \neq b$ is true in M_2. Hence M_2 has exactly $\mathscr{C}$ elements by the Schröder–Bernstein theorem.

THEOREM 10. *Suppose every model for* T *is infinite, and for some transfinite cardinal number* $\mathscr{C}$, *all models for* T *with cardinal number* $\mathscr{C}$ *are isomorphic. Then* T *is complete.*

Proof. (Compare Example 5.) Let S be a statement of T. Let T_1 be the result of adjoining S as a proper axiom to T, and let T_2 be the result of adjoining $\sim S$ as a proper axiom to T. We assert that T_1 or T_2 is inconsistent. Then $\vdash_T \sim S$ or $\vdash_T S$ by Theorem 25.5 and the statement calculus, and T is complete. Suppose to the contrary that T_1 and T_2 are consistent. Then T_1 and T_2 have models M_1 and M_2 by the completeness theorem. M_1 and M_2 are models for T. Therefore M_1 and M_2 are infinite. Then by Theorem 9, T_1 and T_2 have models M_3 and M_4 of cardinal number $\mathscr{C}$. S is true in M_3 and false in M_4. This is impossible because, being models for T of cardinal number $\mathscr{C}$, M_3 and M_4 are isomorphic.

The theory DL of Example 5 is an example of Theorem 10 in which $\mathscr{C} = \omega$. We give an example in which $\mathscr{C} \neq \omega$.

EXAMPLE 11. Let T be the theory ACF^0 of algebraically closed fields of characteristic zero. We use Theorem 10 to show that T is complete. The complex numbers and the algebraic numbers are models for T. T is not categorical because the complex numbers are uncountable and the algebraic numbers are countable. But since T is complete, every statement of T that is true in the complex numbers is true in the algebraic numbers, and vice versa. All models for T are infinite because every field of characteristic zero is infinite. By a theorem of Steinitz, if $\mathscr{C}$ is a transfinite cardinal number greater than ω, then all algebraically closed fields of characteristic zero of cardinal number $\mathscr{C}$ are isomorphic. Hence T is complete by Theorem 10.

EXERCISES

1. Let AG_3 be the result of adjoining $\exists!3$ to AG as a proper axiom. Show that AG_3 is categorical.
2. Let L_n be the result of adjoining $\exists!n$ to L as a proper axiom. Show that L_n is categorical.
3. Give a statement which when adjoined to T as a proper axiom forces every model for T to have 2, 5, 7, or 13 elements.
4. In AG let nx be an abbreviation for $\underbrace{x + x + \cdots + x}_{n \text{ times}}$. The theory of torsion-free abelian groups is the result of adjoining to AG all the statements $\forall x(nx = 0 \rightarrow x = 0)$ as proper axioms. Is this theory categorical? Why?
5. Let T_n be the result of adjoining $\exists!n$ to T as a proper axiom. Prove that $\vdash_{T_n} Q$ if and only if Q is true in every model for T with exactly n elements.
6. Prove that if T has a model with at least n elements for every positive integer n, then T has a model with exactly $\mathscr{C}$ elements for every transfinite cardinal number $\mathscr{C}$.
7. Prove that T is complete if and only if every statement of T that is true in one countable model for T is true in every countable model for T. State the corresponding theorem for generalized first order theories.
8. Let M and M' be isomorphic models for T with domains D and D'. Let the element d of D be paired off with the element d' of D'. Let $p = (d_1, d_2, \ldots)$ be a point of M, and let $p' = (d_1', d_2', \ldots)$. Let P be a formula of T. Show that p satisfies P if and only if p' satisfies P. Then show that P is true in M if and only if P is true in M'.

30 Decidability

T is *decidable* if and only if there is an effective procedure, called a *decision procedure*, for deciding if an arbitrary formula of T is a theorem of T.   In the language of Section 3, T is decidable if and only if the notion of theorem is effective.   In the language of Section 22, T is decidable if and only if its set of theorems is decidable.

Decidability makes sense for the statement calculus, and the statement calculus is decidable because the method of truth tables is a decision procedure.

THEOREM 1.   *Let* T *be a formal first order theory.   Then the theorems of* T *can be effectively enumerated.*

Proof.   Every formula of T is a string in the 12 formal symbols $\sim \rightarrow \forall (\,,\,) \, \alpha \, \beta \, \gamma \, x \mid \#$.   We add a thirteenth symbol, : , which we use to separate formulas.   We write a proof with steps $S_1, \ldots, S_n$ as $S_1 : S_2 : \cdots : S_n :$.   Then every proof is a string in these 13 symbols.   All the strings in these 13 symbols can be effectively enumerated as in the proof of Theorem 27.3.   We feed each string in turn into a proof-checking machine.   If the string is of the form $S_1 : S_2 : \cdots : S_n :$, the machine splits the string into the substrings $S_1, \ldots, S_n$; otherwise the machine rejects the string.   The machine checks to see if $S_1, \ldots, S_n$ is a proof.   If it is a proof, the machine prints the last step S_n.   Thus the machine prints a sequence $P_1, P_2, \ldots$ of last steps of proofs. Every theorem appears in this sequence at least once because every theorem is the last step of some proof, and every possible proof is examined.

THEOREM 2.   T *is decidable if and only if its theorems can be effectively enumerated and its nontheorems* (*i.e., formulas that are not theorems*) *can be effectively enumerated.*

Proof.   Suppose that T is decidable.   Let $P_1, P_2, \ldots$ be the effective enumeration of the formulas of T given in the proof of Theorem 27.3. The decision-making machine examines each P_i in turn and puts it in list 1 if it is a theorem or in list 2 if it is not a theorem. Then list 1 is an effective enumeration of the theorems of T, and list 2 is an effective enumeration of the nontheorems of T.   Now suppose that $Q_1, Q_2, \ldots$ is an effective enumeration of the theorems of T, and $R_1, R_2, \ldots$ is an effective enumeration of the nontheorems of T.   Let P be any formula of T.   The machine goes through the sequence $Q_1, R_1, Q_2, R_2, \ldots, Q_i, R_i, \ldots$ until it encounters P.   If P is a Q_i, then it is a theorem; if P is an R_i, then it is not a theorem.   Hence T is decidable.

THEOREM 3.   *A formal first order theory is decidable if and only if its nontheorems can be effectively enumerated.*

Proof.   Theorems 1 and 2.

The machines that appear in the proofs of Theorems 1 and 2, and 4 below, are mathematical constructs.   Existing digital computers do not have enough memory to execute these effective procedures.

THEOREM 4.   *If a formal first order theory is complete, then it is decidable.*

Proof.   Let T be a complete formal first order theory.   If T is inconsistent, then T is decidable because every formula of T is a theorem. So suppose that T is consistent.   Let P be a statement of T.   Let $Q_1, Q_2, \ldots$ be the effective enumeration of the theorems of T given by Theorem 1.   The machine examines each Q_i in turn.   If some Q_i is P, then P is a theorem.   If some Q_i is $\sim P$, then P is not a theorem since T is consistent.   Some Q_i is either P or $\sim P$ because T is complete. Hence the machine will decide, after examining a finite number of Q_i's, whether or not P is a theorem.   If P is a formula with free variables, then the machine works with the closure of P, because P is a theorem if and only if its closure is a theorem.

The proof of Theorem 4 brings out an important aspect of the notion of effective procedure.   Although we do not know in advance how many Q_i's have to be examined to reach a decision about P, the procedure is effective because we do know that the decision will be made after examining a finite number of Q_i's.

The theories DL and ACF⁰ proved complete in Examples 29.5 and 29.11 are formal, and hence decidable by Theorem 4.   We give an example of a theory that is decidable but not complete.

EXAMPLE 5.   Let AG_4 be the result of adjoining $\exists!4$ to AG as a proper axiom.   Every model for AG_4 has exactly four elements.   A theorem of algebra states that there are exactly two nonisomorphic abelian groups with four elements.   These are the models M_3 and M_4 of Example 29.3.   A formula P of AG_4 is a theorem of AG_4 if and only if it is true in both M_3 and M_4.   The truth of P in M_3 and M_4 can be effectively checked because M_3 and M_4 are finite.   Hence AG_4 is decidable.   The statement $\forall x(x + x = 0)$ is true in M_4 and false in M_3.   Hence AG_4 is not complete.

Two important decidable first order theories are the theory of abelian groups and the theory of real closed fields.

Some undecidable first order theories are number theory, set theory, the predicate calculus, and the theories of groups, rings, fields, and lattices. A theory is undecidable if and only if it has been proved that no decision procedure exists for it. There are many theories whose decidability is unknown.

T is *essentially undecidable* if and only if T is undecidable, and every consistent extension of T with the same formulas as T is undecidable. The theory Q defined below is essentially undecidable.

Q has the same proper symbols as N, and the following proper axioms:

Q1. $\forall x \forall y(x' = y' \to x = y)$
Q2. $\forall x(x' \neq 0)$
Q3. $\forall x(x = 0 \lor \exists y(x = y'))$
Q4. $\forall x(x + 0 = x)$
Q5. $\forall x \forall y(x + y' = (x + y)')$
Q6. $\forall x(x0 = 0)$
Q7. $\forall x \forall y(xy' = xy + x)$

The decision procedures for the theories of abelian groups and real closed fields use the method of *elimination of quantifiers*. We outline a decision procedure for DL that uses elimination of quantifiers.

Let P be a statement of DL. It suffices to consider statements, because a formula is a theorem if and only if its closure is a theorem. Let T be $\forall x(x = x)$. We show that P is equivalent to T or $\sim T$. If P is equivalent to T, then P is a theorem because T is a theorem. If P is equivalent to $\sim T$, then P is not a theorem because DL is consistent. We use the following theorems of DL. 1 through 12 are theorems of the predicate calculus. Only 13 through 18 depend on the proper axioms of DL. We also use the commutative and associative laws for conjunction and disjunction without explicit mention.

(1) $\sim \sim T \leftrightarrow T$
(2) $T \land P \leftrightarrow P$
(3) $T \lor P \leftrightarrow T$
(4) $\sim T \land P \leftrightarrow \sim T$
(5) $\sim T \lor P \leftrightarrow P$

(6) $\exists v Q \leftrightarrow Q$ if v is not free in Q

(7) $P \wedge (Q \vee R) \leftrightarrow (P \wedge Q) \vee (P \wedge R)$

(8) $\exists v(Q_1 \vee \cdots \vee Q_k) \leftrightarrow \exists v Q_1 \vee \cdots \vee \exists v Q_k$

(9) $\exists v(R \wedge S) \leftrightarrow R \wedge \exists v S$ if v is not free in R

(10) $v = v$

(11) $\exists v(v = u)$

(12) $\exists v(v = u \wedge S) \leftrightarrow S(u/v)$ if S admits u for v

(13) $\sim(v < v)$

(14) $\sim(u = v) \leftrightarrow u < v \vee v < u$

(15) $\sim(u < v) \leftrightarrow u = v \vee v < u$

(16) $\exists v(v < u_1 \wedge v < u_2 \wedge \cdots \wedge v < u_j)$

(17) $\exists v(u_1 < v \wedge u_2 < v \wedge \cdots \wedge u_j < v)$

(18) $\exists v(u_1 < v \wedge u_2 < v \wedge \cdots \wedge u_j < v \wedge v < w_1 \wedge v < w_2 \wedge$
       $\cdots \wedge v < w_k) \leftrightarrow u_1 < w_1 \wedge u_1 < w_2 \wedge \cdots \wedge u_1 < w_k \wedge$
       $u_2 < w_1 \wedge \cdots \wedge u_2 < w_k \wedge \cdots \wedge u_j < w_1 \wedge \cdots \wedge u_j < w_k$

In the steps below, T is regarded as an atomic formula, i.e., the variable x and the quantifier $\forall x$ that occur in T are disregarded.

Step 1. Reduce P to prenex normal form $Z v_1 \cdots Z v_n Q$ and replace each $\forall v_i$ by $\sim \exists v_i \sim$.

Step 2. Let Q' be the formula that comes after $\exists v_n$. (Q' is either Q or $\sim Q$.) In Q', use (10) to replace each subformula $v = v$ by T, and use (13) to replace each subformula $v < v$ by $\sim T$. Let Q'' be the result. If Q'' is T or $\sim T$, use (1) and (6) to reduce P to T or $\sim T$. If Q'' is a tautology or a contradiction, replace it by T or $\sim T$ and use (1) and (6) to reduce P to T or $\sim T$. Otherwise proceed to step 3.

Step 3. Reduce Q'' to disjunctive normal form.

Step 4. Use (14) to replace each subformula $\sim(u = v)$ by $u < v \vee v < u$, and use (15) to replace each subformula $\sim(u < v)$ by $u = v \vee v < u$. Then use (7) to reduce to a formula $Q_1 \vee \cdots \vee Q_k$, where each Q_i is the conjunction of atomic formulas.

Step 5. Use (8) to replace $\exists v_n(Q_1 \vee \cdots \vee Q_k)$ by $\exists v_n Q_1 \vee \cdots \vee \exists v_n Q_k$.

Step 6_1. Eliminate $\exists$ and all occurrences of v_n in $\exists v_n Q_1$ as follows. If v_n is not free in Q_1, use (6) to replace $\exists v_n Q_1$ by Q_1. If v_n is free in Q_1, then Q_1 is $R \wedge S$, where v_n is not free in R and is free in S. Then use (9) to replace $\exists v_n(R \wedge S)$ by $R \wedge \exists v_n S$ and consider S. (If v_n is free in every atomic subformula of Q_1, then R does not exist and S is all of Q_1.)

Case 1. S is $v_n = u$. Then use (11) to replace $\exists v_n S$ by T.

Case 2. S is $v_n = u \wedge S'$. Then use (12) to replace $\exists v_n S$ by $S'(u/v_n)$.

Case 3. $=$ does not occur in S.

Subcase 3.1. S is $v_n < u_1 \wedge v_n < u_2 \wedge \cdots \wedge v_n < u_j$. Then use (16) to replace $\exists v_n S$ by T.

Subcase 3.2. S is $u_1 < v_n < u_2 < v_n \wedge \cdots \wedge u_j < v_n$. Then use (17) to replace $\exists v_n S$ by T.

Subcase 3.3. S is

$$u_1 < v_n \wedge u_2 < v_n \wedge \cdots \wedge u_j < v_n \wedge v_n < w_1$$
$$\wedge \ v_n < w_2 \wedge \cdots \wedge v_n < w_k$$

Then use (18) to replace $\exists v_n S$ by

$$u_1 < w_1 \wedge u_1 < w_2 \wedge \cdots \wedge u_1 < w_k \wedge u_2 < w_1$$
$$\wedge \cdots \wedge u_2 < w_k \wedge \cdots \wedge u_j < w_1 \wedge \cdots \wedge u_j < w_k$$

Step 6_i. Repeat step 6_1 for each Q_i to eliminate $\exists$ and all occurrences of v_n in $\exists v_n Q_1 \vee \cdots \vee \exists v_n Q_k$.

Step 7. Use (1) through (6) as they apply. Then repeat steps 2 through 7 for $v_{n-1}, v_{n-2}, \ldots, v_1$ in turn. The result is a statement in which no quantifiers occur. Since DL has no constant symbols, this statement must be T or $\sim T$.

EXAMPLE 6. We apply the decision procedure for DL to $\exists x \forall y (y < x)$.

Step 1. Replace $\exists x \forall y (y < x)$ by $\exists x \sim \exists y \sim (y < x)$.

Step 2. No change.

Step 3. No change.

Step 4. Replace $\sim (y < x)$ by $y = x \vee x < y$.

Step 5. Replace $\exists y (y = x \vee x < y)$ by $\exists y (y = x) \vee \exists y (x < y)$.

Step 6_1. Replace $\exists y (y = x)$ by T.

Step 6_2. Replace $\exists y (x < y)$ by T.

Step 7. Replace $T \wedge T$ by T. Then replace $\exists x \sim T$ by $\sim T$.

Hence $\exists x \forall y (y < x)$ is not a theorem of DL.

EXERCISES

1. Why doesn't Theorem 1 yield a decision procedure for all formal first order theories?

2. Let T' be the result of adjoining to the proper axioms of T a finite set of statements of T. Prove that if T' is undecidable, then T is undecidable.

3. Give without proof an example of a theory that is undecidable but not essentially undecidable.

4. Assuming that Q is undecidable, prove that the predicate calculus is undecidable.

5. Let T′ be a consistent extension of T. Prove that if T is essentially undecidable, then T′ is essentially undecidable.

6. Assuming that Q is essentially undecidable and N is consistent, prove that N is essentially undecidable.

7. Prove that if T is complete, then the following statements are equivalent: (a) T is undecidable; (b) T is essentially undecidable; (c) T is not formal.

8. Prove that if T is consistent and decidable, then T has a consistent, complete, and decidable extension with the same formulas as T.

9. Prove that T is essentially undecidable if and only if T is consistent and no consistent and complete extension of T with the same formulas as T is formal.

10. Suppose T is finitely axiomatized. Suppose that for some transfinite cardinal number $\mathscr{C}$, T has a model of cardinal number $\mathscr{C}$, and all models for T of cardinal number $\mathscr{C}$ are isomorphic. Prove that T is decidable.

31 Gödel's Theorem

We sketch the proof of Gödel's incompleteness theorem and its corollary. All numbers are nonnegative integers, and all predicates are predicates of numbers. We write the closed terms 0, $0'$, $(0')'$, $((0')')'$, ... of N as $\bar{0}$, $\bar{1}$, $\bar{2}$, $\bar{3}$, ... and call them the *numerals* of N to distinguish them from the corresponding intuitive numbers. If $P(v_1, \ldots, v_n)$ is a formula of N, then $P(\bar{a}_1, \ldots, \bar{a}_n)$ is the result of replacing each free occurrence of v_i in P by an occurrence of the numeral $\bar{a}_i$ (corresponding to the number a_i) for $1 \leqslant i \leqslant n$.

An n-place predicate $\mathscr{P}$ is *expressible* in N if and only if there is a formula $P(v_1, \ldots, v_n)$ of N with exactly n free variables such that for every n-tuple $a_1, \ldots, a_n$ of numbers

(i)   if $\mathscr{P}(a_1, \ldots, a_n)$ is true, then $\vdash_N P(\bar{a}_1, \ldots, \bar{a}_n)$;
(ii) if $\mathscr{P}(a_1, \ldots, a_n)$ is false, then $\vdash_N {\sim} P(\bar{a}_1, \ldots, \bar{a}_n)$.

For example, the predicates $x \leqslant y$, x *is even*, and x *divides y* are expressible in N by the formulas $\exists z(x + z = y)$, $\exists y(x = \bar{2}y)$, and $\exists z(y = zx)$.

An *expression* of N is a string or a finite sequence of strings of N. A *Gödel numbering* for N is a function that assigns to each expression

of N a number, called the *Gödel number* of the expression, such that
(i) there is an effective procedure for computing the Gödel number
of each expression, (ii) different expressions always have different
Gödel numbers, and (iii) there is an effective procedure for deciding if
a number n is the Gödel number of an expression, and if so, for
recapturing the expression from n.

The proof of Theorem 30.1 uses a Gödel numbering. Gödel used a
numbering based on the fundamental theorem of arithmetic. We give
a version for N. Each formal symbol s is assigned a number $g(s)$ as
follows:

$\sim$	$\rightarrow$	$\forall$	(	,	)	α	β	γ	x	$\vert$	#
1	3	5	7	9	11	13	15	17	19	21	23

Let $p_1, \ldots, p_n$ be the first n primes $2, 3, 5, 7, 11, \ldots, p_n$ in their natural
order. Then each string $s_1 \cdots s_n$ is assigned the number $g(s_1 \cdots s_n) = p_1{}^{g(s_1)} p_2{}^{g(s_2)} \cdots p_n{}^{(s_n)}$. For example,

$$g(A(x)) = g(\alpha \# (x)) = 2^{13} 3^{23} 5^7 7^{19} 11^{11}$$

Each finite sequence $S_1, \ldots, S_n$ of strings is assigned the number
$g(S_1, \ldots, S_n) = p_1{}^{g(S_1)} p_2{}^{g(S_2)} \cdots p_n{}^{g(S_n)}$. From now on all references to a
Gödel numbering for N are to the numbering just described.

A Gödel numbering enables statements about N to be translated
into statements of informal number theory, and expressibility enables
statements of informal number theory to be translated into statements
of N. Hence the two together enable statements about N to be
translated into statements of N.

EXAMPLE 1. *v is a variable* translates into the number theory predicate
$\mathscr{V}(n) : n = 2^{19}$ or there is a prime p_k greater than 2 such that $n = p_1^{19} p_2^{21} \cdots p_k^{21}$. Suppose $\mathscr{V}(n)$ is expressible in N by the formula V.
Then the true statement $x\|$ *is a variable* about N translates into the
theorem $V(\overline{2^{19} 3^{21} 5^{21}})$ of N.

To state Gödel's theorem we need the notion of ω-consistency. N is
ω-consistent if and only if for every formula $Q(v)$ of N with exactly one
free variable v, if $Q(\bar{n})$ is a theorem of N for every number n, then
$\sim \forall v Q(v)$ is not a theorem of N.

LEMMA 2. *If N is ω-consistent, then N is consistent.*

Proof. Suppose N is ω-consistent. Let $Q(v)$ be a formula of N with
exactly one free variable v. Either $Q(\bar{n})$ is a theorem of N for every

number n, or there is a number k such $Q(\bar{k})$ is not a theorem of N. In the first case $\sim\forall v Q(v)$ is not a theorem of N by the definition of ω-consistency, and in the second case $Q(\bar{k})$ is not a theorem of N. Hence N is consistent.

LEMMA 3. *Let $\mathscr{G}$ be the 2-place predicate defined by: $\mathscr{G}(a, b)$ is true if and only if a is the Gödel number of a formula $P(x)$ with free variable x, and b is the Gödel number of a proof of $P(\bar{a})$ in N. Then $\mathscr{G}$ is expressible in N by a formula G.*

We omit the proof of Lemma 3.

Let P be the formula $\forall y \sim G(x, y)$, and let i be the Gödel number of P. Let S be the statement $P(\bar{\imath})$, i.e., $\forall y \sim G(\bar{\imath}, y)$.

THEOREM 4. *(Gödel's incompleteness theorem.) If N is consistent, then S is not a theorem of N; if N is ω-consistent, then $\sim S$ is not a theorem of N. Hence if N is ω-consistent, then N is incomplete.*

Proof. Suppose N is consistent. Suppose for contradiction that S is a theorem of N, i.e., $\vdash_N \forall y \sim G(\bar{\imath}, y)$. Let j be the Gödel number of a proof of S in N. Then $\mathscr{G}(i, j)$ is true by the definitions of $\mathscr{G}$ and S. Hence $\vdash_N G(\bar{\imath}, \bar{\jmath})$ by Lemma 3. But spec applied to S gives $\vdash_N \sim G(\bar{\imath}, \bar{\jmath})$, contradicting the consistency of N.

Suppose that N is ω-consistent. Suppose for contradiction that $\sim S$ is a theorem of N, i.e., $\vdash_N \sim\forall y \sim G(\bar{\imath}, y)$. N is consistent by Lemma 2. Hence S is not a theorem of N. Therefore no number n is the Gödel number of a proof of S in N, i.e., $\mathscr{G}(i, n)$ is false for every n. Hence $\vdash_N \sim G(\bar{\imath}, \bar{n})$ for every n by Lemma 3. $\sim G(\bar{\imath}, y)$ is a formula with exactly one free variable. Then by ω-consistency, $\sim\forall y \sim G(\bar{\imath}, y)$ is not a theorem of N, contradicting the assumption that $\sim S$ is a theorem of N.

If G is interpreted as $\mathscr{G}$, then the interpretation of S is: $\mathscr{G}(i, n)$ is false for every n. By the definitions of $\mathscr{G}$, i, and S, this means that there is no proof of S in N. Hence S says that it is unprovable. If N is consistent, then indeed S is unprovable by Gödel's theorem. Hence, if N is consistent, then S is true in this interpretation but unprovable.

By using a statement more complicated than S, Rosser replaced the hypothesis of ω-consistency in Gödel's theorem by the weaker hypothesis of consistency. We sketch Rosser's proof.

LEMMA 5

(a)   *For every number* k,

$$\vdash Q(\bar{0}) \wedge Q(\bar{1}) \wedge \cdots \wedge Q(\bar{k}) \rightarrow \forall z(z \leqslant \bar{k} \rightarrow Q(z))$$

(b)   *For every number* m, $\vdash y \leqslant \bar{m} \vee \bar{m} \leqslant y$

Proof. (a) is Theorem 24.24.   Each instance of (b) follows immediately by spec on $\vdash \forall x \forall y. x \leqslant y \vee y \leqslant x$, which is Theorem 24.22.

LEMMA 6.   *Let $\mathscr{H}$ be the 2-place predicate defined by: $\mathscr{H}(a, b)$ is true if and only if a is the Gödel number of a formula $P(x)$ with free variable x, and b is the Gödel number of a proof in N of $\sim P(\bar{a})$.   Then $\mathscr{H}$ is expressible in N by a formula H.*

The proof of Lemma 6 is omitted.

Let P be the formula $\forall y(G(x, y) \rightarrow \exists z(z \leqslant y \wedge H(x, z)))$, and let j be the Gödel number of P.   Let R be the statement $P(\bar{j})$, i.e.,

$$\forall y(G(\bar{j}, y) \rightarrow \exists z(z \leqslant y \wedge H(\bar{j}, z)))$$

THEOREM 7 (*The Gödel–Rosser theorem*).   *If N is consistent, then neither R nor $\sim R$ is a theorem of N.*

Proof. Suppose N is consistent.   Suppose for contradiction that R is a theorem of N, i.e., $\vdash_N \forall y(G(\bar{j}, y) \rightarrow \exists z(z \leqslant y \wedge H(\bar{j}, z)))$.   Let k be the Gödel number of a proof of R in N.   Then $\mathscr{G}(j, k)$ is true by the definitions of $\mathscr{G}$ and R.   Hence $\vdash_N G(\bar{j}, \bar{k})$ by Lemma 3.   Spec applied to R gives $\vdash_N G(\bar{j}, \bar{k}) \rightarrow \exists z(z \leqslant \bar{k} \wedge H(\bar{j}, z))$.   Then modus ponens gives $\vdash_N \exists z(z \leqslant \bar{k} \wedge H(\bar{j}, z))$. $\sim R$ is not a theorem of N because R is a theorem of N and N is consistent.   Hence no number n is the Gödel number of a proof of $\sim R$ in N.   Then $\mathscr{H}(j, n)$ is false for every n by the definitions of $\mathscr{H}$ and R.   By Lemma 6, $\vdash_N \sim H(\bar{j}, \bar{n})$ for every n. Then by the statement calculus, $\vdash_N \sim H(\bar{j}, \bar{0}) \wedge \sim H(\bar{j}, \bar{1}) \wedge \cdots \wedge \sim H(\bar{j}, \bar{k})$.   By Lemma 5(a) and the statement calculus,

$$\vdash_N \forall z(z \leqslant \bar{k} \rightarrow \sim H(\bar{j}, z))$$

Then $\vdash_N \sim \exists z(z \leqslant \bar{k} \wedge H(\bar{j}, z))$ by the predicate calculus (Theorem 18.5, the statement calculus, and the replacement theorem).   But we already have $\vdash_N \exists z(z \leqslant \bar{k} \wedge H(\bar{j}, z))$, contradicting the consistency of N.

Now suppose for contradiction that $\sim R$ is a theorem of N. Let m be the Gödel number of a proof of $\sim R$ in N. Then $\mathscr{H}(j, m)$ is true by the definitions of $\mathscr{H}$ and R. Then $\vdash_N H(\bar{j}, \bar{m})$ by Lemma 6. R is not a theorem of N because $\sim R$ is a theorem of N and N is consistent. Hence $\mathscr{G}(j, n)$ is false for every n. Then $\vdash_N \sim G(\bar{j}, \bar{n})$ for every n by Lemma 3. By the statement calculus, $\vdash_N \sim G(\bar{j}, \bar{0}) \wedge \sim G(\bar{j}, \bar{1}) \wedge \cdots \wedge \sim G(\bar{j}, \bar{m})$. Lemma 5(a), the statement calculus, and spec give (i) $\vdash_N y \leqslant \bar{m} \to \sim G(\bar{j}, y)$. Assume $\bar{m} \leqslant y$. Then $\bar{m} \leqslant y \wedge H(\bar{j}, \bar{m})$ since $\vdash_N H(\bar{j}, \bar{m})$. Then $\exists z(z \leqslant y \wedge H(\bar{j}, z))$ by $\exists$. Then the deduction theorem gives (ii) $\vdash_N \bar{m} \leqslant y \to \exists z(z \leqslant y \wedge H(\bar{j}, z))$. Then the statement calculus on (i), (ii), and Lemma 5(b) gives

$$\vdash_N \sim G(\bar{j}, y) \vee \exists z(z \leqslant y \wedge H(\bar{j}, z))$$

Then the statement calculus and gen give

$$\vdash_N \forall y(G(\bar{j}, y) \to \exists z(z \leqslant y \wedge H(\bar{j}, z)))$$

i.e., $\vdash_N R$. But $\vdash_N \sim R$, contradicting the consistency of N.

The proof of the Gödel–Rosser theorem is constructive: The proofs of Lemmas 3 and 6 give an effective procedure for constructing the formulas G and H, and hence the statement R.

The Gödel–Rosser theorem is not a peculiarity of N. The proof goes through for every formulation of number theory for which Lemmas 3, 5, and 6 hold. This includes formulations both weaker and stronger than N. In particular, the proof goes through if R (or $\sim R$) is adjoined to N as a proper axiom. Indeed, the proof goes through no matter how many statements are adjoined to N as proper axioms, provided the resulting theory is formal.

Gödel's second theorem is a corollary of the incompleteness theorem. Let $\mathscr{L}$ be the 3-place predicate defined by: $\mathscr{L}(a, b, c)$ is true if and only if a is the Gödel number of a formula P of N, b is the Gödel number of a proof of P in N, and c is the Gödel number of a proof of $\sim P$ in N. $\mathscr{L}$ is expressible in N by a formula L. Let $Consis$ be the statement $\forall x \sim \exists y \exists z L(x, y, z)$ of N.

THEOREM 8 (*Gödel's second theorem*). *If* N *is consistent, then* Consis *is not provable in* N.

Proof. We sketch the proof. If L is interpreted as $\mathscr{L}$, then $Consis$ says that there is no formula P such that both P and $\sim P$ are theorems of N, i.e., N is consistent. Recall that the statement S says that S is not provable. Hence $Consis \rightarrow S$ says that if N is consistent then S is not provable. By means of Gödel numbering and expressibility, the proof (Theorem 4) that if N is consistent then S is not provable can be translated into a proof of $Consis \rightarrow S$ in N. Now suppose $\vdash_N Consis$. Then $\vdash_N S$ by modus ponens. Then N is inconsistent by Theorem 4. Hence if N is consistent, then $Consis$ is not provable in N.

The significance of Gödel's second theorem lies in the interpretation: If N is consistent, then the consistency of N cannot be proved by methods formalizable in N. Like the incompleteness theorem, Gödel's second theorem applies to many theories both weaker and stronger than N. In particular, it applies to set theory and every formal extension of N. Although the consistency of N can be proved in set theory, the value of the proof is doubtful, because set theory itself cannot be proved consistent by methods formalizable in set theory.

EXERCISES

1. Show that 4 and 16 are not Godel numbers.
2. State how to distinguish the Godel number of a string from the Gödel number of a sequence of strings.
3. Find the expression whose Gödel number is 46656.
4. Find the Gödel number of $A(x) \rightarrow B(y)$.
5. Let N′ be the result of adjoining $\sim S$ (S is Gödel's statement) to N as a proper axiom. Prove that if N is consistent, then N′ is consistent but ω-inconsistent.
6. Let T have the same formulas as N. T is ω-complete if and only if for every formula $Q(v)$ of T, if $\vdash_T Q(\bar{n})$ for every number n, then $\vdash_T \forall v Q(v)$.

   (a) Prove that if N is consistent, then N is ω-incomplete.
   (b) Prove that if T is consistent and ω-inconsistent, then T is ω-incomplete.

Notes

Chapter 1

Chapter 1 of Rosser 1953 and Part I of Kleene 1952 are excellent introductions to mathematical logic. *Section 2.* For more set theory along these lines, see Abian 1965, Fraenkel 1953, Halmos 1960, and Stoll 1963. *Section 3.* Axiomatic theories are discussed in Stoll 1963 and Wilder 1952.

Chapter 2

General references for the predicate calculus are Beth 1959, Church 1956, Hilbert and Ackermann 1950, Hilbert and Bernays 1934, Kleene 1952, Mendelson 1964, Quine 1940, Rosenbloom 1950, Rosser 1953, Stoll 1963, and Whitehead and Russell 1910. For additional references to particular topics, see Church 1956, especially Sections 29 and 49. *Section 14.* The deduction theorem is due to Herbrand 1930. *Section 15.* The completeness theorem for the statement calculus is due to Post 1921. The proof here is that of Kalmár 1935. *Section 17.* The name *Rule C* is borrowed from Rosser 1953. (The formulation here is not the same as Rosser's.)

Chapter 3

General references for first order theories are Beth 1959, Mendelson 1964, Robinson 1963, and Stoll 1963. For additional references to particular topics, see Mendelson 1964. *Section 22.* For more algebra, see Birkhoff and MacLane 1941, Herstein 1964, Jacobson 1951, van der Waerden 1949, or any modern algebra book. Higher order logic is discussed in Church 1956 and Hilbert and Ackermann 1950. For formal set theory, see Bernays and Fraenkel 1958, Fraenkel and Bar-Hillel 1958, Gödel 1940, Mendelson 1964, Rosenbloom 1950, and Suppes 1960. *Section 24.* For more number theory along these lines, see Beth 1959, Church 1956, Hilbert and Bernays 1934, Kleene 1952, Landau 1951, and Mendelson 1964. *Section 26.* The precise definition of truth is due to Tarski 1936. (An English translation appears in Tarski 1956.) *Section 27.* Löwenheim 1915 proved that if a finitely axiomatized first order theory has a model, then it has a countable model. Skolem 1920 extended the theorem to arbitrary first order theories. The completeness theorem is due to Gödel 1930. The proof here is that of Henkin 1949 as simplified by Hasenjaeger 1953. The compactness theorem is due to Malcev 1936. Theorem 4 is due to Adolf Lindenbaum. (See page 98 of Tarski 1956.) The definition of truth and the completeness theorem form the basis of the *theory of models*. See Tarski 1952 and 1954, and Robinson 1963. *Section 28.* For more on completeness see Robinson 1956. Cantor's theorem is in Cantor 1915 and Kamke 1950. For cardinal numbers and well-ordered sets, see Abian 1965, Bachman 1955, Bernays and Fraenkel 1958, Cantor 1915, Fraenkel 1953, Gödel 1940, Halmos 1960, Kamke 1950, Mendelson 1964, Sierpiński 1958, Stoll 1963, Suppes 1960, and Whitehead and Russell 1910. Theorem 10 is due to Vaught 1954. Steinitz's theorem is in Steinitz 1910. *Section 29.* Euclid's fifth postulate is discussed in Wilder 1952. The consistency of the axiom of choice was proved by Gödel 1940; the independence by Cohen 1963. For more about the axiom of choice, see Rosser 1953, Rubin and Rubin 1963, or any set theory book. *Section 30.* Church 1936a and 1936b gave a precise definition of decidable theory and proved the undecidability of number theory and the predicate calculus. Decidability is an aspect of the theory of *recursive functions*. See Davis 1958 and 1965, Hermes 1965, Kleene 1952, Markov 1954, Mendelson 1964, Péter 1951, Rogers 1967, and Smullyan 1961. Theorem 2 and related theorems are discussed in Post 1944. The decidability of the theory of abelian groups was proved by Szmielew 1955.   A decision procedure for real closed fields was given by Tarski 1948.   For a discussion of the theory Q and the undecidability of various algebraic systems, see Tarski, Mostowski, and Robinson 1953.   The decision procedure for DL is due to Langford 1927.   Exercise 10 is a theorem of Henkin 1955. Several of the other exercises are theorems of Tarski, Mostowski, and Robinson 1953.   *Section 31.* Gödel's theorems are in Gödel 1931. The details of the proof of the corollary are in Hilbert and Bernays 1934.   Rosser's extension is in Rosser 1936.   Davis 1965 includes an English translation of Gödel 1931 and reprints of Church 1936a and 1936b, Rosser 1936, and Post 1944.

References

ALEXANDER ABIAN.

    1965: *The Theory of Sets and Transfinite Arithmetic.* Philadelphia: W. B. Saunders Co.

HEINZ BACHMAN.

    1955: *Transfinite Zahlen.* Berlin, Göttingen, Heidelberg.

PAUL BERNAYS and ABRAHAM FRAENKEL.

    1958: *Axiomatic Set Theory.* Amsterdam.

EVERT BETH.

    1959: *The Foundations of Mathematics.* Amsterdam.

GARRETT BIRKHOFF and SAUNDERS MACLANE.

    1941: *A Survey of Modern Algebra.* New York: The Macmillan Co., revised 1953.

GEORG CANTOR.

    1915: *Contributions to the Founding of the Theory of Transfinite Numbers.* Chicago: Open Court Publishing Co. Reprinted 1952 New York: Dover Publications, Inc.

195

ALONZO CHURCH.

1936a: "An Unsolvable Problem of Elementary Number Theory," *American Journal of Mathematics*, Vol. 58, pp. 345–363.
1936b: "A Note on the Entscheidungsproblem," *Journal of Symbolic Logic*, Vol. 1, pp. 40–41; Correction, *ibid.*, pp. 101–102.
1956: *Introduction to Mathematical Logic*, Vol. 1.   Princeton, N.J.: Princeton University Press.

PAUL COHEN.

1963: "The Independence of the Continuum Hypothesis," *Proceedings of the National Academy of Sciences, U.S.A.*, Vol. 50, pp. 1143–1148 and Vol. 51, pp. 105–110.

MARTIN DAVIS.

1958: *Computability and Unsolvability*.   New York: McGraw-Hill Book Co.
1965: *The Undecidable*.   Hewlett, N.Y.: Raven Press.

ABRAHAM FRAENKEL.

1953: *Abstract Set Theory*.   Amsterdam, second edition 1961.

ABRAHAM FRAENKEL and YEHOSHUA BAR-HILLEL.

1958: *Foundations of Set Theory*.   Amsterdam.

KURT GÖDEL.

1930: Die Vollständigkeit der Axiome des logischen Funktionenkalküls," *Monatshefte für Mathematik und Physik*, Vol. 37, pp. 349–360.
1931: Über formal unentscheidbare Sätze der Principia Mathematica und verwandter Systeme I," *ibid.*, Vol. 38, pp. 173–198.
1940: *The Consistency of the Axiom of Choice and the Generalized Continuum-hypothesis with the Axioms of Set Theory*.   Princeton, N.J.: Princeton University Press, second printing 1951.

PAUL HALMOS.

1960: *Naive Set Theory*.   Princeton, N.J.: Van Nostrand Co.

GISBERT HASENJAEGER.

1953: "Eine Bemerkung zu Henkin's Beweis für die Vollständigkeit des Prädikatenkalküls der ersten Stufe," *Journal of Symbolic Logic*, Vol. 18, pp. 42–48.

LEON HENKIN.

1949: The Completeness of the First-Order Functional Calculus, *Journal of Symbolic Logic*, Vol. 14, pp. 159–166.
1955: "On a theorem of Vaught," *Indagationes Mathematicae*, Vol. 17, pp. 326–328.

JACQUES HERBRAND.

1930: *Recherches sur la Théorie de la Démonstration*, Travaux de la Société des Sciences et des Lettres, Classe III, no. 33.

HANS HERMES.

1965: *Enumerability, Decidability, Computability*. New York: Academic Press, and Berlin.

ISRAEL HERSTEIN.

1964: *Topics in Algebra*. Waltham, Mass.: Blaisdell Publishing Co.

DAVID HILBERT and WILHELM ACKERMANN.

1950: *Principles of Mathematical Logic*. New York: Chelsea Publishing Co.

DAVID HILBERT and PAUL BERNAYS.

1934: *Grundlagen der Mathematik*, 2 vols., 1934, 1939, Berlin.   Reprinted 1944 Ann Arbor, Mich.: Edwards.

NATHAN JACOBSON.

1951: *Lectures in Abstract Algebra*, 3 vols., 1951, 1953, 1964.   Princeton, N.J.: Van Nostrand Co.

LÁSZLÓ KALMÁR.

1935: "Über die Axiomatisierbarkeit des Aussagenkalküls," *Acta Scientiarum Mathematicarum* (Szeged), Vol. 7, pp. 222–243.

ERICH KAMKE.

1950: *Theory of Sets*. New York: Dover Publications.

STEPHEN KLEENE.

1952: *Introduction to Metamathematics*. Princeton, N.J.: Van Nostrand Co. Amsterdam, Groningen.

EDMUND LANDAU.

1951: *Foundations of Analysis*. New York: Chelsea Publishing Co.

COOPER LANGFORD.

1927: "Some Theorems on Deducibility," *Annals of Mathematics*, Vol. 28, pp. 16–40, 459–471.

LEOPOLD LÖWENHEIM.

1915: "Über Möglichkeiten im Relativkalkül," *Mathematische Annalen*, Vol. 76, pp. 447–470.

ANATOLIĬ MALCEV.

1936: "Untersuchungen aus dem Gebiete der mathematischen Logik," *Matematicheskiĭ Sbornik* (new series), Vol. 1, pp. 323–336.

198 REFERENCES

ANDREĬ MARKOV.

1954: *The Theory of Algorithms.* Available from the Office of Technical Services, U.S. Department of Commerce, Washington, D.C.

ELLIOTT MENDELSON.

1964: *Introduction to Mathematical Logic.* Princeton, N.J.: Van Nostrand Co.

RÓZSA PÉTER.

1951: *Rekursive Funktionen.* Budapest, second edition 1957.

EMIL POST.

1921: Introduction to a General Theory of Elementary Propositions," *American Journal of Mathematics*, Vol. 43, pp. 163–185.
1944: "Recursively Enumerable Sets of Positive Integers and Their Decision Problems," *Bulletin of the American Mathematical Society*, Vol. 50, pp. 284–316.

WILLARD QUINE.

1940: *Mathematical Logic.* Cambridge, Mass.: Harvard University Press, revised 1951.

ABRAHAM ROBINSON.

1956: *Complete Theories.* Amsterdam.
1963: *Model Theory.* Amsterdam.

HARTLEY ROGERS, JR.

1967: *Theory of Recursive Functions and Effective Computability.* New York: McGraw-Hill Book Co.

PAUL ROSENBLOOM.

1950: *Elements of Mathematical Logic.* New York: Dover Publications.

J. BARKLEY ROSSER.

1936: "Extensions of Some Theorems of Gödel and Church," *Journal of Symbolic Logic*, Vol. 1, pp. 87–91.
1953: *Logic for Mathematicians.* New York: McGraw-Hill Book Co.

HERMAN RUBIN and JEAN RUBIN.

1963: *Equivalents of the Axiom of Choice.* Amsterdam.

WACŁAW SIERPIŃSKI.

1958: *Cardinal and Ordinal Numbers.* Warsaw.

THORALF SKOLEM.

1920: "Logisch-kombinatorische Untersuchungen über die Erfüllbarkeit oder Beweisbarkeit mathematischer Sätze nebst einem Theoreme über dichte Mengen," *Skrifter utgit av Videnskapsselskapet i Kristiania*, I, no. 4.

RAYMOND SMULLYAN.

1961: *Theory of Formal Systems.*   Princeton, N.J.: Princeton University Press.

ERNST STEINITZ.

1910: "Algebraische Theorie der Körper," *Journal für die reine und angewandte Mathematik,* Vol. 137, pp. 167–309.

ROBERT STOLL.

1963: *Set Theory and Logic.*   San Francisco: Freeman & Co.

PATRICK SUPPES.

1960: *Axiomatic Set Theory.*   Princeton, N.J.: Van Nostrand Co.

WANDA SZMIELEW.

1955: "Elementary Properties of Abelian Groups," *Fundamenta Mathematicae,* Vol. 41, pp. 203–271.

ALFRED TARSKI.

1936: "Der Wahrheitsbegriff in den formalisierten Sprachen," *Studia Philosophica,* Vol. 1, pp. 261–405.
1948: *A Decision Method for Elementary Algebra and Geometry.*   Santa Monica: Rand Corporation.   Revised 1951, Berkeley: University of California Press.
1952: "Some Notions on the Borderline of Algebra and Metamathematics," *Proceedings of the International Congress of Mathematicians,* 1950, pp. 705–720.
1954: "Contributions to the Theory of Models," *Indagationes Mathematicae,* Vol. 16, pp. 572–588 and Vol. 17, pp. 56–64.
1956: *Logic, Semantics, Metamathematics.*   Oxford.

ALFRED TARSKI, ANDRZEJ MOSTOWSKI, and RAPHAEL ROBINSON.

1953: *Undecidable Theories.*   Amsterdam.

ROBERT VAUGHT.

1954: "Applications of the Löwenheim–Skolem–Tarski Theorem to Problems of Completeness and Decidability," *Indagationes Mathematicae,* Vol. 16, pp. 467–472.

BARTEL VAN DER WAERDEN.

1949: *Modern Algebra,* 2 vols.   New York: Ungar Publishing Co.

ALFRED WHITEHEAD and BERTRAND RUSSELL.

1910: *Principia Mathematica,* 3 vols., 1910, 1912, 1913.   Cambridge, England, second edition 1925, 1927, 1927.

RAYMOND WILDER.

1952: *Introduction to the Foundations of Mathematics.*   New York: John Wiley & Sons, second edition 1965.

INDEXES

Index of Symbols

Subject Index

205